For Ted (who he's older)
and Bob, a good read for
two generations of Hemingways.

Firoz
25 May 1992

SECOND GENERATION

*

Raymond Williams's second novel is the story of the families of two brothers, Harold and Gwyn Owen, who, unemployed in the 1930s, move away from the Welsh border country near Gwenton and find work in a car factory in a university city. Here the families are on a new border, between factory and university, as Harold's son Peter grows up and becomes a research student, and as Harold's wife, Kate, moves out into the world of politics involving both factory and university, in 'the traffic of a single city'. The personal stories of Peter and of Kate are, in different but connected ways, the contemporary stories of a 'second generation'.

SECOND GENERATION

A Novel by
Raymond Williams

1978
CHATTO AND WINDUS
LONDON

Published by
Chatto and Windus Ltd
42 William IV Street
London WC2

*

Clarke, Irwin and Co Ltd
Toronto

First impression 1964
Second impression 1978

Published with the support of
the Welsh Arts Council

ISBN 0 7011 1218 2

Printed and bound in Great Britain by
REDWOOD BURN LIMITED
Trowbridge and Esher

Contents

*

PART ONE

Part One

Chapter One

IF you stand, today, in Between Towns Road, you can see either way: west to the spires and towers of the cathedral and colleges; east to the yards and sheds of the motor works. You see different worlds, but there is no frontier between them; there is only the movement and traffic of a single city.

Peter Owen stepped from the bus to the crowded pavement. Twenty minutes earlier he had been in the high white room of the library, closing his books and reserving them, after the long quiet day. He had walked down the squared oak staircase, and out through the quadrangle at the heart of the university, under the weathered dome and the intricate stonework of the central spire. Only a few people were crossing the cobbled square to the high carved gateways and the lawns and rooms beyond them. In the evening light, and the slow movement of shadows, the familiar high walls seemed to press in more closely. In the known intervals of the slow chime of the hour, a silence of enclosure seemed to hang in the air. Then, where the remote marble statues looked down over the curve of the crowded street, he had caught the bus and travelled east, over the long river bridge. In the lines of small shops and houses, in the clean façades of garage and cinema, the urban landscape had changed. He stood now at the crossing, under the orange ball, watching for a gap in the dense race of lorries and cars.

The factory begins at this corner. The first sheds rise on your left, their roofs a series of right-angled triangles, a jagged wave movement above the loading doors of the long bays. The main road runs on, with the buildings on each side of it, until it seems an internal road, within the definition of the works: boundary walls, diamond-wired barriers, numbered gates guarded by uniformed police. There is no pall of smoke; only an infiltration of darker greys into the ordinary light. Along the older buildings, the large black cowls of the ventilators stand regularly spaced like drums. But beyond the great yard, where the new cars gleam in long lines, the new buildings rise in a silvery grey, and at first seem vertically striped, in their regular corrugations. Above them, fantastically, rides a fleet of funnels, the high ventilators, silvery and varying in height. The occasional red stack is warm with its brickwork, in this world of reflecting greys.

Standing at the edge of the pavement, Peter felt the wind of a high transporter, passing close: a giant carrying the little shells of cars on its back. Vans and cars, crowded behind it, edged restlessly out in frustrated efforts to pass. An open lorry, stacked with scaffolding poles, rattled as its offside wheels hit the cover of a manhole. Behind it, almost as high as the transporter, a yellow pantechnicon loomed above the pavement. On its side a huge painted head of a girl laughed back on a pillow that was also a cloud, and the high green letters spelled LITAZARE. Behind its bulk, the crowded cars edged out impatiently, and one hooted sharply as a bicycle swayed to turn away to the right. By the faded stripes on the oil-stained road, there was a quick iridescence where fresh oil was spreading at the water-edge of the gutter.

Peter looked down the road to the factory, where his father and uncle worked. Within its gates it is a world of its own, quite as much as the university. It is large enough to impose its own rhythms: a place of lines and regular intervals, an area rubbed clean and newly designed. It is not the huddle of mills to the course of a river, or the squat of colliery workings to the line of a seam. It needs no natural feature; it is simply a working space that has been cleared and set in order, giving room to move. But out here in the street, there is no man's land: the highway to which everything comes, the shuttle and tension of all the other actions.

At last there was a break in the traffic, and he crossed with the others who were waiting. In front of him a high pram, with a blue fringed canopy, was being eased over the jolt from pavement to road. He looked quickly into the mother's face, and saw a girl of his own age, whom he half recognized or remembered from school. He stepped past her at an angle to the far pavement, through the people still converging on this channel between the waiting lines of traffic. By habit he still hurried, but the delay had forced him into looking around.

His father had come here from Wales, in the thirties; come from unemployment to a job on the assembly line, and to the house in Goldsmith Street, up the hill, where Peter was born. His Uncle Gwyn had followed, and lived in the house next door. Growing up in these streets, Peter had moved in by scholarships to grammar school and university. Now, in his third postgraduate year, he still lived at home.

10

He saw his reflection ahead of him, in the bright windows of a furniture store. The curved and bevelled mirrors, hung at varying heights, were reflecting the street in a multitude of angles. He saw the body before the head: the black serge windcheater, the books under the arm, the grey crumpled trousers. Then the light was harsh on his face, strained and staring under the cropped tallow hair. He looked away, for he could not acknowledge the reflection: it was fixed, timeless, without life. But he looked with more interest at the shop itself, which he passed every day. There was a lattice of red-printed stickers on the long window, repeating again and again *Bedroom Event*. Behind the wide plate glass that shone over marble above the dirty pavement, a pink-quilted bed rested between the mirrored pieces of a veneered suite of two wardrobes and a dressing-table. Curly pink-shaded lamps mixed into the grey of the autumn evening.

At last he walked on. The next shop was empty, and had letting labels, with large crossed keys, on its windows. The glass was unevenly whitened, in opaque sweeps in which the arm could be felt. Next door, in the radio shop, five television sets demonstrated an identical image in unequal sizes—a speaking face though no words could be heard. A record-player rotated slowly on a glittering sequined octagonal column. At the corner, where he must turn, a soft blue electric sign moved again and again through hazy letters before suddenly forming its word: *delicatessen*. On the opposite corner the white shells of the garage were brightly illuminated, above the enamelled pumps. He turned the corner and made his way home up the hill.

Chapter Two

THERE is a fence round the works, but the rhythms cross it, into the first lines of houses. These are stiffly rectangular, cement-faced and identical except for the occasional dark patches of weathering and overflow. From the windows of many of these houses you can look through into the assembly lines, and in the rooms, especially at night, you can hear the muffled beat of the presses. A new school, at the edge of these houses, has the clear functional shape of the factory buildings, and has even a reproduction, in brick, of the funnel shape of the ventilators. But then, beyond it, a different pattern is clear, The pairs of houses are still identical in construction, but hardly one is faced or painted like its neighbour. There are varying patterns of brickwork and roughcast and stucco. The tiles set over the porches or at intervals on the walls are red and blue and yellow and black. The wood-work of doors and windows, the false beams of the gables, are painted in many colours, and the small front gardens are more varied again: some with a cypress as high as the house, some with cut box and clipped privet, some chained and paved except for a central diamond with rosemary and hydrangea and aubretia, some formal and open with rosebeds. Street after street shows new variations, as the houses climb up the hill.

Goldsmith Street runs up to the church and school of the old village, and the fields to High Wood begin at its end. The Owens had settled near the top: Harold in 285, and Gwyn in 287. Opposite them was a small children's playground, shaded by a tall horse chestnut. The doors and windows of the two houses were painted in the same blue, and the roughcast was white. There was an old joke, between the brothers. 'Like we're not semi-detached, we're semi-attached,' Harold said. 'Aye, that way,' Gwyn agreed.

As Peter was nearly home, Gwyn passed him, in his old car, Mag, of which he was obstinately proud. Gwyn waved, as he passed Peter, and turned in just ahead of him. He had taken away the front gate and widened the old entry and laid a ramp to the parking-space in the little front garden, under the mountain ash. He stopped with the bumper just short of the wall under the bay

12

window, just leaving room to get through to the side entry. The path to the front door was thick with the drifting white seeds of the michaelmas daisies that had flowered under the wall.

Gwyn got out as Peter stood by the ramp.

'All right then, Peter?'

'Yes.'

'It wasn't worth stopping, the last few yards. And if I stop her on the hill, she don't much like it.'

'You'll have to invest in your own industry soon.'

'Aye, worse luck. Though no point till about January, that's the best time to buy.'

Peter hesitated. He was looking along the panel of wrought iron that was set on the low wall between the street and the two front gardens. Drops of rain stood out clearly on the gleaming blue paint: separate and tiny reflecting spheres.

'Your Dad won't be home yet, Peter. One of his meetings again.'

'Yes, I think he said.'

'Come and eat with us, then, if your Mam's not in.'

'No, Uncle, I can't keep coming.'

'Go on, boy, we like to have you.'

'I'll just see if Mam's in.'

'All right, but come round if she isn't.'

Peter walked on to his own house, running his fingers along the ironwork so that the drops were broken and moved and ran into each other. He went to the door of the side passage, and as he opened it saw at once that nobody was in. All his life, it seemed, he had looked for the square of light from the dark kitchen, angled over the gravel and the board fence. In the long past it had always been there, coming home like this. But increasingly, these last years, it was missing most nights. And it was not his business; he was not a child to be waited for home. But a dark house isn't easy to go into, when all your life you've been used to coming home to it lighted and welcoming.

He went on down the passage and into the garden to the connecting gate. He lifted the oiled latch and went up the brick-walled steps under Gwyn's conservatory. The glass was misted, and with the light inside it the whole structure seemed of a different substance from the things we ordinarily look at. The neat staging and shelves were lined with pots, which threw sharp angled shadows down on the glass. But around these, seen through the misting, were the intricate networks of the growing plants, and the occasional flash of colour where the light reflected the flowers. Reluctantly, Peter went up the steps to the side-passage, where the light from Myra's kitchen streamed across the big paving-stones. He opened the kitchen door, to a curtain of warm air and the smell of cooking. From beyond, in the living-room, he could hear the tinkle of a toy, probably a puppet film on the television. He hesitated and then walked on, into this familiar house.

'There now, Peter, you've caught me,' Myra said, turning. 'And I only looked in for a minute, I've got my apron on and even my spoon—look—only somehow I stayed.'

Peter smiled. He liked his aunt so much. She was tall, with a high colour. The vivid auburn hair was coarse and springy, and her skin had coarsened from its original fineness. The bright red cheeks gave an impression of flaking, and the curves of the ears were very bright, as if the blood was at the surface. Her teeth were large and very widely set, so that the spaces between them showed clearly when she spoke or smiled. The strong heavy body had become looser and more awkward in middle age, and among other women she often seemed ungainly, though her physical presence was so strong that she cancelled out other people near her. Only the large hands were invariably neat and certain, and to see her fingers working, with great speed and skill, was to see an unusual strength and grace.

'It's you caught me, Auntie, really, coming in through your kitchen.'

'No, Peter, sit down. We can all eat in a few minutes, it's nearly ready.'

Myra turned from the doorway, and went back past him into the kitchen. Peter hesitated, and then stepped into the living-room. Beth was sitting on a stool near the television. She spoke without looking round, as he came up behind her.

'You can watch it for once. It won't bite you.'

'No, it certainly won't bite.'

'You wouldn't want it to bite.'

'No, but come in off the street and straight out to Montana or playing paper patterns on the rug.'

Beth smiled and looked round at him. She was Myra's daughter from her first marriage, and startlingly like her in presence and colouring, though slimmer and neater. She was a few months older than Peter, and they had grown up together in Goldsmith Street and at first gone to school together, in the old building up the hill under the church.

'This is pretty, look,' Beth said.

Peter bent and kissed her on the cheek. She turned away, smiling.

'No, but it is, Peter.'

He stood close behind her, looking down at the screen. A high-winged butterfly, very clearly drawn, moved in a curving rhythm to the high music, through a winding pattern of conventional flowers that were swaying and leaning towards it, the outline shapes continually developing and interlocking. Peter watched, caught by the pattern, until the scene ended.

'There,' Beth said.

'Yes. All right. At least it didn't end as an advert.'

Beth looked into his face. It was clear that nothing he could say in this general way was important to her. She was waiting for him to speak as himself.

'Well, did you have a good day?'

'Not bad. Phyllis is still away. And there seems to be a sort of emigration, to the most unlikely places.'

Beth worked in the foreign exchange department of one of the banks, which she had gone into at eighteen from her grammar school sixth form. Peter had wanted her to try for university, but Gwyn and Myra had not thought of it, and Beth herself, in the end, had not really cared.

'I got the theatre tickets for tomorrow. Is that still all right?'

'Yes, of course, Peter. Thank you.'

As she spoke she laughed, and Peter watched her lips.

'What is it?' he asked.

'Just that we weren't going to the theatre any more.'

Peter smiled, awkwardly.

'Do you mind?' he asked.

'No. It's just you make these terrific statements and then a day or two later you've forgotten all about it.'

'Perhaps it wasn't only the theatre.'

Beth stood, quickly, looking into his face.

'Well, was it?' he asked.

'I must go and help Mam,' Beth said.

'Anything but talk, in fact.'

Beth moved past him, quickly.

'Yes, Peter, anything but talk.'

She went out of the room, and Peter stood, looking down. The television programme changed, but he took no notice of it. He sat on the stool, where Beth had been sitting. Two evenings earlier, they had been walking, after the theatre, slowly back up Goldsmith Street. They were both dissatisfied with the play, and had learned no ways of evading this. They did not turn away to pick out this actor against that, this set against that. It was not the production, it was the feeling they rejected.

'They talk about Aunt Edna in the stalls,' Peter said, 'but it's Aunt Edna on the stage worries me. Every play, nowadays, somebody's marvellous bloody Mum. Dressed up, naturally. Countess Mum. So charming, such long teeth, and when she dies the world dies, because the men all just fold their hands and wither away.'

Beth laughed. They were walking at an easy distance, their fingers casually linked. The street lamps ran ahead of them up the hill, in the clear autumn night.

'It was that this evening, Peter. But not all that often.'

'I don't know. The theatre seems to exist now just to tell lies about women. This young one, beautiful as flame. This old one, spiritual and charming as candlelight on old silver. This middle-aged one, spiritual, charming, beautiful, generous, the lot.'

'It's the actresses, I suppose.'

'Well yes, but it's men writing it. I can see the women striking poses about themselves but I can't understand men accepting them and even elaborating them. Because I've watched women when they don't know the men are looking. I've seen some of the real attitudes.'

'Of course. And anyway women are different, as men are different. Why should there be one kind of truth about them, or one kind of lie?'

'But there is one kind of lie. Either Countess Mum or the beautiful generous tart. I don't think either exists.'

Beth smiled and pulled her fingers away. They were walking more slowly now, on the steepest part of the hill.

'What you're saying really, Peter, is that men make very simple judgements of women—they're all this or that. But I think you're doing the same. If the simple idea breaks down, there's no need to be angry about it. You can just start seeing actual people again, individual women.'

'That's the theory, Beth, but in fact the lies go on, and the men make them go on. If only somebody, for once, would just tell the truth.'

'Do you mean in a play?'

'No, anywhere.'

'Am I included in this then?'

'No, Beth, you're not.'

'Why?'

'I don't know. Because I trust you, I suppose?'

'But nobody else?'

'I don't know. Let's leave it.'

Beth looked across at him, under the light of a lamp. He was not smiling, as she had half expected, for part of his talk had been consciously amused. He was staring forward, but without focus, and he had again slowed his pace.

'The worst of that play wasn't that,' he said bitterly. 'There behind the fantasy was the familiar disgust, that just empties and breaks you. It isn't only the lies about sex but the guilt mixed up with them. First the set speeches against Anglo-Saxons and Puritans. Then the other set speeches, contradicting the first but unnoticed, that unless you're disgusted you're trivial and shallow, some kind of Old English Rationalist.'

'You don't have to work it out from the play, though.'

'It hurts nobody there.'

'It hurts you, Peter. Talking about it.'

'Yes, I suppose it does.'

They had reached the flat of the hill and were looking across at their homes. On the side they had walked was the playground, with the big horse-chestnut tree by the wicket-gate. The tree and the playground had always been part of their lives: so close that there were no particular memories but only the long familiarity, the immediate recognition. On the pavement and in the road, under the lamp, lay dozens of squashed green husks and throwing sticks, and then the occasional shine, like polished wood, of the tiny conkers that hadn't been worth carrying away.

'Do you want to go in yet?' Peter asked, looking away from the houses.

'No, not particularly.'

'Shall we walk round inside?'

'All right.'

They pushed through the wicket-gate, and down the path under the high thorn hedges to the square of open rough ground with its horse, roundabout, chute and swings.

'It's months since I've been in here,' Beth said, as they walked from the grass to the concrete footing of the swings.

'Yes, we're supposed to be past it.'

'Of course,' Beth said, looking up at him.

'Past that but into nothing else.'

'The theatre,' Beth said, laughing.

'Yes, that.'

He stood by the swings, holding the cold tube of the angled frame. Beth sat on the nearest swing, her arms curved round the hanging chains.

'All right,' he said suddenly, and stepped quickly across and pushed her back.

'No, Peter.'

'Yes, go on.'

She had scuffed her feet along the concrete, to hold against his push. But as he pushed again she curved her legs up under the seat and swung free. He stood in front of her, waiting, and as she swung towards him he put his hands on her knees and pushed her hard back. She swung away from him, and then came back with gathering speed. He stood with his legs apart, leaning forward, and waited for her to come to him. Then he pushed her knees again, and she swung away. She swung high back and then again towards him.

'I could go as high as the bar once.'

'Yes, now,' he shouted, running a few paces and pushing her high back.

'Mind,' she called, laughing, as she swung down again. He stood back out of reach, with his arms extended. She kicked her legs forward and just touched his fingers before she swung back and away. She swung again and again, and each time they just touched, lightly, before she swung away. At last she slowed the chains with her arms, and on the second time through Peter caught her and lifted her off. He kissed her as she held in his arms for a moment, and she returned the kiss, quickly, before breaking away and kissing him lightly on the cheek. They stood close, looking out over the lights of the city.

'I feel I don't want to go in at all,' Peter said.

'I know,' Beth said, her hands busy with her hair. They walked on, rather separate, towards the hedge by the allotments.

'Still stuck here like children really,' he said. 'At an age when our own children could be playing here.'

'That's a bit alarming, Peter.'

'Certainly it's alarming.'

He stopped by the horse, a long bench with square handles and a brightly painted head. He put his foot on one of the long side

18

mounts and began rocking the horse. In seven goes, always, he
had been able to get it to such a pitch of rocking that it would
still be moving, minutes afterwards, when he had gone right
away. It bucked violently, in its curiously arrested mechanical
movement. It was almost frightening, for it seemed to come
suddenly alive, the painted head jerking violently.

'You know, Beth, I can't go on living at home much longer.'

'No.'

'In any case it can't last.'

'What can't last?'

'I can't really talk about it.'

'You ought to, Peter. Or it'll break you.'

'We've been broken already. Haven't we?'

'No, not broken, love.'

'It's happened to a whole generation, at least our part of it.
What they call extended opportunities has turned out just an
extended adolescence. I get bitter when I think how many it's
broken. After all, I'm twenty-three. I could have married seven
years ago. So could you.'

'People marry now while they're students.'

'Yes and so they should, though the old men find it comic. If
you're the academic type you can wait for all that. Leave
breeding to the drawers of water. That was their ticket at eleven
plus.'

'It comes all right in the end, surely. Perhaps they'll be better
marriages.'

'That's what I mean about lying.'

He turned sharply and walked away. Beth hesitated, and then
followed him.

'Honestly, Beth,' he said as she came beside him. 'Nobody's
begun to tell the truth about this. The ones who might are
ashamed. Nobody's told what it does to you, in your body, to
have been given that kind of priority. The old men are afraid
of what they call immorality, but this is much worse, this is really
immoral, because it twists your whole body and soul. That's not
to be straightened out by some eventual marriage. The repression
and its fantasies will gave grown in too deep.'

'Then those who marry as students are right,' Beth said.

'Or those who take the other way, as more and more seem to be
doing. And the old call that a moral decline.'

Beth did not answer. They walked on in silence for some time,
following the line of the thorn hedge.

'It's easy to see what that does to them too,' Beth said, at last. 'The few I know aren't really like women, once they've hardened. They get tough and bitter inside, they can't give any more but they need to take. So it's on and on, till it gets mechanical.'

'That sounds too convenient.'

'I'm just saying what I've seen. Love can't just be used to get rid of a difficulty.'

'Are you sure, Beth?'

'I'm telling you, Peter, what I feel myself.'

She turned to him. She was almost crying. He put his arm round her shoulder and she rested her head on him, holding him close.

'It's not just the sex, Peter. You could have that, now, there'd still be the delay. You'd wake up next morning you'd know nothing had been done. Except enough disturbance to leave it emptier than ever.'

'How can you possibly know, Beth?'

'I know what I want, Peter. What I've wanted for years.'

'My fault then?'

'If we'd got married, then, when you got your degree. I wanted it, Peter.'

'Yes.'

'And since, I don't know, it's got more and more difficult.'

'Between us, you mean?'

She lifted her head, and moved back.

'Yes, Peter. Since Rose.'

He looked down at the ground.

'That finished a long time ago. When she married.'

'Its effects haven't. Its effects on both of us. I'm sorry, Peter.'

They walked back to the swings again. They stood, quietly, under the high frames. In the city below them the lights in the side streets were beginning to go out.

'Beth, I don't understand how it is with us,' Peter said quietly. 'It's always seemed we've been brought up too close. Almost like brother and sister.'

'Can it be too close?'

'With the delay, yes. Because then it belongs to the dark.'

'Love belongs to the dark?'

'Not love but the need, the actual need.'

'Too well to pretend then, you mean?'

'Too well to use, what you call use.'

Beth looked up into his face.

'It's not only that and you know it,' she said harshly. 'If it was real we'd have got through by now. Neither of us has been ready. It isn't just me.'

'That's what I'm saying.'

'I'm trying to be fair, Peter. Don't just push it back at me. In spite of everything, you could have taken me if you'd wanted.'

'There are so many lies, Beth.'

'Yes.'

'One child in ten born from sex before marriage. And still, knowing that, we tell lies about it.'

'We can't live by what other people do.'

'No, but that's how it is, how it really is. Only of course not us. Never us. We're the good ones, we shall never get into the bad statistics.'

'None of that matters. We can do what we want. When we agree it's real.'

'But you don't agree.'

'Not living here, Peter,' Beth said quickly, and again turned away.

'Because of them, you mean?' Peter said.

'I wasn't thinking of your Mam, I was thinking of mine. She goes half out of her mind when it's so much as mentioned. And even if she's wrong, I don't see my way. Because I should have to tell her.'

'Then not just your own doubts?'

'I've got no doubts, Peter, what I want for myself.'

'You said when it's real.'

'Yes. Not here.'

'Should we go away then? We could go to Trawsfynydd at Easter.'

'The caravans.'

'Yes. The caravan.'

'Mam would go daft, I tell you.'

She looked up at him, and then laughed. She caught his arm and leaned to him. He held her, politely.

'People do go on holiday, Miss Evans.'

'Yes, Mr Owen. This is the twentieth century. This is the nineteen-sixties. People go on holiday.'

'Even different genders, in the same watering place.'

'Yes, it seems so.'

They laughed again, and stopped walking. They looked out at the lights through the trees.

'It's this mad idea of like school,' Peter said. 'Like my Dad said last week, when you've finished your training.'

'I know. But we must try to be patient. It's all there, in front of us.'

'We don't understand that we're touching altogether,' Peter said slowly. 'Whatever it is, it's made us thoroughly guilty. And we've stuck at the stage when talk is the substitute. When talking about it is in fact the affair.'

'I know.'

They walked on again towards the road, under the shadow of the big tree. The street lamps formed into lines again, away down the hill past the darkening pairs of bushes. Beth stopped at the wicket-gate, buttoning her coat and pushing back her hair. It was strange coming out of the relative darkness of the playground, where they had been able to talk as if for once they were alone. They looked at each other, quickly, getting the secondary recognitions of clothes, hair, features.

'There, you look nice,' Peter said.

'Do I?'

'You know you do. And I love you.'

She leaned forward and kissed him, then turned through the wicket-gate. Peter followed her, looking across at the houses, with the cars parked by the bay windows and the blue and white paintwork picked out by the street lamp. Down the hill to the north they could hear the night sounds of the works, and especially the low rhythmic pulse of the presses, that they had heard all their lives.

'I'll see you home,' Peter said, smiling. Beth laughed and took his arm as he walked her to the lower gate. There was a light on in the greenhouse, where Gwyn was working late.

Peter looked up, hearing a sound from the greenhouse. The television was still on. The girl announcer, compulsively smiling, was giving a preview of that evening's play. His actress wife, erring, guilty, but convincingly human. He got up and switched it off, watching the image fade down. Then he walked to the door of the little conservatory. Gwyn, wearing his light blue working overalls, was working at one of the side benches.

There was a sudden change in the air, in this lighted shell. It was as warm as that of the house, but there was a quite different quality in it, both of humidity and of the smell of growth. Closing his eyes, Peter felt this air as a kind of greenness, and then came the slow, elusive scent—yet hardly a scent, a curious brown tinge in the air—of the opening chrysanthemums. Gwyn was turning a thumb-pot gently on its side, and then he tapped it sharply. There cupped now in his left hand was a ball of black fibre, with young green leaves resting along his fingers.

'What are those, then?'

'Schizanthus. It's an ugly name. In the newspaper adverts they put it "butterfly flower".'

'Yes, I've seen it. You've grown them before.'

'Aye. Though I haven't really got the time for it. These are a week late now.'

More than twenty of the thumb-pots, each with its seedling plant, were set in rows on the bench. A heap of new potting soil lay on brown paper at Gwyn's left hand, and the new pots, scrubbed clean, stood ready under the staging.

'You spend too much time at that other bench, that's what it is.'

Gwyn frowned, and for a moment his hands were still. 'No, no, boy. A man's got his work.'

'You'd rather be here, though.'

Gwyn did not answer. He was re-potting the young schizanthus, working the new soil gently around the ball of black fibre, then levelling it just below the rim with an old white-painted wooden label.

'Like some of these discourage you almost,' he said as he put down the finished pot and took the next in line. 'Like there's good polyanthus seed, there in the box, lying dormant a full year. Just the soil and the glass and the old paper gone yellow with last year's league tables. And I can't throw them away, they might still come.'

'You have to keep a year ahead with them, I suppose.'

'Aye, Peter, when I get the time.'

'Only if you had more time, Uncle, what more could you do? Every inch, already, you've got all these growing.'

'They're not what they would be with more attention.' He had tapped a new ball of fibrous root into his palm, and was scraping it gently with the edge of his broad thumbnail. Behind them, Beth opened the door.

'Come on, you two. Food's on the table.'

'Aye, just finish this,' Gwyn said.

Beth and Peter watched as he filled the new pot with soil and carefully levelled it. When he had finished he looked round at them, rubbing the loose black earth from his fingers.

'Your Mam wasn't in then, Peter?'

'No. Actually I remembered when I got round, she'd said she had a meeting.'

As he spoke, he realized that Gwyn and Beth were watching him carefully. He felt trapped, suddenly, in the warmth under the glass, and wished only that he could get away. He looked down at the staging, and at a particular pot which had a slight chip on its rim showing a lighter colour.

'I'm glad Mam does this,' he said with an effort, leaning back and finding support from the door. 'Not only that it's an interest for her, but that she's right to try.'

'Well, yes,' Beth said.

'I mean the whole society seems to be coming to a stop, jamming up like the traffic all going our separate ways. Somebody's got to get out and make a change.'

'I think it's wonderful, all she does,' Beth said.

'Aye, it's what Harold says,' Gwyn added, looking back round the staging.

'I mean, I feel like this myself,' Peter said firmly. 'Not just because Mam does it. We've all cut ourselves off, getting settled and comfortable in our own places, till we don't even see what's happening any more. We're just dug in and waiting, and we don't even know what for.'

Beth and Gwyn stood close. It was strange how alike they were: the same hazel-green eyes and coppery hair, the same frankness of expression, the familiar ease of this house. They might have been physically, and not only from habit, father and daughter.

'We'd better go or the meal will be cold,' Beth said.

'Aye, and I've to wash my hands.'

Peter followed them up the step into the living-room. He stayed near Beth, wanting to speak to her again. The words were ready in his mind: you keep me right, all of you, in this house. But the place was too familiar, the routine too settled, and he said nothing.

In the warm kitchen Myra was standing at the table, above the bowl of soup and the big pot of tea. Peter sat next to Beth, but he was watching Myra. When she was sure of herself, as now, she seemed to draw every feeling towards her. Even Beth, beside her mother, seemed remote and incomplete.

Gwyn finished washing his hands in the scullery, and came to the table. Myra stood, serving, until all the others had begun. Around the small table, in the warmth of the meal, Peter lost the feeling of separation, of looking in from outside, that was his normal world. There was a cyclamen on the table, crowded by the sugar bowl and the plate of bread and butter and the Welsh cakes. He reached across suddenly, and touched one of the lower buds which was still curving closely above the moist black soil.

'It's the shape,' he said. 'Like the neck of a swan.'

Beth did not answer, but he could feel her very close to him. Gwyn leaned forward, suddenly.

'Them seem to me like flamencos, Peter. Like I saw them once on the pictures, that same delicate pink and the curve of their necks.'

'Not flamencos, Dad.'

'Aye, big birds, waders. On a lake it was, in Africa.'

'That's flamingos,' Beth said. 'Flamenco's quite different—a dance. Isn't it Spanish, Peter?'

'Yes, I think so. It doesn't matter.'

'I might have got it mixed up then,' Gwyn said. 'Only there's a rose called Flamenco, that's the only place I've seen it written down.'

Peter looked at the bud again. What Gwyn had said seemed to rest him. When the meal was over, he stayed for a while, talking to Beth and Myra, but he had work to get on with and when the living-room clock struck eight he went round through the dark to his own house.

Chapter Three

PETER was only a few minutes before his father. He was still
standing in the kitchen when Harold opened the side-door and
came in. Harold was shorter than his son, but much stocker. His
coppery hair had faded, and there was now so little of it that it
was hardly separate, in tone, from the deeply weathered skin.
The face was alert and anxious, and on the thin neck had a
bird-like movement, an odd combination of neatness and
jerkiness.

'Mam not back then?'

'No.'

'That stove's out, isn't it?'

'I think so. I haven't looked.'

'It's that stuff they sent us last time. Just marbles and dust.'

'In any case it's been shut up too long.'

Harold walked past his son to the boiler. He lifted the lid
and looked inside, then opened the damper. As he walked
back he picked up a fork on the table, then quickly put it down
again.

'Where is Mam?' Peter asked.

'It's been the meeting of this working party. On the schools.'

'Have you eaten, Dad?'

'No, we'll wait till Mam's back.'

'I've had mine, round next door.'

'That's all right, then.'

'You've had a meeting?'

'Yes, just the stewards. Look, we'd better sit in the front. With
the electric.'

'All right. I must do some work.'

'I've got work. Letters. The Birmingham people want a week-
end meeting, joint with us. Only it's never that easy to fix up.'

'No, I'm sure.'

Peter turned and went through to the front room, and his
father followed him. Peter switched on the light and the fire, and
sat down.

'It's so damned cold in this house, somehow. Whatever you do,'
Harold said. He crossed and knelt by the fire, and seemed to be

listening to it. As the bar glowed, he leaned across to adjust the thermostat switch on the side.

'I really need an office,' he said, getting up. 'Only it's no use talking while it's voluntary.'

Peter nodded, staring at the fire-bar's glowing crimson reflection in the shining curve of the shield. It was true that Harold's trade union work had become almost another job, unpaid but endlessly demanding.

'The real thing is, Dad, that more of you should be doing it. If it's for all of you, why is the work left to a few?'

'I know,' Harold said, screwing round and sitting back in his chair. He looked suddenly very tired. He took off his glasses and rubbed his closed eyes and the red mark on his nose where the frame had pressed into the flesh.

'You can't tire yourself out for ever,' Peter said.

'It's no use just saying it, boy. We all know it, we've been saying it for years, till we're tired hearing it. It's just a few carrying the whole of it, wherever you look. Like the rest shout when there's trouble, but meanwhile they're off home, got too much to do, and the missus don't like being left alone, or their fishing or their gardens or just the telly.'

'But then that's their life, after all.'

'If you can call it life.'

'Well, it is, surely. It's what they work for.'

'Aye, while the work's still there. But you wait, this winter. We've had the first reports coming in. And it's now, see, the effort's got to be made. By Christmas they'll all be shouting, only then it'll be too late.'

'Except that you can't live just waiting for trouble.'

'Why do you say that?' Harold asked sharply. He had jerked back as Peter spoke, as if from a blow.

'I don't know. I was just thinking about it. Haven't people always been told what to do because there's trouble coming? It's no wonder they're tired of it.'

'And the trouble's come,' Harold said. 'I've had it, I've lived it through. To make out otherwise is just stupid. Just simple thoughtlessness, that's all they are now.'

'Everybody? Uncle Gwyn, for instance?'

'Gwyn was never interested, but he's all right, you can count on him.'

'Perhaps because you know him. Do you know the others?'

'Certainly I know them, I have to,' Harold said impatiently.

27

He got up and went again to the fire. He bent to try to turn up the thermostat, though it was already at maximum setting.

'Mam's late,' Peter said.

'I've heard the same at work,' Harold said, still bending over the fire. 'I've been called names for it, when I'm telling them what they see later is true.'

'It's not you I'm criticizing, Dad.'

Harold sat back in his chair. Slowly, after wiping his eyes, he put on his glasses again. As the naked eyes were covered, the face faded into a familiar settlement.

'They're all old, they seem to me, Peter. All the chaps we ought to rely on, old and set in their ways by the time they're forty. And the young ones, they talk, but they don't understand.'

'Isn't it always like that?'

'No, this is worse. Like a dog crossing the road, he'll jump when the lorry's just on him, and he might squeak away, but till then look how sure he is, in his own sort of world.'

Peter rubbed his eyes. Some feeling was coming through, that he could not name. Physically it was an intense dryness and fatigue.

'I saw a dog killed just now, coming home from work. By the crossing down the corner. And he was really moving, that last second, but of course too late, the lorry right over him. And his scream and the brakes screaming. It was filthy to see.'

'Yes,' Peter said, staring at his father, but seeing also, past the bowed head, the crossing where he had stood and waited: the race of traffic, the lattice of adverts, the soft blue sign.

'There's no trust,' Harold said. 'That's where I'd really put it. We've learned the other too deep. What kick we've got goes as much at each other as anywhere. You wouldn't believe the fierceness inside the few that's doing anything. Though, mind, I know how to look after myself.'

'Has it got to be that?'

'Yes, it's got to be that. You can say what you like, it feels like fighting, and you can't afford to let up.'

'Yet we keep saying it could be different.'

'This is how it is now, that's all I know,' Harold said, and with an effort pushed himself from his chair and went across to his bureau. He took out a bundle of papers from his pocket, and began sorting them through. Peter watched him for some moments, then went out to get his own books. When he came back, Harold was sitting with his pen ready, checking a list of addresses.

Peter sat and opened his book. He read a few paragraphs, but without attention. His mind kept moving back to his father, who was writing now, bending forward over his work so that his whole left forearm covered the lower half of the small page. Peter watched him, remembering what he knew of his history. He and Gwyn had been born in Brynllwyd, a grey huddle of cottages, little more than a hamlet, perched on the limestone scarp beyond Black Rock, looking down into the valley of Gwenton. To the south and west were the narrow mining valleys, along the shores of that lost island of which the coastal swamps are now the coal measures of South Wales, the English Midlands, and Belgium. To the north and east were the green farming valleys of the border country, under the blue broken peak of the Holy Mountain. Back in the 1830s, Brinley Owen, then a farm servant in the Golden Valley, had walked through this country and up Black Rock for a job in the ironworks where his descendants were still employed.

The cottages in Brynllwyd were built in that same period, one of the many settlements scattered along the ridge to serve the ironworks. When Harold was fourteen, and Gwyn twelve, their mother had died. Their father, Mervyn, was a furnaceman and a lay preacher, who had found in Christian teaching a way of accepting the hardness of his life. It had given him meaning and dignity, but equally it had cut him off from his sons as it had long cut him off from his wife. Neither Harold nor Gwyn went to chapel after their mother's funeral; the religion, like school, was one of the childish things they put away. It was a deliberate break, against their father as much as anything, but there was no new settlement to break to, for work was hard to come by and it seemed in the end that they would have to move right away. They got jobs in the ironworks, in the occasional good periods, but in six years after leaving school Harold had work for no more than two, while Gwyn did not get his first wage until he was nearly seventeen. And through all this, in the cold cottage looking down over Gwenton, there was bitter quarrelling with their father and, increasingly, between the brothers themselves.

Harold turned to politics, but could not interest Gwyn, who was sure that would get them nowhere. And it was Gwyn, in the end, who made the first move away. Without telling his father or Harold, he applied to join the police. After an unusually bitter family row, in which both the others were against him, he went on with it, and for two years stayed right out of touch, neither visiting nor writing. In the end he resigned from the force and came back, a few weeks before Harold married.

Harold had met Kate Thomas through politics: she was a clerk in the local Co-operative office, and an active worker in the Labour Party. There was really no question, after the wedding, of Kate moving in and taking over the house in Brynllwyd. The others would have resented it, and there was no place for a woman in the household as it had become. Then, just three weeks before the wedding, Harold was laid off at work, and at last it was clear that he must move right away.

'It's the only way, see; get right out. Here the margin's too narrow, you feel short of breath with it, even if it is your own people.'

On the first day of what could have been his honeymoon, he got a lift down Black Rock into Gwenton, and went on east, through the border country, to find work in England. The job on the assembly line, and then the house in Goldsmith Street, had been the end of the journey. Kate had come up, and Peter had been born, and Gwyn, some months later, had come to lodge with them, on the same job. From the beginning, shaped by his experience, Harold had worked hard and bitterly in politics and in his union.

Peter looked out through the window at the lamps running down the slope of the street. Harold was still writing, and the house was silent except for the occasional click of the thermostat. Peter forced himself back to his book, but could not really settle.

'Mam's very late.'

'Yes,' Harold said, leaning back in his chair and stretching his cramped arms.

'What is it exactly, this working party?'

'They're making a report, as I understand, on the educational service in the city. And then recommendations.'

'Will it make any difference?'

'I don't know. There's some influential people on it.'

Peter smiled. The dry heat of the fire had made his eyes heavy. It was as if hundreds of points of dry grit were pressed on his eyelids, and as he rubbed at the irritation he was reminded of his father's hands, in the same movement.

'Look, it's gone nine, Dad. When was this meeting?'

'I thought she said three.'

'Shouldn't we inquire then?'

'She's been late before. It's always the same with these meetings.'

If you're sitting at home you can't think what's keeping them. She used to say it to me.'

'Yes, but this late. Six hours.'

'It is, yes,' Harold said.

He took off his glasses and walked across to the fire.

'Where is it? Shall I walk down to the bus?'

'No.'

'Are you sure?'

'Of course I'm sure.'

Harold was answering sharply, almost angrily, and Peter looked away. Closing his eyes, he tried for a moment to see his mother's face. As a child, when he was separated from her, he had often tried to get in touch like this. Not just to see her face, which he could always bring into view like a photograph, but her face at this very moment—what she was doing, what she was saying, elsewhere. He found that he could see only a dark room, a long room where there might have been a meeting, and it was as if he was sitting at the table, staring down at it: a yellowish oak, with a scratched polish on it, and with dirt deeply lined in the grain. He kept seeing this, though it was not what he wanted.

As he opened his eyes, a car drew up in the street, just opposite the house. Its headlights for a moment swept across through the room. He stood up quickly and saw his mother getting out of the car. He could not see the driver; only a dark shape behind the wheel as she turned, holding the door, and bent to speak back inside.

'That's Mam, isn't it?' Harold said.

'Yes.'

'We can get the supper on then.'

'I've eaten. I think I'll go on to bed.'

Hurrying upstairs, he had reached the landing before he heard the front door opening. Without thinking what he was doing, he went into his bedroom and lay down on top of his bed in the dark. It was very cold in the room. Through the open curtains he could see the lines of lights down at the works. Directly underneath him, in the kitchen, he could hear Harold and Kate: their voices loud though he could not make out any words. He lay for some minutes, then pushed himself up to undress in the dark.

Chapter Four

KATE got up as usual to cook Harold's breakfast. The kitchen was cold, with the stove still out, and she shivered in her thin pyjamas and dressing-gown. From habit they talked very little at breakfast, and Kate, this morning, ate nothing. When she had put Harold's bacon on the table, she went back to the scullery and stood near the warmth of the gas stove, looking down at the ring of blue jets under the kettle. She saw that the holes needed cleaning—they were half filled with grease and dust—but she did not think about it. She was not really conscious yet, and so she stayed near the ring of warmth, as a child might, preoccupied and alone.

She heard the flush of the lavatory upstairs, and Peter coming down. When he came into the scullery she saw that his eyes were red and strained. He said good morning and she answered, turning a little away as she took his bacon from the pan and served it on a plate from the drying-rack. He carried his plate to the table in the kitchen, where Harold had lit a cigarette and was drinking his tea as he read his paper. As Peter sat down, Harold looked at the clock and got up. As he went out through the scullery he kissed Kate on the cheek, and then went down the side-passage to the car. Peter ate quickly and went back upstairs.

Kate saw the kettle come to the boil, but she did not want to move. At last she set up the coffee percolator and poured in the water, holding the hot handle with a corner of her dressing-gown. She had always to make tea for Harold and Peter, but for herself she waited for coffee. She put the percolator on the stove and watched the slow drip of the dark heavy liquid inside the misting glass. The faint smell of burned gas was absorbed in this new odour, and she was glad to stay near the steam and the warmth of the switched-off ring.

Peter came back into the kitchen, pulling on his overcoat. It was unusual for him to leave so early, though he always got up for breakfast with his father.

'I'm going in to the library, Mam.'

'Now? You'll be too early, surely.'

'No, I'm going to walk in. I feel like a walk.'

The coffee had almost dripped through, and Kate lifted it from the stove. She looked across at Peter, and it seemed that she was coming back from a long distance. When he turned and went out of the kitchen, she put down the coffee and followed him.

'Will you be back for lunch?'

'No. No, thanks.'

'Are you all right, Peter? Have you got everything?'

'Yes.'

He walked to the front door and put down his bag to set up the latch.

'You don't look as if you slept well. Are you sure you're all right?'

She was moving towards him as she spoke, and for a moment she was back in the days of seeing him off to school. He had been as tall then: already at thirteen a head above her.

'I'm quite all right,' he said, turning back to open the door. He had avoided looking at her. She put her hand up and drew together the lapels of her dressing-gown, for she remembered how he had protested bitterly, as a boy, that she came down in only her dressing-gown and night things. But it was more than this. He was always now that bit remote from her, avoiding coming close. In the last weeks this had been very noticeable.

'All right, look after yourself,' she called as he closed the door. She hurried into the front room to watch him crossing the road and walking away down the hill. In his black coat, under the cropped pale head, he looked very cold and exposed. Yet she could see the resemblance to Harold, in the set of the shoulder, the shape of the back of the head. She wanted to go after him and walk with him, but she knew she could not.

She went back into the kitchen and got her coffee. She had a sudden headache, which she associated with Peter, but when she thought about it she knew it had begun earlier, when Harold was going out. So much was wrong, permanently wrong, that she had almost got used to it, but at times the pain broke through.

She picked up the pile of papers and took them, with the coffee, back up to her bedroom. It was Friday, and there was plenty to read: the two weeklies, that they had always taken, and the two dailies, though Harold now only read one. It seemed a release, with so much to read.

She put everything ready on the table by the bed. Harold's pyjamas were lying on the side where he had got out, and she

33

went round and folded them and put them away under his pillow. As she bent near the wall she could hear the wireless music from next door—Myra listened right through in the mornings, from the moment she woke until she left for work in the canteen, and it was always loud enough to be heard all over the house.

Straightening up, Kate caught sight of herself in the wardrobe mirror. Her long black hair hung loosely to her shoulders; she had kept it like this through all the changes of fashion, since she first went out to work—why should she try to look like a different person every few years, according to the shape in vogue? She had always been very pale, and she was so small and slim that in many ways she still looked very young; the first impression of the tiny body and the shoulder-length hair was of a schoolgirl. But the face was mature enough, with its heavy cheeks and prominent dark eyes. In the mask which most people present to the mirror— the set, frank stare—she could see, in the tensions of the skin, all the years of pressure and of waiting.

She got into bed, piling both pillows behind her and pulling the blankets tightly around her body. It had not been easy postponing what she was looking for, but she could not bear to fit it into the rush of breakfast or while the bedroom was untidy. She must get clear first, get as she wanted to be.

But now she turned the pages eagerly, to the reviews of books. It was there, in each of the weeklies and in one of the dailies—the other carried no reviews unless the book made news quite separately, as war, crime or personal scandal. It was strange to see it at last in print: *Sensational Radical—the Life and Works of G. W. M. Reynolds*, 1814–1879, by A. L. S. Dean (Laycock, 35s.).

Kate leaned back again on the pillows. Seeing names in print was so special that she had got to thinking in a different way of the people they stood for. As a girl she had thought that there was a literary world—a phrase she had seen so often—and that the people whose names she saw regularly in print lived in it, quite physically. She knew now that in all sorts of places, all over the country, people put envelopes into ordinary letter-boxes, sending their writing off to be printed, and when they appeared in adjacent columns this was usually the only contact they had. Still, the sense of a separate world had lingered, until now. She had often seen writers at meetings and lectures, but this was the first case of someone whom she had first known as a person, who had got a book into print.

And it was different, the print made it different. There was remoteness in the 'A. L. S. Dean', and then the publisher and the price seemed to put the whole thing in plate glass, where perhaps it really belonged. She didn't know what the L. S. stood for. He had been Mr Dean, and then Arthur Dean. The L. S. came marching out of the birth certificate and the official documents, but on the whole she liked it. The habit of throwing Christian names around in public removed their only advantage—that they marked a stage when you knew someone better, the man behind the initials. It had spread from entertainment—you had to be Mary to be the world's sweetheart—and then of course in politics —you could trust a Stanley but not a Baldwin. It was everywhere now—she glanced over the names on the pages spread on the eiderdown—and in that way the remote A. L. S. Dean was quite welcome. She smiled as she read it again. 'They probably won't review the bloody thing at all,' Arthur had said, last night, just before she got out of the car. 'Unless, of course, the sex carries it.'

Kate read the reviews, carefully, and re-read them. They were quite favourable, though more concentrated on themselves and on Reynolds (whom they only knew through Arthur) than on the book. The most interesting comment, she thought, was this:

'Although his name survives, in the title of one of our Sunday newspapers, little is known of Reynolds, except the bare fact that he was a Chartist leader and that most of his numerous works, which sold very widely in their time, have long since gone out of print. The interest of Mr Dean's book is the paradox he so rightly indicates in his title: that this intense radical and extremist politician, the hero of vast meetings in Trafalgar Square, should have spent most of his life writing pretty lurid fiction, such as—to take only a few titles at random—The Loves of the Harem, Empress Eugenie's Boudoir, The Seamstress or the White Slave of England, and a translation of Paul de Kock. It would be wrong to say that Mr Dean makes the paradox understandable, but he certainly makes it clear, and this in spite of the fact that what he has to say about Reynolds as a man is understandably meagre and could even be called speculative. "All the great radicals have been sexual radicals," Mr Dean observes, somewhat surprisingly, in his conclusion, and this slightly alarming thought (is it really the case, we wonder?) is never really substantiated. Sexual fantasy, in which category one supposes this fiction must fall, can, after all, be generated anywhere: a virginal couch or a plinth in Trafalgar Square may indeed be more likely places, for some prurient reverie, than the corridor of an actual Casanova.'

Was it an alarming thought, Kate wondered? Reviewers had learned, of course, that it was their business to be superior, but who really knew about these things? Did Arthur? It could only be settled from the book itself, but at least, getting this amount of attention, it would probably be a success.

She pushed the papers away, and again lay back on her pillows. The coffee, she suddenly realized, was untouched, but it would be cold now and she did not really mind. Reading, often, was as good a breakfast as any. Yet the effect of the reviews was not really what she had expected. In certain ways they had made Arthur seem more remote, but why should she worry about that? Facing the plain facts, she did not in any case know him well. They had been at the same meetings, over the past four years, and had regularly found themselves on the same side in the increasingly bitter factional disputes. This sense of fighting drew people together; you could become friends in defining a common enemy. But still it had been rather functional. If either had changed sides, on any of the issues that marked the progress of the basic dispute, the intimacies would have disappeared, quite suddenly, and they would have gone off to drink with different people, in the temporary warmth of alternative camps.

It was only in these last weeks, in the working party, that they had really begun to know each other: in the most natural way, since Kate was secretary and Arthur, because of his position in the university, chairman. After the last two meetings, to save the cold wait for a bus, he had driven her home, after the usual drink. Each time, as if he had known her much longer, he had talked very frankly about the book. He had told her so many things about Reynolds that she felt she knew the whole book already, and it was strange, from the reviews, to get things he had not told her. He had not mentioned that general conclusion, which stuck so easily in the mind: 'all the great radicals have been sexual radicals'. But she could hear him saying it, with always that edge of a smile, always likely to shock his opponents but with an incisiveness that, though it had often made him disliked, had always made him respected.

'The fight in the Labour Party,' she remembered him saying, 'is between the genuine radicalism of a quite new conception of human life, and the old solid parochial conceptions of the English lower middle class, which are the nearest the Party has ever come to a set of beliefs.'

Kate remembered the effect of this on all the councillors and officials—old Dorrell, for instance—who had come up to suits and collars through the Labour Party and who enjoyed being councillors and officials, with documents to read, and agendas, and being spoken to nicely by the other side. Talk to them about a new conception of human life and they had terrible visions of danger to their standing orders and their waistcoat buttons and their hearths and homes. Say socialism as more than a new set of committees and welfare offices and they simply didn't know what you were talking about.

Kate slipped down into the warmth of the bed. Closing her eyes she found herself turning over, in what seemed a single movement of mind and body, this idea of a new life. She had every reason to reject the terms of the old life. She and Harold had made the break together: from the grey terraces where the men were kicking their heels month after month, in the long drizzle of poverty. And the break, too, from that stubborn scaling down of expectations which in a whole generation had been the nearest anyone got to any active virtue. Grey endurance and grey hard protest: these were the terms in which she and Harold had grown. The new life had been a phrase in the meetings up on the hill, with the wind blowing the rain like a grey sail through the huddled crowd.

Her own life was to have been different. She had started with more advantages than Harold. Her father was a teacher, and her future was to be in education. She remembered as a very small child riding on the carrier of his bike, every Saturday morning, to the junior library, where he would help her to pick books, and talk to her about them. Then the scholarship to the County School, and the regular competition with Mary Bowen—who had gone on to university and was now headmistress of a big comprehensive school—to be top of the class. All that had ended abruptly, at fifteen, with her father's death. Her mother was too ill to work, and though she tried to get Kate to keep on there had been no real choice. After her school certificate Kate had left and got the accounts job in the Co-op office. Five years later she had married Harold.

It had been good, once the break was made. Once he was settled Harold was ambitious, and she had overcome his resentful memories of learning and helped him through a series of correspondence courses, first in English, then in meeting procedure and chairmanship, finally in the history of trade unionism and the history of socialism. After Peter was in bed, they had settled together at the table in the kitchen with the books and papers. Kate wrote the exercises and essays, but Harold copied them out and they were submitted in his name. She was glad, in a bitter way, that he was so often highly praised. And then, as he had got more involved in practical work, there was Peter: to teach to read, to take down to the library, to help through school. The scholarship at eleven was only a preliminary stage, never really in doubt, and it was the later scholarship, to the university, that Kate always had in mind. When it all came right it was as if she were going herself.

All this had been a quite physical satisfaction. In the deepest sense, it had kept her alive. And she had kept up her own French, her best subject at school, listening regularly to broadcasts from Paris and seeing every French film she could. Hanging on to French had been, really, a way of hanging on to a different life. Not only the easy dream of sun and wine, though this had counted; the Mediterranean was still there, as an idea. But just the ordinary reminder that life could be different, that the English version was neither absolute nor final. And now, perhaps, only the French remained. Harold had made his way, but it had closed in on him: the demands of the work were compelling and narrow. And Peter was suddenly through and on his own, not seeming, any longer, to want her help or even her interest. It was as if, even, he resented what she had done for him. He had accused her once, in a row, of simply using him to work out her own unfinished career; what he wanted had never really mattered, never even been allowed to show itself. In the same period, he had become very physically nervous of her: he kept an embarrassed and awkward distance between them. Then the time comes, as your husband's work settles, as your son grows away, when you know you can't live for ever through others, when the restlessness defines itself and it is your own life you consider.

Kate turned again in the bed. She was lying with her arms folded around her breasts, and her fingers were tight on her shoulders, pulling in to herself for comfort and warmth. What new life could she have, or hope to have, with things as they were? If there were any hope of some general change, things might be more bearable, but all that had faded. At every level it was a long stagnation, an endless series of postponements. The vacuity entered and destroyed. Just at times, for a few brief hours, she could enter through meetings and through print a life where

38

purpose was evident, where the meanings continually defined themselves. But when she came out on the other side, to her own actual day, it was the familiar bleak muddle, in which everybody seemed tired: the indifferent routines of buses and shops, the pervasive hard light of the streets.

With a sudden effort, she threw back the bedclothes and got out. She took off her night things and stood naked for some moments, at the mirror. But she was cold and dressed quickly. As she pulled back the curtains, letting in the grey daylight, she saw Myra, in her new yellow winter coat and blue silk headscarf, turning to close the gate on her way down to the canteen. Myra was touching her eyes as she turned to the street, probably to brush away the fine dust in the wind blowing down from the hill. Kate moved back quickly from the window; she did not want to be seen. But now Myra was looking in her bag as she walked, making sure she had everything she needed.

Kate smiled. Myra wasn't the kind to forget. She had all the domestic virtues. Thoroughly tame, like the rest of them, with their new winter coats and their headscarves protecting their sets. And looking into the bag to make sure all their functions were there: purse, shopping list, key, compact and mirror. Myra was all right, a good deal nicer than most of them, but narrow beyond belief. They would still be looking in their bags when the bomb dropped and finished it all.

Kate folded the papers, made the bed, and took the tray down to the scullery. She tidied the scullery and kitchen, dismantled the gas burners and cleaned them, and cleaned and lit the stove. While the work lasted she was satisfied, but then she walked restlessly back through the house. There was no dinner to get: Harold stayed at the canteen and Peter was usually out. Without intention, she went in to Harold's bureau and stood looking down at his blotter, where she could see the smudged reflection of his awkward writing, at many angles, and in two or three places his signature, with the line under it reduced to dots, like a scratch healing.

There was a crumpled page in the corner, and she smoothed it out and read it. It was a draft for a circular, beginning: 'Having regard to alleged disquieting reports to which reference was made in a communication to the Press by Bro. Kelly . . .' As Kate crumpled the paper again, she smiled and felt suddenly very close to Harold. The best years of their marriage, really, had been when they had sat at the kitchen table, working through the correspondence courses. In many ways it had been too late, but Harold had tried hard, and then had worked and fought through the years, like a hero. Only the heroism was of his place and time: small-scale, fragmentary, awkward.

Kate closed her eyes. It was difficult to think of him as he was now: gone dry in the service of life and the means of life. It was as if she could feel his hand in the rough ball of paper, with its senseless words, and she found suddenly that she was trembling— not only in her hands but right down through her body. She could think only to throw the paper away, as if it were burning her, but when she unlocked her fingers and let it fall, the trembling continued and she had to sit down and cover her head.

When at last she was calm again, sitting in Harold's chair with his papers in front of her, she got up slowly and wiped her eyes. It was as if she had been crying, though the eyelids were cold and dry. She looked at the telephone on top of the bureau, with the directory under it. She lifted the telephone to get the directory, and the bell rang for an instant as it was moved. She wanted to see the number, to know that communication was possible, though she had no intention of making the call or any other definitive move. It was the initials again: Dean, A. L. S. Perhaps it was not just Harold, but everyone. There was nothing, in this print, but the ordinary dry image. Nothing that had to do with her, or that she could imagine touching her. Sitting in Harold's chair, staring at the ring of the dial, she learned the number on her fingers, though her hand remained clenched and still.

Chapter Five

IN the crowded warmth of the canteen, Harold waited in the slow-moving queue. Myra was serving, and she was always slow because everybody liked her and got her talking. When his turn came, finally, he watched her pouring the dark onion gravy over the heap of mashed potato and sausages.

'Makes it look a bit better, does it?'

'Aye, I've been saving enough for you.'

'Do you think I can eat all that, then?'

'Go on, boy, get it down you. You look tired out.'

Harold glanced at Myra as she handed him the plate. She looked very strained, and her eyes were red and inflamed.

'You don't look up to the mark yourself, girl. You all right?'

'I'm all right. I got no time to be otherwise,' Myra said quickly, and at once turned away, bustling a tray of used dishes through to the big open kitchen with its shining equipment. Harold picked up his knife and fork, and looked across for Gwyn. As he made his way across several men stopped him, catching his arm to make hurried arrangements. He listened patiently and answered with his usual seriousness. He was a different man, here, from the man either Kate or Peter normally saw. Everybody knew his integrity and respected him. Even young Dick Manning, who would fight him at meetings, was always respectful to his face. The plate of dinner was getting cold, but Harold made no move. He simply stayed turned to go on until each conversation finished.

'They let you come at last, then,' Gwyn said, as Harold reached the table where his brother had been saving a place. Harold nodded and sat to his food. He ate busily, seeming to cut himself off from the ragging talk that was going on all around. Somebody had spilled sugar on the green plastic table. He brushed it away quickly with the side of his hand.

Gwyn sat quietly beside him. He had taken out a letter and was reading it through.

'Shall I get your pudding, boy?'

'Aye, Gwyn, if you will,' Harold said, emptying his mouth.

'And you might have a look at this letter,' Gwyn said. 'We'll have to fix it soon.'

'What's that, then?'

'The caravans.'

'Oh, yes. Right.'

Harold changed his glasses and took the letter. It was from old Wyndham Evans, the father of Myra's first husband, Jack, who had been killed on a motorbike within a year of their marriage. Old Wyndham still ran the garage, and the local bus, in Trawsfynydd, up the valley, north-west of Gwenton. The Owen brothers and their families, every year, rented his two caravans for their holidays.

Harold looked through the letter.

> *'Kestrel Service Station,*
> *Trawsfynydd,*
> *Nr Gwenton, Mon*
> *Tuesday.*

Dear Myra and Gwyn and Beth,

I have been meaning to write for the last week but there has been a terrible amount of work. This is to say that it is all right about the caravans again, last week in July and first in August as usual, at sixteen pounds ten shillings each for the fortnight. I shall look forward to seeing you all again, it is the best part of my year. Only you must make it definite by the end of the month, because I remember Kate said last year it was about time you all had a holiday abroad and it was just as easy, and I have had some other inquiries for those two weeks, being the Bank Holiday.

You see, Gwyn, I am now seventy-one, and I don't count on anything very much. There is more than ever to do in the garage, and though Phil Evans is very good on the bus and the difficult jobs, it's harder getting a lad on the pumps, young Kidley went off last week, stayed just long enough to get his card stamped, and I'm not as fast as I was getting out to it when the bell goes and some of these touring just sit in the driving seat and hoot and I feel like letting them because if they went on there's no other pump for six miles the one way and fourteen the other so they might as well be patient. What I have been thinking about, Gwyn, is this. When I go, I don't want this place going to strangers, I've been building it up too long since the one pump and the van. I feel I want to get it all straightened out and settled and I know I've said nothing to you but you know how much I think of Myra and Beth is my only grandchild and Jack's gone that it was to be for. I know you're earning good money now, Gwyn, but we are not doing too bad here at the Kestrel and you could go through the books and of course it would all have to be settled up straight with the lawyer, so that it was in the names of

Myra and Beth. Anyhow think it over, Gwyn, and when you come in the summer, if you come, which Kate said you mightn't, we could get it all tied up if that was what you wanted. There's room in the house for you all to live while I'm still here and there's all new equipment with the petrol which is the best of the money. You must work it all out`for yourself, and ask Myra. Of course it would be like coming back home for her.

There is a long letter, but I had to say, Gwyn. Remember me to Myra and Beth, and to the folks next door, I hope you are all well.
Yours affectionately,
Wyndham G. Evans'

As Harold was finishing the letter, Gwyn came back and put down the two plates of pudding.

'Here you are, then. Ginger again.'

'Aye, so I see.'

'You read the letter?'

'Yes. I see it wasn't just about the caravans.'

'No.'

'Had this ever been brought up before then?'

'No, mun, never. Though, mind, he did tell Myra there'd one day be a surprise coming to her. Only she thought perhaps money.'

'What's your own feeling, then?'

Gwyn looked at Harold before answering, and sat down.

'I don't know, boy. What would you say?'

Harold change his glasses again, and looked round the crowded room. The ceiling was low, and with the small windows the lights had always to be on. Sometimes, just looking at it, he felt trapped.

'It's got its attractions, Gwyn. Trawsfynydd's a nice place.'

'Aye, bit better than here.'

'I don't know. You got to take it all to account. What sort of turnover would it be? He don't mention.'

'No, but it's a fair amount, mun, must be. There's a lot of business there now, with the farms.'

'It's the profit I meant, really. Like you'd have to put that up against your wage.'

'Aye, though living, mind, there, would be cheaper. And he don't do bad, you know. You think, with the two caravans.'

Harold looked down, and pulled his plate in front of him. The pudding broke as he pushed his spoon into it, and he looked down into the coarse crumbly grain and the amber syrup.

'I expect Myra'd like it, wouldn't she? Like it would be going back home for her.'

'Aye, that's what Wyndham says. In the letter. Only in fact, see, it's turned out just the opposite. She was wild against it when she read the letter. I thought perhaps it was that old business. She'd be going back, see, to where she was with Jack.'

'All that's a long time ago.'

'Well, this has brought it all up again. She was crying at home when I left. I thought perhaps she wouldn't come down. She even snapped out at Beth.'

'Aye, I thought she was upset about something.'

'So there's a lot to consider,' Gwyn said, looking down at the table. 'Like I keep thinking myself, that field there is, below where he keeps the caravans. If I had that, now, I'd start a nursery, young trees, I've always wanted to.'

'You want to watch. You'd be running a garage, not a market garden.'

'A nursery, I said. And I could manage the both.'

'I reckon the garage would be enough, or you'd neglect it. Though, mind you, make your plans.'

Harold hesitated, and then smiled.

'After all, this place grew from a garage. You never know.'

'I suppose it did,' Gwyn said, looking around. 'Only it isn't that, it's just I'd like the trees. There's a lot you can do that way, with just the space. Like these chaps grow an apple and give their name to it, and there it still is, after them. Only it all still depends on Myra.'

Chapter Six

KATE walked slowly down the street where Arthur had his flat. She had met him the previous day, by chance, in the bookshop. They had talked for a few minutes. He was joking about looking in to see that people bought his book. Then he had to hurry because he had pupils coming.

'I wish I could give you some tea, Kate, but the young men will be waiting.'

'It's all right. I have to get back, anyway.'

In fact there had been nearly two hours to wait before Harold came home. But it had seemed the right thing to say.

'Are you often in town in the afternoons, Kate? Why don't you come round?'

'I am sometimes.'

'Then why not come? Tomorrow, for instance?'

It had not seemed urgent. Indeed she wondered if it was just that he couldn't really put it off, having asked. And he was already, in effect, hurrying away.

'Yes, all right, then.'

'About two. You know where I am.'

'Yes.'

'We can talk about the working party and so on.'

Then he had waved and was gone. And the difficulty now, Kate thought, was to know just what had been said. For the tone was so light, so matter-of-fact, that it was difficult to find any real significance in it. Of course that was always the way he talked. But the invitation couldn't be entirely casual. It wouldn't be so in her own world.

She crossed the road to the theatre, where she could easily stand for a few minutes until it was time. She remembered how bitter Peter now was, when he came back from the theatre. Of course he went with Beth, who always drove him to that kind of frustration. And no wonder, really, for she was exactly like Myra in her mind and feelings. Narrower than you could believe until you actually touched it.

She was looking at the box of theatre photographs. Only they weren't much help in getting an idea of the play. They were just selected poses of the players, hardly even in character. But of course graded in size. One star mouth equals one bit part shoulder. 'We used to have Dame Schools, now we have Dame Theatres,' Peter had said, in that long tirade.

The glass of the display box was reflecting the street, and she caught sight of her own reflection for a moment before turning away. She seemed very small and vague, against the gloss of those emphatic photographs. They were of course enlarged, blown up. It didn't leave you much chance, but forget it. She pushed her hands deeper into the pockets of her white raincoat. At least she wouldn't walk like that lot. Not mince, not glide, not stride, not hobble. If you kept your arms still you could get along as yourself, making nothing much of it either way. If only she could know why Arthur had asked her.

The clocks were striking two, and she crossed the street again. She had marked the door and now she opened it quickly and went along the passage to the stairs. Edwardian furnishing seemed to last longest in hallways. This conventional feeling—the old hall-stand, the fern—didn't fit with Arthur at all. Still, go on up. Only at each landing slow down and wait a bit. She didn't want to be out of breath when he came to the door. Yet she was breathing too fast, in spite of all her controls. She waited some moments before she at last rang the bell. There was a long delay, but she would certainly not ring again. Then the door opened suddenly.

'Kate. Of course. Come in.'

'I'd made up my mind you were out.'

'I'm sorry. Only it could have been anybody. It's all very well being central but they look you up, you know. Only here for the day and expect you to care.'

'Except that we'd agreed this time,' Kate said.

'Yes, I know. That's fine. Well, do come in.'

She slipped past him as he held the door open. She walked to the middle of the sitting-room and pushed her hands even deeper into her pockets.

'You know and I know but they don't know,' Arthur said, coming past her. 'Anyway, sit down, Kate. Let me get you a drink.'

'No, thank you.'

'Really? Well, let me take your coat.'

'I can manage.'

She unbelted the tight raincoat, and unbuttoned it quickly and folded it over a chair.

46

'I knew a man once,' Arthur said, 'whenever the doorbell rang he used to put on his overcoat. Then he'd go to the door, a bit flustered, with his hand on the buttons. If it was somebody he didn't want he was terribly sorry, he was just going out. If it was somebody he wanted he'd just come in. Do come in.'

'You ought to try that yourself sometime.'

'I wonder, Kate. I wonder if it would really work. Suppose it had been raining, for example?'

'If it means that much, you could try it and see. Or just tell whoever it is to go away.'

'All right, Kate. You're not amused, forget it.' They were standing facing each other, and in the pause of conversation this was awkward. 'Sit by the fire, Kate. You look cold.'

'Thank you.'

'I'll put some coffee on, shall I? It won't take a minute.'

'Yes, thank you.'

He smiled and went out. Kate let out her breath and sank back in the deep chair by the fire. She closed her eyes for some time, trying to get back her bearings. Had he really forgotten that she was coming? She pulled herself up suddenly, and looked round the room. The bookcases on two sides were wall-length and ceiling-high. The furniture was very ordinary, though quite comfortable. Very much like her own sitting-room, though this one was bigger. She had been once to his room in college, for a meeting, and that had been better, more like her idea of him. But he had lived in this flat while he was married, and stayed on since the divorce. Perhaps this, except for the books, was the wife's taste, though Kate knew nothing about her. She stared into the fire, thinking back to herself at that time.

When he came back with the coffee, she started up. She should, of course, have offered to help make the coffee, but it hadn't occurred to her until now. She pulled up a table for him to put the tray on, and then watched him sit down. Everything he did was very clear and firm. He moved and sat like a much younger man, and the clothes emphasized this: the light fawn tweeds, the pale orange shirt with the thickly knotted green tie, the light brown handmade shoes. The hair was close and curly: like a packed cigarette end, she found herself suddenly thinking. The face was still handsome, though deeply lined. Every man of my kind, she remembered him saying, gets in his late thirties this ravaged look, that used to be called intelligence.

'Would you like to see to the coffee, Kate, or shall I?'

47

'I will, Arthur, of course.'

'It's not very good, but it'll be warm and wet.'

'Who cares?' she said suddenly.

She poured two cups and set them on opposite edges of the table. He offered a cigarette, and leaned across with a light.

'What did you think of the reviews, then?' she asked, more easily.

'My dear, I don't think of the reviews. I know the people who write them.'

'One or two weren't bad.'

' "This slightly alarming thought",' Arthur said, laughing. 'But any thought seems to alarm them, especially in that department.'

'It's understandable,' Kate said.

'Of course it is. It's because they can't tell the truth. So they go all prim in print, or else when they lash out they're wildly, consciously naughty.'

'They shock quite enough people as it is.'

'Of course, but that's the whole point. In a completely guilt-ridden society literally nothing can be said. And these old boys who see the devil at work are quite right. There is this literal connection between diabolism and radicalism, though they've drawn all the wrong conclusions. Since the devil has our animal parts, he's quite plainly subversive, and an attack along those lines really does threaten the social order. As indeed it deserves to be threatened.'

'I don't really see that. I mean, is it connected?'

'Oh, yes. And one's only protection is that they don't quite get the point. Like an old boy in college who congratulated me on my life of Sir Joshua. Presumably the only Reynolds he's ever heard of.'

'Did you tell him?'

'No, of course not. I have to live with him. And to his dying day he'll have me and Sir Joshua linked, instead of some prurient radical. Oh, that was the other, wasn't it? "Some prurient reverie". God, what must their minds be like?'

'I don't know, Arthur. You know them better than I do.'

'Yes, but tell me, Kate. All sorts of people are going to read it. What would the average member of a Women's Co-operative Guild make of the founder of their Sunday paper?'

'I don't know.'

'Perhaps like the Women's Institutes, adopting a hymn to sex as their national song and not even knowing?'

'Do they?'

'But now the Co-operative Women's Guild, I can really see that.'

'Yes, but why should you expect me to know?'

'Don't you really?'

'No, Arthur, I don't.'

She pushed back her hair, looking away. She wanted to answer, in real terms, but she could not find the words. Perhaps he had asked her just to know this, and that would be really insulting.

'I don't know at all, Arthur. I'm as cut off as you are. My sister-in-law, Myra, belongs to the Guild. But she reads a quite different Sunday paper, more like Reynolds' own stuff, I'd imagine.'

'Oh, well, it'll all wear off,' Arthur said. 'Do I know Myra?'

'I don't think so. Harold's brother, Gwyn, he's her second husband.'

'Divorced?'

'Goodness, no. Her first husband was killed, on a motorbike, soon after they married. He left her a little daughter and then she married Gwyn.'

'Is she nice?'

'Myra? I don't know, really. In her way she's been very attractive. She seems like a wild thing gone tame. You can't believe her narrowness when you look at her.'

'That comes in all forms, surely?'

'Yes, I know it does, but I didn't mean it that way. I mean, really, she's a very passionate person, she must be, and it's as if it's all gone to fat. Like, for example, she was pregnant with Beth when she married. Yet now she goes crazy if sex is so much as mentioned.'

'Perhaps for that reason.'

'I don't know,' Kate said, looking down. 'She and Gwyn have never had children. I don't really know why. She'll never talk about it.'

'More his fault than hers, perhaps?'

'Don't put it like that.'

'How should I put it?'

'Don't put it at all. I've no right, really, to sit here talking about her. Nor have you, you don't even know her.'

'All right, Kate, all right. Don't get so worked up.'

Kate stood and walked to the window. There was a fine view,

from close up, over the old red and grey roofs to the crowded towers of the colleges. She stared out, biting back her anger.

It was all coming out so disastrously wrong, and she could hardly bear to look at what was now quite evident. When she arrived he had virtually forgotten that she was coming, and then he had simply settled down to patronize and insult her, as if she were a delegate from the Women's Co-operative Guild. This must be how he really regarded her, and not as a woman at all. Yet it had never come out before, in all the times they had talked after meetings. It had always seemed, quite simply, that they were people on the same side, sharing the same way of looking at life, and able to respect each other from that. Now, suddenly, all the emphasis was on their difference: that they came from quite different ways of life and could not really communicate.

Well, when it came to it, she belonged more with Myra and Harold and Gwyn than with him. She couldn't join him in his distance from them. But she was angry because she saw that she had wanted to do just this. Wasn't this, in a way, why she had found him attractive? A man with just that difference from a way of living she could no longer stand? Forced for this moment to look into herself, she was angry and ashamed.

Arthur had stayed in his chair, watching her, but now he got up and stood behind her.

'It's quite pleasant, isn't it?' he said easily. 'We normally don't see roofs enough.'

'I ought not to have come, Arthur. I knew it would bring all this out.'

'All what, Kate? I really don't understand.'

'Only it was easy enough when it was all quite general. I could pick up your tone. But when I mentioned Myra it was suddenly as if she was here in the room. And Gwyn and Harold too.'

'Well, of course,' Arthur said, 'they're your family.'

Kate turned sharply and looked up into his face. He held her look for a moment, still with the trace of a smile that was probably not even conscious.

'I got myself into this, Arthur. It's my own fault. You asked me and I said I'd come. And you said to talk about the working party, but I knew perfectly well—I thought I knew perfectly well—that wasn't really why you asked. I'm not a green girl but I'm sometimes, I think, more stupid.'

'You're certainly very explicit, Kate.'

'Yes, because I thought that was what education was for.'

50

'Education?'

'You see, you don't even understand that. You can take it all for granted. What do you think drives me out of my home but that there are things to say, things to do, that are simply impossible there? Do you think I'm just on the loose?'

Arthur hesitated, looking down at his shoes.

'Of course not, Kate. I've too much respect for you to think anything of the kind.'

'Well, what do you think then?'

'Very much as you've put it yourself. That you've got gifts you can't use where you are.'

'Look, I don't see them as gifts. They were worked for, such as they are. And I'm not giving anything either. The margin's too narrow.'

'Of course, I agree.'

They were standing facing each other, but Kate avoided looking at him.

'I'm asking why you invited me, Arthur.'

'Well, now, is that so difficult? After all, we know each other quite well, and we've always got on. I just thought it would be pleasant. Say to meet for once without an agenda.'

'Yet you'd forgotten I was coming.'

'No. No, really.'

'And all that about the guild. It was as if you didn't see me as myself, but as a sort of contact. Some of my best friends live the other side of the river.'

'How can you really say that, Kate? The easiest thing in the world is that abstract contact. I can get that all the time at meetings.'

'What then? Tell me.'

'Look, let's sit down. This standing confronting each other puts everything out.'

He smiled and went back to his chair. After a brief hesitation, Kate followed. She sat deeply back, with her legs curled under her.

'I'm not very good at this, Kate. I never understand people's explanations of each other. But isn't it back to what I was saying? That the society is so guilty that literally nothing can be said. I mean, whatever we formally believe, in fact, as we live, we meet this same difficulty. I ask you to come and you agree, and at that level it's easy. I think, for myself, it could stay easy, but I'm not in the same situation. I may be wrong but I think you got angry

51

because you felt guilty. And you were guilty that you were here with me at all.'

'Why should I be, though? I've done nothing wrong.'

'Yes, you've called on a colleague. This is the nineteen-sixties and it's quite often done. Men and women have to work together, so they learn new conventions. That's what we all believe.'

'Because it's true. Isn't it?'

'Certainly it's true but it's not all the truth. For many people it's all so recent that they still have the old reactions. That when a man and woman meet privately it's just for one thing.'

'No, that isn't why I was angry, Arthur. Really.'

'It seemed so to me. At least neither of us was quite certain which convention this was. The confusion was a way of sorting it out.'

'But it wasn't only that. Really.'

'Maybe it wasn't. I don't know. But the thing is, surely, to stop letting the guilt run us. Since the whole atmosphere is guilty, we all think we must ask for a statement of intentions. But life isn't like that. Nobody, at the beginning of a relationship, can possibly be tied down. The thing just has to be lived through.'

'It wasn't that I was meaning.'

'Well, Kate, relax. All I mean is, I asked you because I wanted to.'

'All right,' Kate said.

She looked down at her hands, which had been tightly clasped over her ankles. Slowly, she let the fingers go loose. The tension had gone, suddenly, and she could feel and enjoy the warmth of the fire.

'What are you thinking about?' Arthur asked, some minutes later. He had been watching her carefully, but she seemed quite withdrawn and unaware of him.

'Thinking?' she repeated, looking across at him. 'About Peter, actually.'

He could not understand the way she was looking. She seemed strange and distant, but also as if she were trying, under pressure, to reach and recognize him.

'Your son?'

'Yes. I told you about him.'

'I remember you saying he's researching. Did you tell me who's supervising him?'

'Dr Lane. Robert Lane.'

'Ah, yes,' Arthur said, and smiled.

52

'What does the smile mean?'

'You wouldn't know, Kate. Never mind. At least he's very able.'

'Well, of course he is.'

'He's also the last of the Mohicans, and that's not so funny. Still, I expect it's all right.'

'You'd better say what you mean.'

'I don't know how to, Kate. You either see through Lane or you don't. He's a preacher really and of course quite persuasive. I should have thought the young men would be tired of it, but I suppose they need it, in a way. You see, he's an old style utopian, and completely self-righteous about it. But he manages to wrap it all up in a jargon of his own. It sounds quite impressive till you come down to cases. I don't think he sees the actual world at all. He's just tuned it out and let his phrases take over. All you can respect, really, is his persistence: that he goes on exposing himself in that kind of vague simplicity, and seems not to notice. You could say it takes courage but in fact it takes his wife. She has to live with the consequences of it all, and in fact it's breaking her. He's the last to notice, of course.'

'What sort of consequences?'

'Well, just that he knows nothing about the world and nothing about people, but he goes on predicting their future. Can you imagine what it's like to live with a man like that?'

'No, Arthur, I can't.'

'You should take a look at May Lane. Or at him. It's pretty appalling.'

'Perhaps I will,' Kate said.

She closed her eyes, and again relaxed. They were both silent for some time. Arthur leaned across and tidied the fire, putting on two new logs. As he sat back, he realized that she was watching him again, and he smiled.

'Go on,' he said.

'It's nothing. I was just wondering if you really know as much about people as you seem to.'

'No. But in that case it isn't difficult. You only have to look at them together, or see him without her.'

'Yes, but how do you tell when somebody's being broken?'

'It's different, I suppose, in each case. With May Lane it's just utter fatigue.'

'Is it? Then what would you say about me?'

Arthur looked at her again. In the warmth of the fire, and

53

curled in the big chair, she had lapsed into a softness which was very unlike the woman he ordinarily knew. She was like a girl asking, really. And with her tiny body, in its simple dress, and with the shoulder-length hair, she looked, in the shadows, very much like a girl.

'Not breakdown, Kate.'

'Then what? Tell me.'

'I don't know, Kate. Really I don't.'

She moved suddenly, uncurling her legs and leaning forward.

'It can come on something quite small,' she said, and now he could see her face more clearly—the staring dark eyes, the pale heavy cheeks, the tightness around the mouth. 'All my life I've wanted a holiday in France, and it really isn't difficult, we could save up for it and my French is good enough. But every year, without fail, we go to a couple of caravans by Myra's father-in-law's garage, in Wales. We play cards round the calor-gas lamp, in those poky caravans, because of course it's usually raining. But I've made up my mind. This year I won't. I'm going to France, if necessary on my own.'

'I think you're very wise,' Arthur said, reaching for a cigarette.

'No,' Kate cried, and her sudden intensity frightened him. Her whole body was coiled tight and trembling. 'How can you just sit there and tell me I'm wise? It isn't only in the caravan I have to sit and play cards, sit on and on in that poky world.'

'What else should I say, Kate? Should I offer to take you?'

'No, thank you.'

'You see. That's why vague approval seemed just about right.'

'You calculate your tone too much, Arthur. It makes it very difficult to trust you.'

'Does it? I'm sorry,' he said, colouring. But his voice was ironic, making it clear that he felt no need to apologize. He stood up and carried the tray to a table near the door. He looked less attractive now, with the clash of his angered skin against the lightness of his clothes. The agile body seemed also suddenly tired.

'I'd better go,' Kate said, and got up.

'Must you?'

'Yes. Though I'm glad I came. I don't often get the chance to talk like this.'

He turned and looked at her. She was putting on her raincoat and belting it tightly round her tiny body. She put up her hand quickly, and pushed back her hair.

'You're very intelligent, Kate. Perhaps that's the real difficulty.'

'I can work things out. It never seems to help.'

'It's not over yet. There's still plenty of time.'

'I don't feel it. Not in myself.'

'But you're still young, Kate. You can live as you want.'

'No.'

She moved as she spoke, and went quickly past him.

'Shall I be seeing you again?' he asked, following her. But it was as if the words were forced from him. He could not welcome this quickening which was also fear and despair.

'Yes, I expect so,' Kate said. 'The committees will keep coming.'

'But otherwise?'

'I don't know. You said these things can't be planned.'

'To meet can be planned.'

'We'll just have to see. I don't know.'

'I'll ring you,' Arthur said.

Chapter Seven

THE mountain ash by the house was still bright with berries. Kate looked across at the tree, as she hurried through to the entry. Gwyn, working bent over his car, looked up and waved. She smiled and went in. She didn't want to talk.

Gwyn leaned back, straightening his arms so that he could get the right control on his fingers, working in the last lead. He was putting in a replacement battery. Worth more than the car, Harry Campbell had teased him.

Only they were always on at him, teasing old Mag. What you want, boy's, a Minnie. Or afraid of seeing that face of yours in the chrome? Don't take no notice, there always has to be ragging. Certainly Harold's is new, but that's the difference between us. He never wants to look under the bonnet, scared of it there like a woman. Just click and go, that's his option, so of course it has to be new. Only with me it's keeping the old one going. Old Mag, it's like more than a car. Thomas Edward Chalmers, 15 Smuts Close, Banbury, February 1939. New World Products, Walsall, 1942. Tudor Alexander Roberts, 47 Estate Approach, Slough, 1949. Gwyn Brinley Owen, 287 Goldsmith Street, 1953. Like a pedigree almost, and she's been well used.

Only starting now in the autumn, the bits of lights just draining the old battery. Easy enough, see, in the mornings, just jumping her a bit to start down the pitch. Only the other night, the old starter grinding like an out-of-work harmonium, and the swing only flooded her, apart from nearly breaking my arm. Of course the other chaps laughing and coming round quick to push. We make them, boy, you wreck them. It always is funny and you can't get away from it. Only let the clutch up quiet or you'll half rupture them pushing. And take it easy home, up the hill.

Not a bad battery, by the look of it. At three pound ten, reconditioned, it should see old Mag out. Only it meant going to the post office, and the usual bloody entry on the wrong side of the page. If this garage business came off, with old Wyndham, there'd be no need to worry. But Myra had to be left on her own, making up her own mind. No use having rows, it wouldn't make a farthing of difference. It was only to wait, really. Hang on to

56

what you'd got. Like Harold saying there'd be more short time before Christmas. It's all of it living a bit at a time.

There was the quick sound of a horn: Harold driving in next door. Kate just home in front of him, that makes a change. Can't make out where she gets to, but it's her own business. Only tooting like that, sounds a bit too cheerful for Harold. It's going bad in that house. Only see him on holiday, get his sandals on and a drop of beer inside him, he's as lively as the next. This bloody politics kills people.

It does, whatever you say. It used to be heaven they were saving up for. No time to live here, boy, we're getting ready for the next. Do anything, have anything, it's marked against you, wrong side of the book. And the same with this lot. Like when the Labour was in they used to say girding, girding our loins. Against the serious situation ahead. What the hell you gird your loins for against that? Only no use saying. They talk you down. Like now, nearly ten years after, still half worrying what you heard them say: nineteen-fifty-two, the year of decision. Old Cripps on the wireless. We can look ahead to that crisis year. Fifty-two, the make or break of the British economy. And we must be steadfast and watchful and above all wholehearted in energy. All brothers together, in this sacred cause, in which we cannot afford to fail. Fifty-two. And now, ten years after, there's none of them can remember what happened that year. Not that anyhow. And old Cripps dead and not to see it, but the rest of us still, with the new years, going through the same bloody motions.

'You got the battery then?'

'Aye.'

Harold stepped across the low, dividing wall. Gwyn stepped back to meet him.

'You got one at Bywater's?'

'Aye, three pound ten.'

'Be all right, I should think.'

'Last out the car, anyhow.'

Harold took off his glasses, and wiped them. 'It's nice, that tree, isn't it?' he said suddenly.

'Aye, though it's getting a bit too big. A chap was saying the other day, Edwards along the road, there's as much tree below ground as there is above, the roots going down. And you can hardly credit it, can you, if you look at it? With it only that bit from the house.'

Harold put on his glasses again.

'We might drop round a bit later on, Gwyn. If it's all right with you.'

'Aye, we'll be there.'

'It's this writing about the caravans.'

'Aye.'

'Best talk it over, see, the four of us.'

'Is she still against it?'

Harold nodded.

'Mind, I see her point, boy,' he said quickly. 'Lots of people do go abroad, there's nothing unusual about it. Only the other's got like a habit.'

Gwyn turned away, pulling down the bonnet and fastening the spring hooks.

'Beth was saying something about Easter. Her and Peter.'

'No, I haven't heard that,' Harold said.

'I said it's all right with me, if Beth wants it. Only Myra, well. I suppose it's the way women see it.'

Harold was staring down at the wheel of the car. Gwyn looked into his face. He was getting, now, more the look of their father.

'We can talk about it tonight then,' Harold said, at last.

Harold and Kate came round, as arranged, after supper. Harold had changed, into his new sports coat and flannels. Kate had come in the tight black jersey and jeans she often wore in the house. She looked very pale as she stood talking to Myra while Harold went off with Gwyn to look round the conservatory. Peter and Beth were still out. He had met her from work to go straight to a cinema. They had said they would be back about eight.

Until the men came back, Kate and Myra avoided the question of the holiday. They never talked easily and in any case, on Myra's side, it always seemed that the decision was for the men to make. But Harold and Gwyn, also, seemed to be avoiding talking about it. They stayed alone together much longer than was necessary just to see round the conservatory. But then at last they came back.

'Let's have some beer, then,' Gwyn said. 'There's some bottles out the kitchen.'

'I'll get them,' Myra said, and went out.

'And how you keeping, Kate?' Gwyn asked, trying to make things easy.

'I'm not keeping, Gwyn, I'm a bad keeper.'

'Get away, you look like one of these rock girls.'

'I do not look like a rock girl.'

'You do to me. And very nice too.'

'Oh, shut up, Gwyn, just shut up,' Kate said. She moved away, and sat by the fire. There was hardly any real anger in her voice. She and Gwyn had always talked like this, and had got used to it.

'You don't want to go to Trawsfynydd, I hear?' Gwyn said, coming across.

'No, Gwyn, I don't.'

'Well, there it is then.'

'Except that I don't want to spoil it for the rest of you. If it breaks up it may do none of us any good.'

'Look, between us it don't matter. I mean, Harold and me it won't affect, and if you can't go where you want for your holiday it's not a holiday at all.'

'All right, then, Gwyn.'

'Only it isn't just us. That's what I'm trying to say. What this is really about, look, is Peter and Beth.'

'I think so too,' Harold said. He was still standing, nervously, in the centre of the room. There seemed no way in for him, to the quick talk of the others.

'What about Peter and Beth?' Kate asked.

'Well, Beth told her Mam that Peter was asking her to go down there Easter.'

'Well, why not?'

'And still leave marrying till the summer?'

'Why not, Harold? Let them do as they want,' Kate said. She sat back in her chair and curled her legs under her. 'After all, they're old enough now to make their own decisions. And they're going to get married.'

'They're not actually engaged,' Harold said.

'No, that's what I said,' Gwyn added.

'But people don't get down on their knees and propose, Gwyn, not now. They're committed to each other, aren't they?'

'I'm not sure what that means,' Harold answered. 'Like it isn't I'm against it, they're old enough as you say to make up their own minds. Only we want to be fair to Myra and Gwyn. And to Beth, naturally.'

'And to Peter,' Kate said.

'Well, yes, of course. Fair all round.'

'It's their own decision,' Kate repeated.

59

'Well, no, Kate, not altogether. You say they're old enough, they can do what they want. But nobody, when you look at it, is ever old enough for that.'

'With their own lives.'

'Aye, but in fact their lives are bound up with other people's. It's that we're talking about.'

'Look, at their age we were all four of us married,' Kate said. 'Myra was married twice. We've got no right to go on interfering.'

'Nobody's interfering.'

'If you say that, Gwyn, you're a hypocrite.'

'I'm no bloody hypocrite, Kate. I'm just trying to get it square. And as Harold said, they're not really engaged. Beth don't wear a ring.'

'Because they can't afford it,' Kate said. 'They've better things to do with the money. Do you think it's the ring holds anybody? It's what they feel.'

'You wear a ring,' Gwyn said. 'All married women do, and the girls when they're engaged. It isn't just the ring, it's setting it out open in public. And don't tell me either they can't afford it. We both married on less than they get.'

'Well, you want them to marry, then?' Kate said. As she spoke, Myra came back, with the bottles and glasses on a tray.

'Want who to marry?' Myra said, setting down the tray.

'We were talking about Peter and Beth.'

'They'll marry when they're ready,' Myra said. She began pouring out the beer, and the others watched her, not speaking. It was as if her return had changed the whole atmosphere in which they were talking.

'And when do you think that will be?' Kate asked, at last.

'They said the summer.'

'Yes, Myra, but now they're talking of this holiday at Easter.'

'No, they don't want to do that.'

'But they do want to. That's what we're talking about.'

Myra took the glasses from the tray and passed them round: first to Harold, then Gwyn, then Kate.

'I thought we were going to talk about our own holiday,' she said, looking at Gwyn.

'Well, yes, love, only this other came up.'

'I'll see about that with Beth,' Myra said. 'What I want to know is, are Harold and Kate coming with us?'

'Well, they're here, look. Why don't you ask them?'

Kate said nothing, but sat quite deliberately still. Harold was

sitting on the stool by the television. He had not touched the
beer he was holding between his knees.

'We were thinking, perhaps, about a holiday abroad,' he said,
at last.

'I knew Kate was,' Myra said.

'Aye, well, we both have. There's chaps in the works go to
Spain and Italy, and once they've tried it they keep going. Like
I said to them the other day, Harry Purdom, you know him,
Gwyn. There's more goes to Spain now for their holidays than
went out to the Brigade, when there was the fighting.'

'Well, of course,' Gwyn said, 'the end of the journey's a bit
different.'

'Aye, that's what I said.'

'And not only different, it's better.'

'There's no need to bring that into it,' Kate said.

'And old Harry was saying, the first time it was like Everest or
something, they were all tensed up. Only once it started it was
easy.'

'Exactly,' Kate said.

'I don't think I should like it,' Myra said suddenly to Harold.

'You don't know till you've tried, Myra.'

'Well, no, I don't think I should. And anyhow, Gwyn's got to
go to Trawsfynydd, with this about the garage.'

Kate laughed, rocking back in her chair. She had pulled up her
knee and was resting her chin on it, while her fingers were tightly
clapsed around her bare ankle.

'What's funny about that?' Myra asked, looking down at
her.

'Not just that, Myra. It's the way it's all working out. Because
none of us, really, will talk straight.'

'I'm talking straight, what you mean?'

'Just that you were against this garage idea, when it first came
up.'

'I said Gwyn had to go, that's all.'

'But you'll go with him?'

'Yes, because he's my husband.'

'All right then.'

'And Harold will go with you, because you're his wife.'

'Harold will do what he wants.'

'Except that you've made up your mind.'

'No, I've just said what I wanted. Like Gwyn's said what he
wanted.'

'Yes, that's the difference.'

'What difference?'

'If you don't see it, it's no use talking,' Myra said, and turned away.

The front door opened, and Peter and Beth came in. They were lively and laughing from their walk from the bus, and the cold air had put colour in their cheeks. They seemed surprised to see the others together, and they picked up the tension in the small, crowded room. But they didn't intend to be affected by it. They seemed, tonight, very sure of themselves.

'You two won't have eaten,' Myra said.

'Yes, Mam. We got coffee and hot dogs from the stall.'

'What's that? A bit of pig's leavings and breadcrumbs in a wad of sour paste.'

'No, they're not that bad,' Peter said.

'Beth persuaded me once,' Myra said. 'Only never again.'

Peter looked across at his mother.

'Was the film good?' Kate asked.

'All right. I didn't think you'd be in here.'

'We've been talking over a few things,' Harold said.

'What?'

Myra moved quickly.

'Never mind all that, Peter. Look, sit down, and you, Beth. We'll have a game of cards, take our minds off it.'

'Aye, let's have a game of whist,' Gwyn agreed.

'We're too many,' Kate said. 'I won't play.'

'I won't either,' Peter said. 'You four go on.'

'No, I'll sit out,' Harold said. 'You play, Peter.'

'I don't like it much, Dad. Go on, you relax.'

Harold was in fact stiff and tense on the edge of his chair. His face was blank and tired behind the heavy glasses. But it was clear at once that Peter had said the wrong thing. Harold's mouth tightened, as if Peter had betrayed him. But almost at once he made the effort and got up, setting his feelings aside and adjusting to the others.

'No relaxing playing whist with Myra,' he said. 'She's a terror on it, aren't you, girl?'

'Aye, well, you be my partner, Harold. Then we'll get on all right.'

As she spoke, Myra carried the folding table from behind the television and set it up near the fire. The cards were ready, on the crowded mantelpiece.

'You and Harold against me and Beth, then,' Gwyn said, taking the cards. Beth agreed, and went to her place.

They all settled around the table. Kate had to move, and went and sat on the stool by the television. Peter went across and sat near her. As the dealing finished, and the others were picking up their hands and talking, he turned to her.

'Was it important?'

'It's important, all right.'

'The garage?'

'Not only that.'

He looked into her face. They were talking closely, quietly, as they had formerly so often. But there was a look in Kate's face that Peter could not understand: a subdued excitement that was on the edge of open delight.

'May I know?'

'It isn't just one thing. It's suddenly all come together. Each thing tied up with the next.'

'Am I involved?'

'Yes, you and Beth.'

He looked away. In the activity at the table, there was a sudden curse from Gwyn. Myra, smiling happily, was gathering in an unexpected trick, her hands beautifully assured and controlled.

'You're a devil, you know, Mam,' Beth said.

'Aye, it's my wickedness coming out,' Myra said, happily.

Kate smiled, with an edge of contempt. It was clear how quickly Harold had adjusted to the atmosphere Myra had created. She had set up the table, with the glasses and the cards and the fire, and Harold had accepted it all, as if coming home. He and Gwyn seemed suddenly more like each other. As they would be, Kate thought, if it was only Myra's world.

'Did Easter come up?' Peter asked quietly.

'Yes, I shouldn't worry about that.'

'What's the problem, then?'

'There isn't one, really. It's all working out.'

Peter smiled, disbelievingly.

'I'm probably just being selfish,' Kate said. 'But your Dad did say we might go to France. And that's something, anyway. It gives me something to count on.'

They looked away and watched the cards. Even to them, out on the edge, the liveliness of the game came through. Myra and Harold were winning, quite regularly, but still Gwyn and Beth were excited and happy. It was a surprise to see how lively Beth

63

was, how concentrated and satisfied, in that quick circle. Peter could understand, for the moment, how reluctant she must be, always, to go against Myra's world. As the play went on, he and his mother seemed more and more isolated, away on the edge of things. Gwyn came across once to give them beer, but his mind was still back on the table. Harold was getting more and more excited, in his winning partnership with Myra.

At last the game finished, and Myra folded away the table.

'Bed, I should think,' Harold said.

'Aye,' Gwyn agreed. 'That was very nice.'

Peter stood up, watching Beth.

'I hear that Easter's all right, love,' he said.

'Is it?' Beth asked, turning to Myra.

'We'll talk about it tomorrow,' Myra said, picking up the glasses.

'Why not now?' Kate said. 'We're all here.'

'No, look, we've had a nice evening,' Harold said, picking up two of the glasses and holding them in front of him, on the fingers of one hand. He was withdrawn and stubborn, as he often had to be in his union work. Peter stood, bewildered. Beth was looking anxiously at her mother, and the colour had rushed through her face.

'We want to do what's right all round,' Gwyn said, still holding the cards.

'If you're thinking of getting married in the summer,' Myra said easily, 'you can come with us, have the other caravan. Harold and Kate are going to France.'

'That isn't definite,' Harold said. He was turned towards Myra, but his face was still blank and tightly set. Peter saw Kate's expression for a moment, as she looked at him. It was suddenly very cold and hard, though she said nothing.

'You're thinking of going, though, aren't you, Uncle?' Beth asked.

'That depends on a good many things, Beth.'

'What things?' Kate asked, and the hardness in her voice came through, as if at last the edge had been reached.

'Whether we get a full winter's work, for a start.'

'Don't you think you will, Uncle?'

'I know we shan't.'

'Then it doesn't depend at all,' Kate said. 'You're in fact saying no.'

'It may be all right,' Gwyn said, trying to head off the row.

64

'Like you don't know either way, in this trade. It's as bad as ice-cream or paraffin. It is, you know. And if we're short this winter that don't mean anything final. They'll have us back on overtime in the spring, catching up.'

'It can take a long time to catch up the money,' Harold said. 'And France would be that much more expensive.'

'Yes, Harold, it would be,' Kate said. 'Only it's time to make up our minds. I should have thought we'd had enough of our lives being run by the works. You all sit and take it, whatever they decide to hand out to you. But I'm not waiting any longer, not on that. Every damned thing, in our generation, we've had to wait for, and after twenty-five years I've been waiting enough.'

'I know,' Harold said. 'The margin's always been narrow. Only we can't alter it, not by talking.'

'I'm beginning to think we don't want to alter it. After twenty-five years they've got us used to the cage.'

'There's no cage,' Myra said irritably.

'Isn't there? You wouldn't know if there was.'

'Don't talk like that to me, Kate?'

'Why, are you afraid to hear?'

Gwyn stepped forward quickly, to the centre of the room. 'Look, both of you, there's no use in this. It's getting like work, just arguing at each other. It only makes things worse.'

'You don't understand, Gwyn,' Kate said. 'We've got to say these things out.'

Harold went across to stand beside her. 'I think we'd better go,' he said. 'We've had a good evening, we don't want to spoil it.'

'I don't, Harold, anyway,' Myra said simply.

Kate started to speak again, but then stopped. Harold was already moving to the door, and she followed him, saying goodnight. Peter stood for a moment, undecided. He looked across at Beth. They had stood, these last minutes, embarrassed and helpless and silent. It was as if the few feet that separated them were impossible to bridge. Each could only acknowledge the other's presence and distance.

Part Two

Chapter Eight

AFTER working all day at home, Peter was going down to the city, to see Robert Lane. The time suggested had been a quarter past five, a normal enough university time though it was also the hour, each day, when the streets were jammed with home-going traffic. Sitting in the top front of the bus, looking down at the hardly moving lines of cars and buses and bicycles, Peter knew that he was bound to be late again.

It didn't matter, he decided. The appointment, at Robert's house, was now always informal. Peter had always been worried by lateness. Two minutes late, for his father, was fifteen minutes' pay. The point had been learned and taught. Yet now, finally, it was different. For if he arrived punctually, to see Robert, the sense of time would be immediately lost. Or at least, for a fairly exact hour, mislaid.

The first five minutes, in any case, would be taken up by Robert's ludicrous attempts to get his pipe going. Perhaps the thing to do would be to send some signal, sound the factory hooter, to suggest and even insist that it was now time to light up. Then, when he arrived, he would only have to see the completed pile of barely used matches, overflowing the square glass ashtray. Except that then, in the first minutes, they would have really to meet; the long sidle of the pipe would not be available.

He had been going to Robert for two years now: irregularly but often enough to establish some kind of relationship. He had learned only recently that Robert had been reluctant to take him on, but that was nothing exceptional—it was the general response, once he had said what he wanted to do. As an undergraduate he had read Politics and Economics, because that had seemed his own world, his father's world. Then, when he was accepted as a research student, he had switched to Sociology— 'one more to fall into the twentieth century's favourite parlour game,' as his college tutor had put it.

It was funny to remember that remark in the light of the negotiations that followed. For he had wanted, 'naively and all too predictably' as his first possible supervisor had told him, to study the social patterns of his own community. He had even written, in outline, 'A Study of Growth and Tensions in a Recent Industrial Community'. And what precisely would that be, he had been asked, beyond a few anecdotes in a sea of easily available but not particularly significant statistics? 'It would be what I've seen and learned, put into some disciplined shape,' he had answered, but that, apparently, had been said too often before.

After further arguments, during which he had almost given up and gone to a newspaper job in London (as Rose had wanted; they had then been talking of marrying), he had been sent to Robert, as a last chance. Robert was by training a philosopher, but he had written on social questions. His most important book was a difficult theoretical study of Social Method. Comparatively few people had read it but it had been very widely discussed. He had also contributed to a symposium on 'The World in A.D. 2000', which had been widely sold and had brought him some reputation as a minor public figure. He was working now on a second volume of the Social Method.

Peter respected and liked him, at that first meeting, but so far as his own plans went he had not got what he wanted. An actual study was quite out, Robert thought. But it might be possible to do something quite interesting and useful: a comparative analysis of method and technique in such studies, with a view to establishing their underlying theoretical assumptions. This had been done in America, and might be usefully repeated here. The only drawback, really, was that there were so few studies of British communities, as a basis for analysis, by comparison with the wealth of American material. Still, for a thesis of reasonable length (and reasonable modesty, Robert had added, smiling), there might be just enough. Would he at least think about it, as a possibility? After all, if he eventually wanted to do a study of his own or some other place, he would be that much better equipped by this theoretical preparation.

In fact this project, on which Peter had been working now for two years, had been quite satisfying, intellectually. He had not previously realized, in any abstract way, the complexities involved in the observation of others, or in the subtle relationships between the observer and what he observed. And Robert had been intelligent and helpful beyond all expectation. His first awkwardness of manner and his extreme hesitancy in conversation had behind them an immense, almost implacable persuasiveness. You came away from him with your way of looking at the world really altered, at least for a time. It was as if you at last realized what at quite deep levels of yourself you were doing and thinking and meaning.

Past the centre of the city, and into the long residential streets of the northern suburbs, the bus gradually emptied. When he got off at Robert's road, Peter noticed at once the width of the pavement, a full nine feet, although there were comparatively few people about. If you got away that far, you got room to move.

A few leaves were drifting down to the pavement: perhaps plane or sycamore. And at the bend just before the house the whole road was covered with the litter of a great horse chestnut tree: the big leaves, yellow and brown; the green spiky cases, many crushed by the wheels and edged with a milky juice; fresh nuts in the sour white pith, exposing the bright curve of sheen and bloom; a few piebald and crushed in the gutter, immature, where the layered leaves were beginning to blacken with rot.

Robert's red brick villa stood behind a screen of shrubs and small trees. There was no latch on the unpainted gate, which stood permanently open. Someone had pasted a rectangular nuclear disarmament sticker on the post, and someone else, half-heartedly, had tried to peel it off. (Rectangular, multilateral or whatever, there was still no disarmament.) Robert's car, and two bicycles, stood in the gravelled drive. Five empty milk bottles formed a half fence across the open front door.

Peter rang and walked in, to the high dark hallway. He could hear voices in the open room at the back of the house. As he hesitated, May Lane hurried out. She was very small and dark; like his mother in some ways. But until she made an effort her face was very drawn and tired.

'Peter. Yes, of course. Robert said you were coming. Do come and sit down. He's just in the garden, I'll call him.'

'No, no, I'll go out,' he said awkwardly. He did not find it easy to look directly into her face.

'Come and sit down, Peter,' a new voice called.

'Rose?' Peter said, following May into the far room.

Rose got up as he came, but they stayed at some distance from each other. The other person in the room was Robert's seventeen-year-old daughter, Frances, who had not looked up. She was sitting on a cushion under the window, her legs wide apart and her head bowed over a book, so far bent forward that her hair had fallen and almost hidden her face.

'Of course,' May said, 'you know Mrs Swinburne. You were the same year.'

'Yes,' Peter said, looking across at Frances.

'I nearly married Peter,' Rose said. 'But that was a long time ago.'

She was very assured and smiling: tall, with very clear skin and untidy sandy hair. She looked still in many ways adolescent, though this was largely deliberate, a conscious adoption of a quite common style.

I nearly married Peter. Like Brittany instead of Pembroke this summer. It was now more than two years back. When she had married Michael Swinburne, she had left, almost at once, on his new job. He had gone from a research fellowship to a secondment in the International Labour Organization. Now, with his staff fellowship, they had come back, after their two years in Switzerland. Brittany, Pembroke, Geneva.

'But it seems longer ago than it was,' Rose said, easily.

'Sure.'

'You're well though, Peter?'

'Yes thankyou. And you?'

'As well as might be expected, thankyou.'

'Sure.'

'And hoping it finds you as it leaves me.'

The conscious mimicry of the phrase had behind it the mimicry of accent which Rose's friends—they had once all been Peter's friends—liked to practise, for fun. Frances looked up, as Rose laughed. Peter caught the girl's glance. It was one of quick, absolute contempt.

'I'll just tell Robert you're here,' May said.

'No, no, really, I'll go out,' Peter said at once. He walked on to the double doors which led through the small conservatory into the long walled garden. He had to step past Frances, who looked quickly up at him and nodded. He could see Robert below him in the garden, and he stopped for a moment.

The short, stocky body, with very thick greying hair. The bright Norwegian jersey, with light fawn trousers and wellington boots. Standing at a bright blue fibreglass barrow, into which he was dividing roots. A pile of stringy bindweed root by his feet, and a small fork with a bright red handle.

He went on down.

'Good heavens, Peter, is it that late?'

'I'm sorry. I was late too.'

Robert brushed off his hands.

'Yes,' he said. 'I'll soon have to choose between being a teacher and a gardener. One can hardly be both for long.'

'It looks all right, doesn't it?'

'It's not bad. At least I successfully grow peaches, to the despair of at least four of my colleagues.'

'Why? Don't you give them any?'

'I'd better come in, I can see,' Robert said, smiling.

Peter followed him, and stood waiting in the kitchen. It was like a gleaming workshop, with the quiet hum of machinery: the throb of the refrigerator, the deeper and harsher beat of the oil central heating. Against the white enamel of the fitted sink and the electric mixer the blue of the curtains and chairs and the long plastic table was clear and bright. Robert left his wellingtons, with pads of earth and gravel still sticking to their heels, and began to walk in his socks towards the main part of the house.

'I saw you taking stock of the kitchen, Peter. It's a bit of a showpiece, I'm afraid, but on the whole it justifies itself. Though still the result of our year in America, in more ways than one. By our standards, that's still damnably profitable.'

'You're not really complaining about it.'

'No. Except that one might equally do a visiting year in India or Ghana and somehow one doesn't.'

'One?'

'All right. Most people don't, and I didn't. All one can say, I suppose quite reasonably, is that intellectually, academically anyway, it makes sense. Their social sciences are the best in the world.'

'While in India or Ghana they only have social problems.'

'No, Peter, that won't do. It's much too bitter. Or let's not say that—bitterness can sometimes be justified. But in fact, as you know, it's too narrow.'

'Sure.'

They had reached the big sitting-room which Robert used as his study. Robert pulled on his loose green slippers, and felt for his pipe.

'Though maybe you're right,' he said suddenly. 'Perhaps there is an inverse relation between social science and social purpose. At least their sophistication may be related.'

Peter didn't answer. He had let the thing go. The usual hail of matches, into the big glass ashtray, made him want to laugh more than talk.

73

'No?' Robert asked, making one last successful attempt.

'In this place, perhaps,' Peter said.

'Your contrasts again. Your tale of two cities.'

'We've been over all that. We got nowhere.'

Robert nodded and was silent for some minutes, staring along his legs at his slippers.

'It's just which of the two is more of a treadmill,' he said at last, in a quite different voice. Or at least,' he continued, 'you're off the more obvious one, and have time to think about both. And you can get others off it, since you're at a point of leverage.'

'You can't still believe,' Peter said sharply, 'that any of this is done to help anybody.'

'Well yes. One could hardly go on if one didn't. Perhaps I'm wrong to be an optimist still. Everyone says I'm wrong. But what I'd say myself is that I'm an optimist four days a week, I just manage to hold it at that.'

'You must be pleased, to keep it that regular.'

There was another silence, long enough to get pointed.

'And how's the work?' Robert asked, finally.

'All right. There are never any real problems about.that.'

'You're lucky, then.'

'Sure. Except that the work's not the point.'

'How far have you got with the draft?'

'I've done it. I've brought it for you to tear up.'

'Not literally, I hope?'

'No. I'm not wasting it now, whatever it is.'

Peter took his manuscript from his case, and passed it across. It was all easier now it was formal. He respected Robert too much, in spite of the obvious mannerisms, to want really to fight him. As he watched his hands turning the pages of the manuscript he got an immediate sense of control and direction. Robert began asking questions, about details of the draft, and they were soon into the kind of close discussion which Peter invariably found useful. Behind the surface blur of Robert's manner there was an unusually hard and tenacious mind. The only question, perhaps, was why it seemed to operate, at anything like its real power, only when paper was fed to it. Hearing the central heating start up again in the kitchen, Peter came back to his ordinary doubts.

The door opened, and May came in with a tray of tea. She came, Peter thought, like a servant, not speaking. He got up at once and took the tray, but this seemed only to irritate her. She

74

smiled but at once tightened up still more. Robert had scarcely looked up from the manuscript, where he was re-reading over the turn of a page. But then, as she was going out, he got up suddenly.

'Darling, you needn't have carried that in. I'd have fetched it.'

'It's all right. You have it here.'

'No, we can't sit here like hermits. We'll bring it in to you. I'll leave the script here, Peter. I'll ring you when I've been properly through it.'

May was still standing by the door. She watched as Robert picked up the tray again, and then held the door as he walked through, carrying it with a slight air.

They took tea together in the long sitting-room, overlooking the garden. It was an awkward occasion, with very little real contact. As soon as he decently could, Peter got up to go. Rose immediately said that she too had to run. This was greeted with audible relief by Frances, for Rose had been asking her about school. 'It's all right' and 'Well not bad, actually' were about the clearest answers she had got. But she had kept asking, partly to keep up some conversation, for both Robert and May were silent, and Peter was embarrassed and withdrawn.

'I put my bike down the side,' Rose said, as they left the front door. She smiled as she moved away past the ragged laburnum. Peter waited for her, looking down the road to the horse chestnut, where the leaves were still falling.

He had met Rose in his first undergraduate year. From the beginning it had been a game between them: a game of making an imaginary world, of argument and affection, of which they both knew the limits. Rose was so different from Beth, and from everyone else he had previously met, that she seemed to belong in a different dimension: at once a release from his ordinary world and yet no permanent alternative to it. At first they had been two in a group, and the game was general. But each, for different reasons, took the game further, until it was more wholly personal. It seemed then to others, though hardly ever to themselves, the kind of relationship that would grow into marriage. It was in fact a safe and limited kind of affection: real enough to be continually replayed, yet, when their interests were touched, not so deep that it could threaten the original balance. When they were not together, the game seemed impossible, but they had only to meet to begin it again and to value it. They would talk and argue about everything but themselves, and while they held the world in their own words they could touch without disturbance, keeping a continually affectionate distance. Only in their last month were the rules questioned. It was as if Peter had been living in two worlds, which now suddenly came together. It was even a version of marriage, this game they had been playing. To others it certainly seemed so, and especially to Beth, who in the end was outraged. What seemed to them a game seemed to her trifling, but a dangerous trifling, since it could not be so isolated as Peter seemed to believe. Under Beth's protests, and with the imminent ending of their undergraduate years, which in their special atmosphere had made the playing easier, they tried, briefly, to make the game into fact. Peter had been offered a job on a newspaper in London, and it seemed to Rose that he could take it and they could marry. But what then came out, in Peter, was hardly attractive. In the prospect of actual involvement, his real confusions were at once precipitated. It had always been difficult for others to reconcile his ease with Rose and his critical tension with everyone else. All that happened, as the game became fact, was that they lost what they had previously valued: the security of their artificial dimension, which could now be seen as from the beginning protective. He had outraged Beth, by what she saw as his capacity to trifle, and so as an incapacity to love. He now confused Rose by his evident inability, once his whole life was in question, to accept the way in which, for so long, they had kept everything, including themselves, at so entertaining a distance. What had seemed so easy broke into recrimination, and Peter was seen, understandably, as having been false to both sides. His own nerve broke, as he saw himself in this way, and his whole personality seemed to age and change. The worst quarrel was with Rose, for Beth had withdrawn into silence. Rose took his refusal as a simple refusal of life; he was being destroyed, she said, by a nostalgia and a regression to a narrowness he had wanted to break out from; a narrowness, of guilt and anxiety, they had in fact for so long escaped. Peter replied that their game had indeed been a release, but a release to nothing. As they tried to make something real, all the ordinary conditions returned, and it was the same with her as with anyone else. As now, he added, in just this quarrel.

So it had ended, more than two years back. At the end of that summer, Rose married Michael Swinburne, who was three years older and already established in a college. Peter, slowly, had tried to rebuild his earlier relationship with Beth, though that too had been permanently changed. The crisis had not been forgotten, but in the lapse of time it seemed over.

Rose came back, wheeling her bike, and they turned along the road.

'Well,' she said, 'am I glad to get out of there!'

'The Lanes? Then why did you go?'

'You don't know, Peter boy, how much university wives have to love each other. May and I are on the same committee, seeing that American visitors aren't lonely.'

'How do you manage that? Traditionally?'

'That's enough,' Rose said, wheeling her bike to the other side of the road. She bent down to pick up all the loose conkers she could reach.

'But it is ghastly, even you'll admit,' she said, looking up at him. She was still squatting over the conkers, her bike leaning against her back. Her full skirt was pulled lightly up over her knees. Peter didn't answer, but took hold of the bike.

'He's killing her, that benevolent devil,' Rose said.

As she spoke she jumped briskly up, like a child at a game.

'I don't know,' Peter said, looking away. 'I feel that kind of tension too often.'

'Not often that bad,' Rose said, rubbing the tiny nuts in her long fingers. 'And the fantastic thing about it is that nobody knows how it's done. He's like some fantastically skilful poisoner, you only get on to him by seeing the results.'

'Perhaps she's ill.'

'Yes, in effect. All I know is she's entirely unloved, and it's killing her. And from him of all people. Who loves all the world.'

'I don't know enough about it,' Peter said, looking down at the slow pattern of spokes as he wheeled the bike.

'Still very cautious, Peter.'

'I don't know. There are some things I've learned not to touch.'

'Such as?'

'All this discussing people, for one thing. I listen and listen to it, and I know it's impure in some way. In any case, it's completely disintegrating.'

'It's a bitty sort of life, all this, at the best.'

'You're probably missing Switzerland.'

'Yes, though it wasn't much different. Except that now we've come back to our own kind of poison.'

Peter laughed, letting the tension go. He kicked at an old newspaper, that had moved about eighty yards along the road since he had seen it when he was walking down from the bus. 'Talk now, West urge,' he read on the crumpled headline. Rose stepped off the pavement, avoiding a woman who was wheeling her child in a push-chair.

'Do you run into Michael at all?' Rose asked.

'No.'

'He's so fantastically busy it's almost the same with me. In term, anyway, I feel lucky if I meet him in the street.'

'Rose, don't be so bloody silly.'

'But it's true, Peter. Yes, he comes home at night, and we quite invariably have breakfast together, but beyond that, not much.'

'Most men go to work, don't they?'

'It depends how much of themselves they bring back.'

'All right, so people get tired.'

'It's more than that. It's this whole set-up. I think Robert Lane isn't the only poisoner. Perhaps it isn't even his fault, but just the same process twenty years on.'

'Nobody loves you, Rose, is that it?' Peter said, smiling.

'As a matter of fact, no.'

'Then don't tell me about it. Tell somebody it concerns.'

'Have you ever tried doing that? You said there were things you've learned not to touch. You're not the only one.'

'All right. But it's still your own affair.'

'Is it?' Rose said. She walked on in silence for some time, holding the bike with one hand on the bar and one, with the fingers spreading, on the high saddle.

'Anyway, I wanted to tell you,' she said suddenly. 'I've been married two years and I wanted a child from the beginning. It isn't embarrassing. People think we're just waiting. Only we're not waiting and there's still no child.'

Peter walked on, staring down at the pavement. In the heat of summer the tar mix had buckled and cracked, and grass was beginning to shoot along the rough lines. In one place a plantain had burst the crumbling surface from below, and had drawn the dull black fragments around it into a broken hill.

'You're still terrified, Peter, aren't you, when anyone says something wrong? Something we're supposed not to say?'

'There was nothing wrong in what you said. Except perhaps that you said it to me.'

'Really? Well that's a compliment. Or at least the nearest I'm likely to get.'

They had reached the main road, with its rush of traffic. They hesitated at the corner, watching a postman emptying the crammed wire basket of the pillar box. Rose got on her bike, but kept one foot on the pavement.

'It isn't my fault, Peter, that I've not had a child.'

'I don't know. It's between you and Michael.'

'Well I know that,' Rose said, stepping hard on the pedal. 'I know quite well all that's happened. Go on, hurry, you might miss your bus.'

She rode off, without looking back.

A week later, Robert sent Peter a note. 'I've now read your draft, and it's coming quite well, though I've a few points to discuss. Could we vary the procedure for once? I should quite like to come to you. What about Tuesday at seven? Yours ever, Robert Lane.'

Peter was so surprised by this that he didn't know how to answer. His first idea was to refuse, to put him off somehow, perhaps by suggesting a meal somewhere. But the push was so definite that this wouldn't be easy, and there were moral limits on any absolute turning-down. Still he didn't want Robert mixed up with his home. The better he behaved the worse in a way it would be. In the end, still surprised at himself, he asked Kate what he should do.

'But there's no problem, Peter. Of course let him come. You can have the front room.'

'Yes, keeping it for the courting couple and your supervisor.'

'I just don't understand,' Kate said. 'It's all perfectly easy.'

So Peter replied, though he got through six drafts before posting. 'Thanks for your note. Of course I'd be glad to go over the points you mention. I get so used to routines (and in a way prefer them) that I probably need criticism more than ever. Yes of course do come on Tuesday at seven. P. H. Owen.'

Robert came, walking, soon after seven. Peter went to the door as he rang, but Robert had walked away, and was standing by the low wall that divided the garden from the street.

'Peter, there you are. I was just looking round. It's rather pleasant up here. I didn't realize.'

'Yes, it's quite nice.'

'It's the hill, of course. So much less oppressive than down in the city.'

'Yes, or just down in the works.'

'Of course.'

'And even here, if the wind's the wrong way from the paint shop.'

Robert nodded, looking down the hill to the works.

'Shall we go in?' Peter asked.

'Yes, of course. Thankyou.'

Peter led the way into the front room, where he had switched on the electric fire an hour before. Kate was still somewhere in town, and Harold late again at a meeting. The house felt empty and cold, but it was easier this way.

'Yes, well,' Robert began, sitting in Harold's chair near the fire. 'This is good, Peter. We shall get it all right.'

'Tell me the worst.'

'But there isn't a worst. You're so tense about it. You keep forgetting, Peter, that you've a very good mind. You've proved that again and again, but still you go on being frightened. The real situation, as you know quite well, is that you're quite as capable of putting me right as the other way round.'

'That's not how it's set up,' Peter said, bending and adjusting the thermostat on the side of the fire.

'Well anyway, three points,' Robert said, spreading the manuscript on his knees. There was the usual slow but perceptible tightening up, as he concentrated towards paper. Peter knew, as he listened to the points being made, that this was a man to respect, quite impersonally, as you might respect a highly trained runner, or the control and consciousness of a judge.

'But I may be wrong,' Robert said, looking up. 'You mustn't take this as more than it's worth.'

'I know straight off when you're right, Robert. It's just it gets me down a bit, having to keep restarting, working it all over, like it's straight from the lungs or the stomach. It's just I don't know why I'm doing it, that's what makes it all doubtful.'

'This time should do it,' Robert said, getting up and putting the manuscript carefully on the mantelpiece. 'Are you alone?' he then asked, casually.

'My mother and father are at meetings. This is a very militant family.'

'Yes, I've heard of your mother's work. Thank God somebody's doing it.'

'Yes of course,' Peter said, hesitating. 'Except that next door there's just the opposite, everything that we write down in the notebooks as apathy. Only the place is warm and alive and it's like people living there, that's the difference.'

80

'Who next door?'

'My aunt and uncle. My Uncle Gwyn, my father's brother.'

'I see. Is he at the factory too?'

'Yes.'

Robert relit his pipe. He seemed not to want to talk. Peter saw, looking up at him, the soft clear skin under the thick hair, and then the very tired eyes, grey and dull.

'Come through a minute,' he said, getting up.

'Yes, thankyou.'

They went down the passage to the living-room, which had a low coal fire.

'Here, look,' Peter said, going across to the window.

The lights of the works extended over the valley, but Peter was looking the other way, towards Gwyn's conservatory. The glass was misted, but he could still see the shapes of the nearest plants, the intricate shadows which had remained so clearly in his mind.

'If a man can put that much into anything, don't you think? Some feeling that the effort is worth it, something active and personal.'

'The conservatory?'

'Yes. Though it isn't only that.'

'Quite. We get misled by the metaphors of gardening and so on. I do myself, so I can say this neutrally. Often it's no more, really, than the child's sandpit. It's very nice but we don't make an issue of it.'

'Come round and see it,' Peter said.

'I'd like to. But won't it be disturbing them?'

'I'll run round and ask. If you'd just hang on.'

He hurried out of the room. He was like a boy, suddenly, very sure and eager. Robert watched him pass in the garden below, and then looked down again at the lines of the works. Peter came running back, out of breath.

'Come on,' he said quickly.

They went out through the kitchen and down the side passage to the gate between the gardens. Gwyn was standing by the outside door of the conservatory, in his overalls with a long grey jersey pulled tight at his shoulders.

'Uncle, this is Dr Lane.'

'I'm glad to meet you, sir,' Gwyn said. 'Peter tells me you're a gardener.'

'How are you?' Robert said, putting out his hand.

Gwyn shook hands quickly, and then turned to let them into the conservatory.

'Shut the door, Peter,' he said, when they were crowded inside.

Robert looked around. The chrysanthemums were just coming to their best, and the air seemed full of their bursting colour.

'But this is wonderful.'

'Yes, they're not bad, sir.'

Robert noticed the 'sir', but appeared not to notice it. An apparent friendliness, in not wanting the title, would only come through as insulting. Politeness was to accept Gwyn's judgement.

'I do a bit myself,' he said easily. 'But nothing like this.'

'I've only the limited resources,' Gwyn said.

'You've more than I have.'

'Aye well, perhaps. But I've been building it up eleven years.'

'Yes, I can see.'

As he spoke, Robert walked slowly along in front of the staging, looking carefully at each plant. Gwyn stayed close beside him, and soon they were talking easily, about varieties and dates. Peter stayed at a distance, watching them. It had been a sudden impulse, to bring Robert round here, and in a way it seemed to be working out all right. Yet in another way he was not relieved, but quite tense and still, as if seeing the two men together was something long foreseen, something important and uncertain, within the guarded area of his most private feelings.

When the visit was over, they went back through the garden.

'I'll walk down the hill with you,' he said, and led the way through to the street. The evening mist seemed gathered around the lamps, and the lights of the city, below them, had merged into a soft orange glow.

'I liked your uncle,' Robert said. 'He's so absolutely genuine.'

'I'd not thought about him like that.'

'No, but what I find reassuring, Peter, is that it's possible just to meet as people, with a common interest. The real evil of class, in a society like this, is that it sets up the barriers before we can even see each other. I used to think we could only talk across the barriers, but just occasionally one finds oneself there, and really in touch, without any of the usual problems.'

Peter was counting the steps between the lamps, as he had often done before. The reckoning had changed, over the years.

'Even that,' Robert continued, 'is a classbound way of putting it. What strikes me most, and what we'd do well to admit, is that there's no longer much difference, in the way most people
82

live. Once we see that, then class comes through as a sort of property ghost.'

'Which we talk about all the time, however. Our endless ghost story.'

'Yes, perhaps,' Robert said, glancing at him. The young face was very pale, under the drawn artificial light. The roughness of the cropped hair and the worn black jacket came through only occasionally in the voice, which was usually very soft and precise, though sometimes so low and anxious that it was a strain to hear. But just occasionally, as now, he seemed to speak with his whole body.

'We've got to stop it, Robert. Somebody must have the guts to stop it. Not to be enlightened and tolerant. Not any kind of humane killer. Just chuck the old skin and live it straight, whatever it costs.'

'I think many of us are trying to.'

'Yes, it's what they say about your ideas. But is it true?'

'It was true this evening, I thought. With your uncle.'

'God, no. That's just the point. If you think that you're not only deceiving yourself, but you want to deceive yourself.'

'How, exactly?'

'It's more than chrysanthemums, that's all,' Peter said lamely. His certainty had broken again, and his tone was peevish.

'Well, of course, Peter. I agree. But we all get in touch through some particular interest. It widens from that.'

'Like the squire going down to the stables and finding he has a lot in common with his groom? Eighteen hands of horse.'

'You see,' Robert said, smiling, 'to make your point you have to go archaic. But the squire is on the wall with his gaiters, just for tourists to look at. About as relevant as the horse brasses in the flash Tudor bar.'

'You don't have to imitate to get in touch, Robert. It's best to stick to yourself.'

'All right, I will stick to myself,' Robert said, with more edge. 'What you said was ridiculous because I'm not a squire and your uncle's not a groom. My father was a compositor and I'm a teacher. Your uncle works in a factory. And from all that, in fact, we go home to very much the same way of living.'

'No.'

'All right, my house is larger, though the conservatory's exactly the same. Not even a conservatory, a lean-to, and he has more equipment than I have. We shall eat much the same things

83

for breakfast, when we get up tomorrow. We shall worry about the same things, the insurance and the mortgage payments and the ageing car.'

'No.'

'Yes, Peter. You must see this. Because otherwise it's only too plain. You're projecting your own tension as a national difference. You're playing out your own situation and reading it into others.'

'I'm not a bloody materialist, that's all. I don't care what you eat for breakfast or whether you both get your suits from Burton's. I care how you think. How you think and how you feel.'

'And what do you really know about that?'

'I'm not certain. I'm just trying to understand. But I think for Gwyn the chrysanthemums and so on are just a corner of his life, that he's worked to keep good, and that all the rest contradicts. For you it's just part of your pattern: writing, thinking, growing, within a protecting wall you don't even notice and can't think about.'

'Possibly,' Robert said, and was silent for some time. They were approaching the main road, and there were people passing more regularly. 'Except, perhaps, that we don't know enough about the effects of work, different kinds of work. All the evidence is that routine work, like your uncle's, is quite often welcomed, for its very monotony. It doesn't involve a man too much, and so he can think about something else and build his own life round it. The nature of the work is accepted, because it can be seen, quite frankly, that it pays. And of course that it makes things worth buying, when the wage has been earned. I don't know, but I think the rest is just sentiment, looking in at it all from outside.'

'I've not looked from outside.'

'In a way you have, Peter. You were taken out of it very early, as I was. You're related but you haven't lived it yourself.'

'I'm talking about the effects. On Gwyn and Myra, and on my father and mother. But it's no use, I can't talk about them.'

They had reached the main street and the bus stop. The mist had thickened to a light drizzle, and they stood back in the doorway of the furniture shop. Robert took out his pipe and turned into a corner, cupping his hands, to light it. Peter saw the fine drops of water on the thick grey hair, and the gleam in the light of the match.

'Robert, if you're right about factory work, we can solve this city's problems. It's a simple, even elegant, solution. The university can work on the car lines. Its hands can be occupied with

84

this paying process and its mind, by grace of the monotony, can be left free to think. This will be real rationalization.'

'Yes, it might be,' Robert said, smiling.

'Except that not a man jack of you would do it. You take bloody good care to stay clear.'

Chapter Nine

In the dark bay, the raw grey shells that were being made into cars were lifted and set into lines. Climbing the steep stairs, Harold watched the latest body being lowered by the short, black arms of the mobile crane. There was a long streak of heat along its lower left side, and this caught the dusty light as it was set gently down. He overtook it and walked on under the high bulk of the dipper. Earlier bodies were already in position there, on the powerful rods that would lift and move forward, turning the bodies like animals on spits, lowering them into the first bath and then heaving them up towards the sprays, where they went out of sight. Beyond the sprays was the great oven, where the heat came down as a vibration as he walked quickly beneath it. The newly sprayed bodies were dried by this heat, without any pause in their long slow turning, and then they emerged above the turntable, at the junction with the next line.

The advantages of the dipper were immense, yet the trouble it had caused, in the complicated re-negotiation of piece rates, was clearer in his mind that its extraordinary technical mastery. Gwyn had been directly involved, as one of the new team, but this had made little difference to Harold's thinking about it.

A problem of this kind was necessarily impersonal, like the new machinery itself. The intricate technical process had to be translated into relationships which the piece-rates would define. But there were no real precedents, either for the process or the relationships. The machinery defined its working team, but to express their values, to interlock them with those of others defined by other machinery, was a close, difficult negotiation, in which the taut experience of other definitions was the only guide yet still insufficient.

He looked for precedents, in everything he did, but this wasn't because he was unadventurous. His whole working life, after the bareness of the early years, had been a continual negotiation of unknown and changing conditions. First to establish the bargaining network, and then, through its intricacies edged with hostility, to try to reckon the working values of men engaged in wholly new ways of work, under the powerful and relieving pressure of the new machines.

A man's price, now. An hour of him, working, in that particular team. This price against that, this effort against that production. And at the root of it, nothing to fix on. Only the fight to get what you could, and then say a man's price.

Across where Gwyn was standing, the spit came to the end of its journey, with its bodies now coated and baked russet. Harry Campbell, who had once been a professional footballer, crossed the turntable to release the great locks, and stepped quickly back with a wave to Gwyn who had been watching each of his movements. When Harry was clear, Gwyn operated his main lever, and the turntable moved, slewing the bodies towards the black pincers of the next overhead cranes, while the long spit, caked with repeated paint and heat, was automatically lifted to heavy squat forks. These, when they had settled their load, moved steadily forward in an arc which cleared the spit from the path of the cars. Then, in a smooth interlocking lift, they launched its return to where it had started, to take on new bodies.

No hand had touched the smoothly rolling process since Harry had released the locks and Gwyn had pushed forward his controlling lever. Now, as the spit was lifted and sent back along the side of the oven, the lifting cranes were humming into position above the bodies, and the locking tackle was being fixed around them, by men who stepped in to make one practised movement and then quickly withdrew. Up went the bodies again, on to the long overhead tracks that carried them slowly round, just under the roof, to the next shop. As Gwyn reversed his lever, the forks and the turntable moved slowly back into position. Already, from the vibrant heat of the oven, a new spit was poised to emerge, with its identical russet bodies.

'Tell Kate about seven,' Harold shouted across.

Gwyn nodded. While he stood at his lever, he was so set and unmoving that he seemed part of the solemn process of the machinery itself. He was deeply impressed by it, for its power and complication had at once created an awed respect, which repetition did not weaken. Harry Campbell was different, always ready for a joke after his quick rush to release the locks. But there was little enough time for anything, as the next delivery began.

Harold walked on down the narrow lines, stepping over the circular roller rail on which the finished bodies moved slowly towards assembly. On the far side of the paint shop, a masked

87

figure stepped from the sliding doors of one of the closed spray sheds, and pulled off his mask and gloves to sweat in the ordinary warm noise of the shop. Above him the overhead line of bodies curved towards the second assembly line, which Harold was making for.

Dick Manning was in the first team on this line. The body was lowered to these five, and there were two minutes for each to complete his particular fitting. One threaded and connected the multicoloured sheaf of the wiring cables. One inserted and locked the three external chrome handles. One placed the lamps in the sockets that stood out from the eyeless body. One, squeezing quickly inside, pasted the first layers of trim. Dick Manning, the fifth and the charge-hand, fitted the curving windscreen and its moulded rubber mounting, moving quickly from one side to the other and sealing the mounting with a sharp elaborate gesture that marked the brief interval before the next body came.

Dick stood with the length of moulding hanging from his neck. He was easy and confident, for he could always just beat the two-minute schedule. Like most of the men on this line he was young. Very few older men could stand this speeded-up pace, and even the younger men worked on it for much shorter periods than elsewhere. The money was good, while you could stand the speed, but after a few weeks most men made other calculations. Dick, with eight months on this line, was one of the longest stayers. He often said that it was never going to break him. He could keep up with anything that anybody cared to work out. He could even beat it.

'Five-fifteen then, Dick,' Harold called, while the moulding was being fitted.

'I didn't know you was there, Harold,' he said, completing the operation with his usual elaborate gesture, and then stepping down.

'Five-fifteen.'

'Aye, I got it. I just thought for a minute you was the new egg-timer.'

'You think I'm all sorts of things, Dick.'

'Aye, that's right, Harold,' Dick said, grinning. He was already turning away as the body he had been working on moved forward and the next body was being lowered behind it. He lifted his hands to steady it as it hovered above the rollers, and as it touched turned at once for the next strip of moulding, which he coiled round his bare neck with darkened fingers.

88

Harold walked on down the line. At each station the empty body became more like a finished car, as a new team crowded round it, with a quick dominance, adding its quota of fittings. At the far end of the line, near the big double doors to the yard, Len Weekes, who had come from Taunton in the same month as Harold had come from Brynllwyd, and who lived down the hill in Goldsmith Street, was sitting at the wheel of a finished model on the test roller. He was racing the engine until the wheels spun into a black blur, the equivalent of fifty miles an hour on the road but here meeting only the fast counter-movement of the rollers, which kept the car where it was. As the revs rose and fell, Len checked each instrument and completed his test sheet.

It was the last along the line for the day. In just about a minute the hooters would sound all over the works. Harold had slipped away five minutes early, to remind the other stewards of the meeting. It was sometimes possible to do this, on the paint inspection line where he had worked since the war. Your eye got so quick on a finish you could get that bit ahead or catch up on a few minutes aside. There was always trouble if he was seen away, but the messages had to be passed.

Len Weekes switched off the test engine, and stepped out. He was holding the test card, on its worn black board, very stiffly across his stomach. He nodded to Harold and they stood together for a moment, as along the shop the race of the machines slowed and died. Len was always very settled and quiet: one of the many that got fixed by forty; a kind, gentle, wholly reliable man. Only old. Old and learned to cut down the strain. It was always nice to see him, nice to talk to him. But if there was trouble, you could never count on him for real help, though he would always do what he was asked. If there was never trouble, if the work was even a bit less like a sort of guerrilla war, Len would make sense, in his settlement.

The sharp high blasts of the hooters cut across their few words. Within their immediate range, the blasts seemed to come through to all the senses at once, like a sudden tearing of fabric, in the acrid air. All over the shop, tools were being laid aside. The voices that had been subdued by the machines were swelling and loud. There was a steady movement down the lanes towards the doors, and then outside, in the yards, from all the other shops, there was a scattered, thickening movement.

In the first minutes the tracks were separate, men walking unevenly, cars starting, bikes crossing in oblique paths: a weaving, gathering movement, inside the chain-link fencing, converging at last along the concrete roads to the numbered gates and the directing police. After the sharp revving of the turn to the road, the traffic streamed away down the hill. The first cars got quickly away, ahead of the long drive of bikes, four and five abreast, that nearly filled the roads. But the later cars were lined sullenly behind, and only scooters and motorbikes moved up on the outside of the long lane, edging unevenly past, like eager dogs at a flock.

In the central road that turned down to the estates, the hundreds of bikes filled the carriageway, like birds wheeling, dark and silent, in a down wind. Since the hooters had torn the air there had been this sudden release, an outward-streaming energy that for its set time, its negotiated day, had been contained and organized in the work-lines, and that now burst out and flooded the roads, before gradually dispersing again into separate channels. Within the complicated lines of the traffic, the individual feeling was clear and simple: to get home and a meal and by the fire.

Harold stood by the double doors, watching, and then turned and walked across to the shed where the stewards were meeting. The business that evening was mainly routine: a complaint from the paint shop, about the effects of a new paint being used on the more expensive cars—its fumes were said to be particularly bad, and there had been several cases of sickness; a problem referred from the toolmakers, where a nineteen-year-old youth had been transferred to a drilling job which he had previously been doing in the machine-shop and was still being paid at machine-shop rates though by agreement he should now be paid as an improver; a petition from nineteen men in the machine-shop that Holmyard, a machine setter, was so often inaccurate that they had a very high percentage of rejects and a consequently considerable loss of pay; a complicated insurance problem, affecting part-time married women employees in trim; and a renewed complaint, through Dick Manning, about the timing of the wiring assembly on the new line. Harold, in the chair, took the meeting slowly through each item, and next steps were agreed. It was already late when they came to other business, but he asked permission to make a brief statement on the danger of increasing short-time working by December, for discussion and subsequent report.

There was a full moon over the yard as they walked out to go home. Harold stood for a moment, changing his glasses, before he got into his car. He had just opened the door when Dick Manning came running up to him.

'West Longton's out again.'

'What?'

'Old Edwards, at the gate, heard it just now on the news. The day shift walked out, just before five.'

'It only needed that.'

The factory at West Longton made most of the electrical components required for two of the production lines. There had been many disputes there, and there had been a difficult wage claim in for the last eight months. But this sudden stoppage was surprising.

'Did they say what?'

'If they did old Edwards wouldn't know. He just got the name.'

'At any other time,' Harold said wearily.

'No, don't be so miserable, Harold. We have to keep them on the mark, don't we?'

'We have to keep ourselves on the mark, for this winter.'

'Anyway, catch the bloody wireless giving the reason for a strike. It'd be that idle-sounding bugger licking his lips round twelve hundred men idle. And in an official statement the management has referred to the activities of known trouble-makers.'

'Aye, we've been called it, haven't we? I was met at that gate, in thirty-seven, and told no bloody union men wanted here.'

'That was in your militant days, boy. Not like looking after the part-time women.'

'Don't start all that. I'm going home.'

'Well, if West Longton's out, it won't be long coming here.'

'You can say that again.'

'It's all right, boy. We'll handle it.'

'We'll do what we have to,' Harold said, and put on his glasses and got in the car. It was so light in the yard, under the full moon, that he had started the engine and was moving away, without putting on his lights, until Dick shouted. Harold reached down for the switch, and waved. He drove slowly home, and had his late supper with Kate.

Kate moved as soon as Harold woke. It seemed that for years she had never really slept. She could close her eyes and be still, and sometimes her mind would go quiet. But her body, always, was tense and alert. Whenever Harold moved, she was on edge, waiting and anxious. But there was never any kind of relief.

He had woken early, because of the news overnight. She could still see the bewilderment in his face, which without the glasses was so defenceless that it hurt to look at him. The reality of the news was plain in every dark line of the face. Kate wondered if the other men were like this, at the first recovery of their waking world, and with sleep still numbing the flesh so that it could not set into the looks of the day. For it was always a world of conflict they woke to, in one way or another. Would they all lie like this, numb and afraid, for the few minutes, the ritual minutes, before they had to go out and fight things through?

'You awake, love?' he asked, his eyes still closed.

'Yes, I'm awake.'

He cleared his throat and sat up, then reached to the table for his glasses. As he put them on he began coughing, a deep inner cough that seemed to go on and on, a low rocking of noise. Kate saw that his eyes were wet at the corners, behind the glasses.

'I'll get up and make some tea.'

'It's all right. I'll come down.'

But she slipped quickly out of bed and hurried across to the door. She did not want to see him dressing, and though she wanted to ease the coughing she could not bear it so close to her. She stood over the kettle, getting the warmth from the burning gas. But before it had boiled he came after her, into the cold scullery.

'We'll hear the news at seven, then.'

'There'll be nothing fresh,' Kate said. 'They've all been in bed, with better things to do.'

'They had better things to do yesterday,' Harold said angrily. All the uncertainty had now gone from the face and he was again sure of himself.

'What it is, see, there's no bloody co-ordination. Over and over I've said it, I've told them. Act together we're strong, but them, well. It's more like a bunch of little boys going off half-cock. There's no men left are strong enough to take proper decisions.'

'You sound like the paper or the wireless, Harold. On any strike whatever.'

'That's just daft. You got to keep a sense of proportion. This strike is crazy, coming now.'

'Every strike looks crazy, to the ones not involved.'

'Yes, but this one really is crazy.'

Kate made the tea and passed him his cup. He took it without saying anything. Then they listened to the bulletin on the wireless. The voice was harsh and rasping, on the tiny transistor. It was clear enough, but it seemed to create its own patterns of meaning, its own unfamiliar rhythms, around the most ordinary words. There was, in fact, no news.

'They'll get no bloody support here,' Harold said, switching off the voice as it passed to a crisis in Germany.

'How do you know? It's not just for you to decide.'

'Don't you bloody start, woman. I'll run this thing in my own way. I'm the only one here, and I mean this, with any real idea of what we're in for. And I won't see our plans just buggered about.'

'Calling me woman,' Kate said, smiling.

'Well you are, aren't you?'

There was a flicker of amused understanding and sympathy in his eyes. Against her will, Kate was excited by this. Quite suddenly and completely, an instinctive response ran through her whole body. It was very rare for there to be any contact between them, like this. They were used to each other, from day to day, but otherwise there was nothing between them, any longer, to make sense of sharing the same house and bed.

'I thought I'd been locked out,' she said, laughing.

'What d'you mean then?'

'Don't you get it?'

He had darkened again, and slipped away from the moment of attention. She stood watching him, letting her dressing-gown hang loose, and then leaned across him to fill his cup.

'They'll come here first, you watch,' Harold said. 'And it won't be me. It'll be our friend Mr Manning. See, if they can get us with them then they're cushy. Only they won't. I can manage Mr Manning.'

'You don't know all the facts yet, do you?'

'Enough,' Harold said, sipping the hot tea.

'Would you like me to try and find out for you? Then if you get involved you'll have the facts to back you up.'

'You won't find the facts about Longton. Nobody will, except the chaps involved.'

'Well, some of the facts. And, you know, the background. What you said about the prospects this winter.'

Harold began coughing again. He closed his eyes and clenched

93

his fists to try to control the coughing. When at last he recovered he gulped down the rest of the tea.

'Well, shall I?'

'Shall you what?'

'Get out a summary of the facts for you.'

'Aye. All right. If you think you could.'

'Look, I've done it before.'

'Aye, you have,' Harold said, and smiled for a moment.

Kate, also, was thinking back. In their first years she had thought he would go a long way in politics. On to the council certainly, and with a bit of luck perhaps Parliament. He was exactly the convinced, experienced, determined man the party needed. And in those early years she had seen her own life along this same line. Helping him with the reading and fact-finding, for which he hadn't been trained. Going to London as a team and part of a team, in the critical struggle to bring a new thing through.

All that was a very long way back now. Men like Harold weren't asked or even encouraged any more. The wheel had turned full circle, back to the point where it seemed absurd, by definition, that such men might be a parliament. Arthur, for instance, though he had no interest in a political career, and indeed often referred to it as the refuge of the second-rate, would in fact have ten times Harold's chance of a nomination. None of it was as simple as it had once seemed. For, ironically, the worst men in the party were the ones like Harold who had somehow got through. They bore all the marks of that unacknowledged contract. When they put on the businesslike glasses, and the dark suit and the familiar way with papers, they lost, almost always, their own real values, but still had the narrowness, the suspicion, the crippling lack of real education. To look back over these years was to realize how swiftly and silently the idea of a new politics had been changed and dragged back. Whatever their origins, the men of the agendas and the accommodations were back in control.

'I'll get on with it today, then,' Kate said, aloud. There was a stubborn loyalty in her voice, and she was very consciously, even abstractly, aware of it.

'All right, girl. It may do some good. Except that you can't always reason with them.'

'I can't always reason with myself.'

'You don't do bad,' Harold said, and went out to the scullery

94

to shave. He could see down over the back gardens, and the lines of roofs, to the big grey yards of the works. Over the hill beyond ran the new bypass, to the main trunk road north. Out beyond there, somewhere—a name like home, though he had never been there—was West Longton, and the strike. Harold looked at the hills in the distance; the low blue hills, very like the hills above Gwenton. That was much too far back. He must live and look in this different direction. Only now it seemed not so much a country; it was more like a large firm. Not only the roads in the towns, but the roads between the towns, seemed part of a single system. The factories were separated by hundreds of miles, yet they were entirely dependent on each other. A breakdown in one place meant a general breakdown, very quickly. Over a whole region, this network defined nearly all the lines of communication.

Kate worked more than nine hours on the report she had promised: first in the library, then telephoning people, then calling on two Labour economist friends in the university, who could help her interpret some of the facts she had collected. The whole problem got steadily more complicated, in the course of the day, and by seven she was tired and confused. She had got a sort of outline, but whether it was what Harold wanted, or anything that could really help him, she couldn't now judge.

The worst thing was that there was a Party committee at seven forty-five, which she ought to attend. She had meant to get home, cook a meal, and see Harold, before the meeting. But now she could only ring up, leave a message with Peter, and get a coffee and a sandwich before the meeting started. Still carrying her notebooks, and only a little refreshed, she arrived at the hall to find the meeting had started.

She sat beside Arthur, at the end of the crowded table. Over the years the committee had tended to separate out, physically, into the known groups of opinion. Though the lines were never quite absolute, and there were individuals who weren't predictable, the separation was almost as clear as the separation of parties in Parliament, though with the same assumption of an over-riding common cause and common loyalty. It was often difficult to remember, in the long struggle for supremacy, that this was not a deciding forum; that it was only a single unit of less than half a parliament and less than half a nation. For it often seemed, in the intensity of the struggle, that a whole world could turn on this resolution, this nomination, this local decision.

Kate was very tired and almost at the limits of her interest.

Once or twice she found herself noticing that she was sitting by Arthur more than the business of the meeting.

Since the visit she had often thought about him, but with a new edge of questioning and suspicion. Too much had been said : that was really the trouble. And while in the main it was her own fault, there was something about him that made any ordinary relationship difficult. Perhaps it had seemed satisfactory before, just because it was so limited. Looking at his hands resting on the table beside her, feeling the ease and confidence of his whole presence, she felt surprisingly bitter and distant from him. And when she heard the familiar control in his voice, making a key point in an otherwise straggling discussion, yet having made it saying no more, letting it go, she had to fight to stop herself crying out in protest. If he treated the meeting as a game, at which he happened to be better (and knew himself to be better) than anyone else taking part, what did this argue, really, about his essential quality? To accept his tone would be quite disastrous, if you were at all involved. The informed voice was entirely convincing, until the very last moment, when you went over the edge.

Or was that fair? In part, at least, it must be the result of his work. Every kind of job shaped a man, and sometimes crippled him. She tried to think of Arthur's real situation. To know more, almost always, than the people who came to him, if only because he had been learning it longer. To have to mark people, and grade them, summing them up, through the relaxed conversational teaching, as possible firsts, poor seconds, straight thirds. And then to know, from sheer repetition and the obligation to correct, the most common errors so quickly that they were hardly even errors but the expected material he must work with. None of this could be good for a man, however necessary it might be. None of it could be easily set aside in the rest of his life, where he might be wrong and in any case had to deal with his equals. The pleasanter he was, the more easily and tactfully he made allowances, the more intolerable the relationship became.

What would his voice be like, Kate wondered, if there were some one thing he must urgently, breakingly, have? If there were some need he could not grade but must give himself to, nakedly and completely? Yet he didn't look as if this often happened. Perhaps the needs too, impressively and inexorably, went through the same process of sorting.

They were nearly at the end of the meeting. Then, under other

96

business, Dick Manning tried to raise the question of the possible stoppage at the works. There were immediate objections, from all round the table. For it was clearly understood, by nearly everyone, that the Labour Party regarded labour questions as outside its sphere. Such matters belonged, constitutionally, to the other wing of the movement. ('The other pigeonhole,' Arthur whispered to Kate.)

But it was very difficult to keep Dick Manning quiet, on anything. What the hell were they there for, giving up their spare time, but to protect the interests of the working class? To listen to some of them if they saw a worker they'd tell him to go home and get cleaned up. And the workers' votes weren't their bloody dues, whatever some of the officials might think. It was no use telling him he was out of order. The whole bloody system was out of order, that was what they were there about.

Kate sat on the edge of her chair while Dick was speaking. She was so excited, suddenly, that she had forgotten she was tired. It was as if she could feel her own blood again, and she hardly noticed Arthur's reaction. He sat back from the table, smiling. I support these sentiments, the smile seemed to say, but I question their tone. She turned away and joined eagerly in the argument, on Dick's side. Even Dick seemed surprised by her vehemence. For it was clearly much more than the habit of fighting to support her own group. Everyone knew Dick was wild, but he was the only active trade unionist on the left of the committee, and it was vital to keep contact with him. But Kate was beyond this sort of calculation. She had forgotten, even, all the long inquiry and the complications of the day. It was only while she was speaking that the complications forced their way back. She remembered that Harold had spoken of this issue as between himself and Dick. She did not change her arguments, when she remembered this. But against her will the pressure seemed to slacken and die away.

It was not clear what would happen, if the discussion were allowed to continue. But at last, after several attempts, the chairman established his ruling, and the matter was dropped. The meeting was then closed, and Kate jumped from her chair to go round to talk to Dick. But he had been even faster, hurrying round the table to continue the argument with the chairman, shaking his hand into the pinched grey face. Other people gathered round them, joining in the argument. Kate hesitated, and Arthur spoke from behind her.

'We might as well go, Kate. We can supply the cursing ourselves.'

'But he was right to be angry. He's absolutely right, what else are we here for?'

'Come along and I'll tell you,' Arthur said, and smiled. 'Anyway, I like my militancy neat.'

'What does that mean?' Kate asked angrily, but he did not answer. She went back to her seat to pick up her bag, and then went with him down the narrow stairs to the street.

She was still roused, physically, from the excitement of the argument. But she supposed that as so often this must be talked away, cold, in the indifferent street. To be angry on the plain, ordinary pavement, with the rest of the city going home in peace, might be useful but was never possible.

For a brief, unexpected moment she seemed to be standing outside herself. She did not know what she, Kate Thomas, was doing here. Arthur, Harold, Dick, Peter: they were all strangers, they had nothing to do with her own real life. To step into the car with Arthur; to go home to bed with Harold; to go on, blindly, with the endless rush of talk: none of these things seemed more than a sleepwalking from which one day, dangerously, she must wake.

Only what if this moment were now? Here, with this stranger? She would be suddenly hurt and exposed. She would be naked, knowing nothing, yet in some way committed.

She saw, as if from a distance, Arthur bending across towards her. The close fair hair glinted under the light. The face was deeply shadowed.

But then she had come to the wrong car, and this was a stranger. She had better turn quickly and run, while there was still time. There would be people about, along the street. One of them would look after her, if she asked. Look after her and take her home.

'Come on, Kate,' Arthur called, impatiently yet with a familiar confidence that she would come.

The voice broke the moment of distance, and her ordinary focus was restored, though she was still tired and shaken. And if, as she still felt, it had little to do with her own life, still that was normal; there was never that much connection. It was only getting into the car.

She stepped in quickly, pulling her skirt tightly over her knees. It was pleasantly warm inside. Arthur leaned across her, to close the door properly. She smiled and relaxed. The hesitation, really, had been just an odd moment, because she was so very tired. And she had hardly eaten all day. There was always the danger of making a mystery out of these things, which when you looked had quite simple physical causes. Arthur gave her a cigarette, and held his lighter close to her face. She inhaled deeply, and leaned back, closing her eyes.

What mattered, really, was to get things straight. If the Labour Party ignored the workers then the workers would ignore the Labour Party. Dick could have quoted, quite fairly, the significantly low figures of total poll, in all the working-class wards. The majority was there, all the time, if you could get the people out. But you could only get them out if you made real contact with them, if the political relationships had some living substance in them. If only hate or anger; these, anyway, if there could be nothing better. But some real contact, some conviction and involvement for once. It was acknowledging the person beside you as a member of the same living body as yourself. Getting through to real feelings, past the usual talk.

'You look tired, Kate.'

'Yes.'

'You've been working on the facts of this strike?'

'Not the strike. Just the general prospect, in the industry.'

'That makes sense, I suppose. Since you're bound to be involved.'

'Yes, Harold will be in the thick of it.'

There was another pause. Kate had still not opened her eyes.

'I've heard he's very good on all that,' Arthur said. 'It needs such a vast amount of detailed local information.'

'Yes, he's done marvellously really. He knows almost everything there is to know about that kind of politics.'

'Well, politics?'

'It is, Arthur. You'll never see this, because it doesn't affect you. But it's the beginning of everything.'

'Yes, I used to think so.'

He had switched on the ignition, but seemed in no hurry to start. He straightened and stretched his arms in front of him, his hands resting lightly on the serrations of the thin white circle of the driving wheel.

'But not now?' Kate asked, opening her eyes and looking across at him.

'No. You see, what I ask myself, Kate, is this. Is it anything more, really, than a late form of . . . what? *bourgeois arrivisme*?

99

That's a terrible phrase, but only the French have done any political thinking. What I mean is it seems so wholly material, so narrowly material. The one consuming interest, in all the union work, is just money and position. They're bargaining with the employers on the employers' terms.'

'What else can they do, for goodness sake?'

'I know. I'm not blaming them. All I'm saying is it shows what a fortuitous connection there really is between radicalism and the working-class movement. It looked like a connection, at a particular historical stage, but it isn't one now.'

'Then why do they all say that strikes are a threat to society? If it's all part of this materialism, why don't they just accept strikes? Accept their motives, I mean?'

'Indeed, why not? I must try to say this somewhere. The strikes and so on are part of the British Way of Life: that's the whole point. They're within the terms that we've all accepted. They may be one of the cruder parts of the market mechanism, but that's where they belong.'

'They can't all be fools, the ruling class, all seeing them as a threat.'

'They are fools. They should be glad of them. While it's only strikes there's no real danger at all. This is the whole point about capitalism, that it runs the economy by putting contradictions to the test of the market. Capitalism grew originally, and now survives, by collapsing one side of the tension. By cutting out all reference to growth, by submitting everything to the terms of the market, it stays strong.'

'Then why do they say that we shall get to a breaking point? That the wage demands will force up costs so far that the whole system will break.'

'But nobody believes that, Kate. They say it from time to time, as part of the bargaining, but nobody believes it. The compromise, you see, is built in from the beginning, and they know it. They know what the trade unions are like. There will be no breaking point; that's what the system is for. Capitalism regulates, almost perfectly, the percentages it can afford, and then the unions fight with this terrific militancy towards the compromise which is all they're ever really asking. The victory will always be three per cent when they'd asked for five per cent, or redundancy pay when they'd asked for no redundancy. And it will stay this way, because in fact they have no absolute demands.'

'What would an absolute demand be?'

'I don't know. Nobody can know, in this kind of society. It isn't a system in which thinking of absolutes is possible.'

'But you must have thought of it, to see a difference.'

'I don't know. Some human claim, I suppose. Blok thought the Bolsheviks had it, and couldn't bear it when he realized the truth, that Christ was leading the insulted and the rejected into yet another respectable bourgeois society.'

'You still haven't said the alternative.'

'There isn't one really. Don't let me corrupt you.'

'If you're right, we're corrupt already. And I think you probably are right.'

'I mean if you think what we were doing tonight,' Arthur went on, quickly. 'Just hanging around the Labour Party like a gang of calculating relatives. Keeping in touch with this tired old auntie, but an auntie with a legacy. It just may be, you see, that she's an unconscious instrument of something new, some kind of new start. She hasn't got quite enough, but she's a good deal better than nothing.'

'You don't really think that,' Kate protested, shocked. 'That would be really corrupt.'

'It would be ugly, I agree, but then the whole situation's desperate. It's only when everything above ground is withered that we go back to the roots. And that's never a beautiful process. Necessarily it is cold and dark.'

'But not mean,' Kate said.

Arthur leaned forward, and switched on the engine. Kate watched the windscreen clearing an arc in front of her. The deserted street looked cold and bare, and the drizzle was keeping the roadway black. She sat very still, not daring to speak again. She did not want to hear any more of Arthur's ideas. Everything he said seemed finally depressing and disintegrating. Yet it was more than this. The orthodox talk of the time was almost always depressing and disintegrating, but at least, there, she could feel some active opposition. She belonged with people who were fighting against it. Here, with Arthur, it was different, yet she could not say why.

Unconsciously she framed the words to herself. It is because he is saying what I really feel. It is just that he has the courage to admit the corruption, as I won't do. Even if admitting it is the only way of beginning again, and I must begin again, however corrupt it may be. For I've passed that breaking point at which belief goes, faith goes.

Yet as the words came she rejected them. She could not bear any break except an attempt at something better, something she could believe in and respect herself for.

They were climbing Goldsmith Street, and the power of the car seemed to flatten the pitch. Kate remembered how often she had struggled up here in the rain, with the pram and the shopping. It didn't seem the same place.

'Here we are, then,' he said, pulling in fast to the kerb.

'Yes. Thanks.'

'Is it that side your relatives live? Your sister-in-law, did you say?'

'Yes, Gwyn and Myra.'

'You seemed a bit critical of Myra. Is it always so?'

'We're as different as could be. She's all right, but I don't know. If it wasn't for family she'd be in a different world.'

'You must learn to accept being isolated, Kate.'

'Must I?'

'It's like loving your neighbour, which all the faiths seem to agree on. All the religions and all the political parties. The only snag is that all of us, quite by chance of course, seem to be living in just the wrong place. We could all love our neighbour, but never the actual person next door.'

'No, it's not as bad as that,' Kate said, and went in.

The next few days were very tense with waiting. It became gradually clear, to everyone concerned, that the strike at West Longton was going to last for some time. And this was having immediate effects, over the whole system. By the beginning of next week, at five other factories, production would start to slow down, and the majority of the workers would be laid off. Already, here, a warning notice had been posted.

Yet the Longton strikers themselves were also moving out, directly, into the rest of the system. Delegates were being sent to each associated factory, to explain the dispute. They had already had some success, in getting support for their action. For nearly all the men they spoke to agreed that they had a strong case. All the weight of experience was on their side. You could hardly approach a man, in this vast network, who did not start by believing that the grievance was real, for when he listened to others it was like listening to a story of himself and his own world.

But of course there were immediate differences when it came to what should be done. Dick Manning insisted that the Longton men should be given active support. It was pointed out that this would weaken everybody for later on, in their own inevitable fight over redundancy. But 'what happens to them today will happen to us tomorrow,' he said. 'Why let the management pick us off one by one in their own time? Why not choose our own time, and fight when we're strong?'

Harold led the opposition to this. It was just muddling separate issues, and you could only get a good fight if the issues were clear. He was as ready for a fight as anyone, only let it be on something where they would get hundred per cent support, and where there was a chance of swinging public opinion against the employers.

'He sounds just like a bloody Fabian, the old Fabian tortoise,' Dick said, meaning the remark to be overheard.

'No,' Harold said, keeping his temper as a matter of policy. 'Just one who's fought more issues than you've ever heard of, and knows how it has to be done.'

The crisis came over a request from the Longton delegates that they should be allowed to address a general meeting of the men, in the Monday dinner hour. Harold insisted that this was impossible, but he was outvoted. What was wrong, after all, in letting everybody hear what the Longton chaps had to say? Harold accepted his defeat, but at once decided to turn the meeting into a different path, giving the first public warning of the scale of the redundancy ahead. When the meeting was announced, he worked as hard as anybody to make sure it was a success.

Kate would not go to the meeting, though in the old days she had gone down to listen, whenever she could. Surprisingly, Peter asked her if she would come down with him, but she had made up her mind not to go.

'Though it's a change you wanting to go, Peter, isn't it?'

'Why? I've always been interested.'

'Not that I've noticed. You turned your back on it all as soon as ever you could.'

'You can say that, Mam? After years of living in the same house you can tell that kind of lie about me?'

'It isn't a lie. It hurts because it's the truth.'

'And you want to hurt, I suppose?'

'No, Peter. Why should I? I even wanted you to turn your back on it, because I know what it does to people. The way you could help was to get your degree.'

'Yes, I've noticed the help.'

'It's the only way. Don't contradict me, Peter. After all, I know this other right through. To make a difference where it matters you need a different kind of mind, and it takes years to train.'

'So many years, in fact, that we forget what it's for. That's why I want to go down there, to see.'

'It will sicken you, Peter. You just know, listening, that the issues are too difficult for them, and it isn't really their fault. If the workers knew enough, if as a class we'd been really trained and intelligent, we'd have done it by now, done it a generation ago. Only we haven't done it, and you'll find out why. Don't go down there thinking of some virtuous assembly. You'll find just waste and confusion, and an aimless sort of anger that's blowing itself to pieces.'

'I find all that where I usually am,' Peter said, and went out.

The loudspeaker van that had been hired for the meeting was in position early. Harold was one of the first across and went to talk to the driver. He gave him a cigarette and they stood out of the wind, behind the van, chatting.

Slowly, keeping together, more men moved across to the meeting place. The general mood was quiet, reserved, sceptical, in the grey light and the keen dry wind. Dick Manning, arriving with the two Longton delegates, was like a sudden patch of colour in the drained light. His eagerness, his confident voice, his clear refusal to be disheartened, were all encouraging in a way, and he was quite well liked though still carefully watched. Slowly, the meeting assembled. It was already ten minutes after it was due to start.

Then, unexpectedly, from the road past the old assembly bay, came a straggling procession: almost all young people, mainly students though several looked even younger. Two tall young men, in high sweaters and loose black coats, carried the familiar nuclear disarmament banner. Behind them, along the line, the black and white circles moved at uneven heights above the loose march. They brought another and different silence, that impinged strangely on the wary, bitter silence of the men waiting for the meeting. The leaders turned the march round the edge of the crowd, and a picket line was formed, all around them. Now the banners and placards were lifted, tilting high in the air. The lettering was very sharp and distinct: '*The Basic Enemy of the Workers—War*'. '*The Peace is in Your Hands*'. '*Let's Mind Our Own Business—Let's Stay Alive*'. In the first minutes the surprise was complete, but as the marchers stood still the men began calling to them, especially to the girls.

'You've come to the wrong place, Miss.'

'Aye, Trafalgar Square's the other way.'

'No bombs here.'

The silence of the boys and girls in the picket was disconcerting. Every face was tense, but it was an inward tension, brought to this single point.

'Never miss the beatniks,' one young worker shouted, laughing with his friends. But again there was no reaction. The girls in their jeans and coloured stockings, the boys in their dark coats and several with beards, merely held their line. It was almost as if they were not present, as if what they were doing belonged in a different dimension. Then the loudspeaker boomed suddenly, and the tension of waiting was broken.

Harold was standing on the low stone wall, holding the trailing microphone. Peter could hardly recognize his father's voice, in the distorted boom of the amplifier. He was introducing the Longton delegates, and the first of these, Meeson, a small, dry, elderly man, not unlike Harold himself, was already climbing up beside him. The shouted words came—the unpractised shout into the microphone—and boomed and echoed through the cold air of the meeting. But the familiar phrases were points of recognition and understanding, beyond the details.

'The point comes, brothers, when your own wages and conditions have got so far away from you, so damn near lost in parallel agreements and further study and God knows how many consultative councils and standing joint committees and any other name they like to think up. So far away from you, you damn near wonder if you exist at all, except in some bloody file in London. So we reckon we've waited long enough about this, and it's time they heard from us. Let them call us wildcats. What do that matter? We're responsible men. We just ask them to be straight with us. Because I tell you, whatever they say, when we come out then things start to happen. That's what we're here for, and thankyou for your attention.'

Meeson stepped back. What he had been saying seemed right to the meeting, but his presence and voice, even distorted and amplified by the microphone, seemed so unemphatic, so deeply resigned, that there was only a spatter of clapping. The second delegate, Rathbone, a tall, florid man in his thirties, took over the microphone, and there was at once a tightening of attention, for this voice was vivid and its quick rhythms powerful. Like Meeson, Rathbone gave an account of the complicated situation which had led up to the strike, but some extra feeling began to come through, bringing the realities nearer. Still, the facts and figures of this remote dispute were not easy for anyone to follow. Rathbone, in immediate touch with the mood of the meeting, sensed the drift away from attention. Suddenly he switched his tone.

'And I know quite well, brothers, that this is boring you. It's marvellous, isn't it, how wages can bore you, unless they're your own.

'So let me tell you a little story, definitely true I guarantee. I've been saying the management, but what's that? Let me tell you about the man we actually go and talk to, though I won't tell you his name. About my age, and definitely a coming man. He went over the three thousand and under his double figure handicap in the same week: that'll show you. And his kids, you should see his kids, in their private school uniforms—all fast dye, you know, guaranteed not to fade. Mind, remember, brothers, he didn't produce them all on his own. He needed the co-operation of a lady, and from what we can tell he got it. If they called for co-operation in industry with her around, you'd all come to work the night before. That is, if you like them glistening. As you do.'

There was the first real laugh of the meeting, though still an uneasy laugh.

'Not me, of course,' Rathbone added, smiling. 'I'm a happily married man, as my wife would tell you.'

There was a further laugh, and he seemed to breathe more deeply. He waited for silence, with his hand held out in front of him, and the thumb raised.

'An happily married man,' he repeated, looking sideways at his thumb until everyone seemed to be following his look. 'That's just it,' he said, and let his thumb subside.

The whole mood of the meeting had changed now. There was a direct relation between speaker and audience, for the first time.

'Well now you've got some idea of him, brothers, I'll just tell you what he said. Because I'm not one to waste time, even if old Harold Owen did think there was a dirty story coming.'

There was another quick laugh, but Harold was standing quite still and unmoved, smoking in the shelter of the van, as if his name had never been mentioned.

'What he said, when he'd got his moustache well up, every hair on parade and looking us straight in the eye, what he said, brothers, was this. "I can only repeat what my masters have decided." Honest truth. "I can only repeat what my masters have decided." And he's quite a big boy too, under them padded shoulders.

'Only the point, brothers, the point of why Brother Meeson and myself have come here to you today, the point is after all that he was speaking the truth. You might have one of these lads here yourselves, and you think it's him you got to impress. He's got kids too, you wouldn't want them to be taken away from that nice school. "I can only repeat what my masters have decided." Well, remember that. Say it over to yourselves. Say it over every morning when you're kissing your missus. Only for Christ's sake get it into your heads. Hammer it in. Hammer it in so it'll never come out. Then you won't be led away by the usual bloody nonsense that even some leading trade unionists come out with. Because you know the facts quite well for yourselves. If we stop work, you stop work. And why? Because it's all the one system, and all the decisions lead back to the few people that lad calls his masters. His masters, my masters, your masters. That's it, brothers, whatever they say about local issues, keeping local disputes separate, and all that bloody nonsense. Because where we are, brothers, is where you are, and don't you forget it. It'll be Black Monday, Black Tuesday, Black January to December, whenever the working people of this country forget that one simple fact. Where we are is where you are. Remember that. It's your own business we're asking you to mind.'

Rathbone stepped down from the wall without even waiting for the reaction. He seemed quite certain of it. He seemed to know in his body that the meeting was with him, that the thing had been done. And indeed at that point, if only sympathy had mattered, there was no more to do. A good few of the men even turned and went away: the climax that mattered had been reached. There was some argument in the little group around the van, but then Dick Manning was speaking.

'I wish to formally propose,' he shouted into the microphone, 'that this meeting affirms its support for the Longton strike, and pledges itself to take all necessary measures to carry that support into practical effect.'

Harold took the microphone, slowly, and spent some time clearing his throat. His voice, when it came, was flat and dull.

'I know that is what we all want,' he said slowly.

Dick Manning and the Longton delegates were watching him

with open surprise. Harold did not often switch his line this suddenly.

'We would be less than men, less than brothers, if we wanted anything else. And so I have much pleasure in seconding the motion, adding an instruction to our stewards' committee that they discuss, as a matter of urgency, the necessary measures.'

Dick Manning and Meeson were smiling. The victory seemed all the better for being so unexpected. But Rathbone had flushed angrily. The florid good humour of the speech had quite disappeared.

'I can't actually second the motion, formally,' Harold said. 'Is there a seconder from the meeting, for the motion as I put it.'

Several voices called out.

'Right,' Harold said quickly. 'Those in favour?'

A clear majority of the men put up their hands in assent.

'Carried. And that concludes the business. Thankyou very much.'

Harold stepped back, smiling, and lit another cigarette. He still had his hand to his face as Rathbone came over and began talking earnestly to him. Dick Manning, listening, was frowning. But the meeting was over, and the men were walking away. The boys and girls in the picket line were distributing leaflets, and most of the men were taking them but after a quick glance folding them in their pockets.

Peter stood, as the crowd dispersed, trying to sort out his feelings. As the crowd thinned, the picket line stood out more clearly, and he suddenly saw Robert's daughter, Frances. He walked across to her, and waited until she had finished distributing her handful of leaflets.

'Hullo, Frances.'

'Oh, hullo.'

She was very jerky and embarrassed, as she had been at the house.

'I wonder what you thought of the meeting.'

'It was very interesting.'

'Whose idea was it, to do the picket?'

'Well you see,' she said, each word tumbling over the next, 'it's a sort of general policy, to sort of extend the campaign. To try to kind of put it on a broader basis, socially I mean. Our weakness had been you see that we haven't made proper contacts with the workers. It's been too, you know, middle-class, and the students and so on. So we came.'

'And have you made the contacts, do you think?'

'I don't know.'

'Nor do I. I don't understand these meetings.'

'Well we did what we could,' Frances said, and her embarrassment had deepened. 'I mean . . .' But she broke off, as the others in the line began moving away. 'I must go now,' she said quickly, and hurried away.

Peter felt rebuked, but there was so much, still fresh in his mind, that rebuked him, that he could not really centre his feelings. Over by the loudspeaker van the little group including his father, still argued fiercely. He watched for a few moments, and then walked slowly back up to the house.

Two evenings later, Kate waited up for Harold, while he was at the meeting of the stewards to which the question of supporting the West Longton men had been referred. Kate sat in the front room, with her back to the bay window. She had not drawn the curtains, though the street was dark and wet. Here, in the limited circle of light from the standard lamp, in the narrow area of dry heat from the electric fire, she could hold herself for a while. The rest needn't be looked at, till she had to.

Peter was round next door again; probably just the other side of the party wall, with much the same lamp and fire, and with Beth. Harold was still at the decisive meeting. He had taken her memorandum, but it would stay in his pocket; decisions weren't made from memoranda.

She looked back at the article she was reading, on an experiment in decision-making by production workers in a factory in Jugoslavia. She knew how Harold would react to an article like this. It would be so remote and abstract as to be comic. She felt this also, at times, but in another part of herself she knew that it was the reaction which was really remote.

This, really, was the whole trouble. It was like being two persons in one world. Every scrap of English belittling, of narrowness, of philistinism, she felt quite active in herself. All the destructive derision, pettiness, complacency of this English world kept coming to the surface, as her own thoughts. But at the same time there was this quite different drive, towards belief, energy, action. The one mocked the other, perpetually, but not in any external conflict. What might have been a division in the world was in fact the ebb and flow of her own mind.

If only this tension could be seen, heard, felt, for an instant even, there might be some result, some demand, some absolute demand. And what would that be, exactly? Kate could hear the precise intonation, of this question that looked for no answer. Some absolute demand, yes. But show me the cash value of that. I mean, in the way of direct use to the sort of people we are. And in the end, perhaps, there was no cash value, and there was nothing direct and exact. It was only a cry: give me back my life, give me back my world.

Harold's car turned in from the street, and the headlights swept through the room. He came through the front door, hurrying in to her, as if he could not wait to tell her his news. Yet she felt that she knew it already, had always known it.

He seemed so alive and eager, so completely absorbed in what he had been doing, that she responded at once, without thought. He seemed surprised that she was smiling at him, but the rush of excitement carried him through.

'It was all right then?' she asked.

'Yes, twenty-two to nine. A statement of support for their claims, and a request to union headquarters to do everything possible to back them up.'

'But no more?'

'Not by us.'

Kate hesitated, wondering at his eagerness, though still responding to it.

'I'm glad for you, love,' she said, and went across and kissed him.

'Yes, it is pretty good.'

She held his neck and kissed his lips, with a passion they had both almost forgotten. He could not find his bearings, and began drawing his body away. Really it was making him ridiculous to do this, when in fact he wanted to talk. She still held his neck, her fingers locked so tightly and pressing into the flesh that she was actually hurting him. Her lips were wet and moving, and seemed to be drawing him into her, changing the feel of his skin. Like the first moment under water, he remembered. His arms were still at his sides, but he lifted them and held her across the shoulders, to keep his balance.

Only it had finished, all this, years before. Yes, the desire came back, quite sharp and clear sometimes, but always with too much care attached to it, too much consciousness, and all the business of the world in the way. He patted her shoulder, reassuringly, but he did not know whether he was reassuring her or himself. Still she clung to him with a kind of madness, as if she was really not herself. He looked out over her hair at the uncurtained windows, spotted with rain against the yellow lamps of the street. He could see, looking back, that her eyes were closed, and the long black hair had tumbled over her face.

He tightened his fingers on her shoulders, and gently eased her away, smiling down at her. She was reluctant to move away, to let go of him and open her eyes. But he bent over her, soothing her, and took her back to her chair. He crouched beside her, resting his head on her knees, holding her leg tightly against his cheek. She was very still and quiet, and at last he looked up to her face.

'It's all coming right,' he said.

'What is?' Kate asked, as if the words had no meaning.

He drew away a little, afraid.

'Look, I didn't get to use your notes, love. But I'd got up the redundancy figures and I really let them have it. It was just one fact after another, face up on the table. Your Manning hadn't got a leg to stand on.'

'Yes, I'm glad you got what you wanted,' she said, indifferently.

'It was the only possible decision.'

'Anyway, it was what you wanted.'

'And what the majority wanted.'

'Yes.'

'The thing is, Kate, they're worked up now for the next step, the vital step, when the redundancies start. Without this it'd have been ten times harder.'

'Yes, I know. The next step.'

'Well, you agree. You agreed when we went through your notes.'

'Yes, Harold, I did. Let's hope, that's all, they stay worked up that long.'

She pushed up from her chair, pushing him away. It seemed to her like an end, this moment: a final line drawn. Yet nothing could happen, to bring this feeling out. Everything would go on just as before.

'I expect you're tired,' Harold said.

'Yes, we shall need that holiday.'

'Aye, I suppose.'

'It's come down to that in the end. That different life, that life in its own right, is just a thing we can hope for in a week or two of the year.'

'It's the rest,' Harold said.

'No, this is the rest.'

'Not for me it isn't.'

'It's not how busy we are. Can't you see? It's how much of it amounts to anything.'

'We get some things done,' Harold said, stubbornly.

'Like tonight, for instance? When all you did was to stop something happening? I've noticed that, with most of the people I know. Their achievement is that they've managed to stop something. It's the English genius.'

Harold was too hurt and angry to speak, but he could feel her estrangement. There had often been difficulties between them: failures of sympathy, periods of coldness barely disguised. But this was something else. This was a different voice and a different woman.

'I'm sorry, girl, that you see it like that.'

'You should be sorry it is like that.'

'But how can I be? I know what has to be done.'

'Yes, that nothing has to be done. That's what you've all arrived at, for the most plausible reasons. And what will you fight for, tell me, when the great day comes? For a bit of redundancy pay? For no sackings before Christmas, to keep the compliments of the season? For what, really? What demands have you actually got?'

'We say no redundancy, no sackings.'

'Of course you say that. And the employers just calculate how many weeks they must wait before they can get you talking their language. They've got you as far as redundancy. Then it'll be severance payments, adequate preliminary information, full and frank consultation, like the butcher and the pig. Perhaps they'll even buy you your little tin swords, to wear on your watch-chains.'

'For Christ's sake, Kate. You talk like somebody who's never lived any of this. Like the militancy of some kid.'

'Which will in any case never even be listened to, behind the mumblings of all the old men.'

'What old men? Do you mean the leadership?'

'No, Harold, I mean you.'

He closed his eyes. While they were still closed he took off his glasses and rubbed his strong fingers across his nose. Kate wanted to go to him again, but she could see him too clearly, too nakedly, and could not find the courage to touch him. He opened his eyes and looked across at her. He had clenched his fists and there was open anger in his face. For a moment she thought that he would come forward and hit her. She imagined the blow, and was ready for it. However afraid she might be, she wanted some decisive action, at last. But he did not move. He put his glasses slowly back on.

'I think it's only fair to tell you, Kate, I've agreed with Gwyn about the caravans.'

'Agreed what?'

'I've said that so far as I can see at present we shall want the other caravan. I was going to tell you. Only Gwyn had to write that day.'

Kate went to the mantelpiece, and took a cigarette. She lit it, stabbing the match down on the box so that it hissed and flared. She inhaled deeply, tasting the acrid dryness of the smoke.

'And with things as they are,' Harold said.

'Look, if you're trying to hurt me,' Kate interrupted him, 'you can just forget it. It doesn't matter to me what arrangements you make.'

'Doesn't it?'

'Not now. Not from now.'

Harold rubbed his hand back over his hair. He did not want to look at her. He did not want to hear any more. It was a mistake, always, to start talking so late. Whatever was said, tomorrow would still be the same.

'I think I'll go to bed, Kate. It's no use waiting up.'

'All right, if you want to.'

'Are you coming?'

'No.'

'Don't be so damned silly. You can't wait down here all night.'

'I can do whatever I want. I shall do whatever I want.'

Chapter Ten

AFTER the latest meeting of the working party, Kate was sitting with Arthur in their usual pub. She had said she was in no hurry to get home, and they were staying late. They sat on a window bench in the corner of the comfortable saloon. Arthur did most of the talking, while Kate watched the other people or looked out through the window. She could just see, over the roofs, the corner of a floodlit college tower.

Arthur talked mostly about himself. He had several funny stories about his childhood, and especially his more distant family. There was one of his uncles, on his mother's side, a quite wealthy man who had made his money in rubber in Malaya. He had never married though he once had a child by a Chinese girl that he's kept for years as his mistress.

'But things really happened when he retired and came home. In his last years in Cornwall he started a rite of spring. No, really. On the first of March every year he had a nest built in his bedroom. A substantial thing of interwoven hazel branches, lined with straw and moss. Then for the next six weeks, he lived in the nest. A servant he'd brought back used to take up his food, and he ate and slept there, everything.'

'I don't believe you, Arthur.'

'Honestly. I saw it. Of course only after it was abandoned. Or do they say deserted? Actually he died peacefully enough in his bed, one February, just before the nest was due to be made. He left me a lot of his books.'

'What happened to the child?' Kate asked. She was looking back through the window at the floodlit tower, where the beautiful stonework seemed transformed into solid light.

'Which child?'

'Didn't you say he had a child by a Chinese girl?'

Arthur picked up his drink.

'Yes. At least so it was always said, in the family. I never heard any more about her.'

'A girl child, was it?'

'No, I meant the Chinese girl. I never heard any details about the child.'

114

Kate nodded, and looked back across the bar. She seemed still quite distant, taken up with her own thoughts.

'One more notch against the foreign devils, I suppose,' Arthur said, finishing his drink.

'Well they were foreign devils. At least that sort.'

'Oh, I don't know. He was a harmless old boy. Yes, the nest got pretty foul, but only he had to put up with it.'

'I meant the girl and the child.'

'Yes. Though actually what he paid her probably saved her from starving. Not that that excuses it.'

'The rest of us will pay for every penny of all that.'

'How?'

'To have been exploited oneself, and yet to have been born into a guilty nation. That, for us, Arthur, is the really damnable thing.'

'Well yes, but they'll merely ignore us, they have better things to do. And while our bit lasts, we'll build our own nest and creep into it.'

Kate sat up, tightening her fists on the table.

'You sound as if you're acquiescing in it.'

'I just don't want this damned guilt, Kate. It's been nag, nag, every day of our lives. What we did to the Indians, what we did to the Irish, what we did to damn near everybody. And we didn't do it, Kate. You and I didn't do it. I used to have Indian students here, nagging away about the British Raj and the wrongs of their country and I'd say yes, of course, you're quite right, you should have your independence. And they just fixed you again, with the same nagging eyes. "But you must understand, the British power in India . . ." And that mad accent went on: the famine, the children dying, the men sleeping and starving in the streets. Well yes, it is so, but I didn't make those conditions, I supported Indian freedom even before it was fashionable. And I've had enough, we've all had enough. I didn't send children down the mines, I didn't put the ropes over the backs of those women hauling trucks. I stick on this. I'm weary of all the cant. I have boys coming to me now from working-class homes, well-fed, well-dressed, as comfortable young gentlemen as the world could conceive. And they think they have some birthright to nag me, about the depression, the hunger marches, mass unemployment. There, while they're drinking my sherry. And I've had enough, we've all had enough.'

'We'd better go,' Kate said, picking up her handbag and gloves.

'Yes, all right.'

They made their way out through the crowded tables. Several people looked at them as they passed, and it was in being looked at that Kate suddenly felt her relationship with Arthur. It was as if they were being confirmed together in public; this was how it was going to be, from now on.

Arthur was easy and happy in the street. The eager talk seemed to have cleansed and satisfied him. He took Kate's arm, and they walked easily together. He felt tender and protective towards her, because she had helped him towards this release. Kate, in herself, hardly thought about it. Certainly she did not care any more about the attitudes and the arguments. That they were together, like this, was enough, for the time.

The street was cold, but they walked slowly and without speaking. Steadily they adjusted their pace, until they were walking in a slow, easy rhythm. Kate was aware of this first, and as she walked she looked down at her legs and feet, and at his legs moving beside them. It was strange to become aware, like this, of so familiar a movement. Aware of it as a physical action, an end in itself, bringing its own satisfaction. It seemed to warm her suddenly, and she felt relaxed and happy. She even wanted to laugh, in pure pleasure. She would not have believed, until now, that this kind of satisfaction existed, in anything so ordinary and so simple.

She could feel quite clearly, as if in a definite place at the back of her brain, the pressure of a quite different consciousness: questioning what Arthur had said, relating his attitudes to her own life, relating the arguments to what they were actually doing. But, just as she could feel this quite physically, she could feel also the barrier, again quite physical, that prevented it coming forward. It was there, but it could not break through and connect. Every active feeling was in the slow rhythmic walk, the feel of his arm on her elbow, the slow smile and warmth of her face, where the lips were full and the skin alive.

What could break this now? What could ever break in and destroy it? The world was there, but it had no power over them; it was little and distant. There was only the walk, the continuing adjustment and discovery. She had walked so often along this street. She had walked it quite often with Arthur. But it seemed no longer the same. Its pressure had gone, though also she felt more in touch with it, saw its buildings with more interest and affection, as if they were extensions of her own feelings. The towers and spires were floodlit, above the uneven dark roofs. The slow steps of the walk seemed the centre, with the street moving past and around them.

She took his hand and guided it, still holding hers, into the deep pocket of his coat. He smiled and held her close.

'Is there really no hurry, Kate?'

'No.'

'Will you come up for a while then?'

'No.'

'Why not? If there's really no hurry?'

'No.'

She stopped suddenly. They were almost opposite the car, on the other pavement. They still avoided looking at each other.

'Are you sure, Kate?'

'Yes.'

She was gripping his hand very tightly as she spoke. As they waited, he could feel the pressure and movement of her fingers, opening and closing very tightly around his hand.

'Kate.'

'No, don't say anything.'

'Are you sure you won't come?'

'Not tonight. Take me back.'

'But Kate.'

'Please,' she said, and quickly released his fingers, pulling her hand from his pocket.

They walked slowly across the road. Arthur felt for his keys and unlocked the car doors. She kept her face turned away from him. She did not want him to look at her. She got into the car, quickly, and sat very still. Arthur hesitated, then got in and drove off without speaking. On the journey back he tried once or twice to start talking again, but she did not answer. He drove very carefully, watching the road. At the bottom of Goldsmith Street he stopped, and switched off the headlights.

'There's no need for explanations, I suppose?'

Still she did not answer. He turned and kissed her. She kept her eyes open for a moment, then closed them and moved quickly towards him, returning the kiss. As he drew back, she let her head rest on his shoulder.

'I'm glad of this, Kate. I wanted it to happen like this.'

'No, don't say anything.'

'But you'll come? Soon?'

'I'll try to.'

'Is there a reason for waiting?'

'I have to know, Arthur. I have to know what I'm doing.' He still had his arm round her, but she sat up suddenly and moved to open the door.

'Can't I drive you on up?'

'No, I'd rather walk.'

'Are you sure?'

'Yes.'

'But you will come?'

'I'll try to,' Kate said, and opened the door and stepped out.

'Thursday. Thursday evening,' he said quickly.

'I will if I can.'

Gwyn and Harold were late that Thursday. It was one of the things nobody could ever explain, or at least ever bother to explain. There was the slowing of orders, and the certainty of sackings or short-time in front of them, but still, in these weeks of waiting, two shops were working overtime. The strike at West Longton had ended, the men being ordered back to work by their union so that new negotiations could take place. So there had been only a brief interruption of production, and this, it seemed, they were now making up. Nobody in the shop could understand what was happening, but almost everybody was glad of the overtime, because of the extra money.

Myra was waiting for Gwyn in the kitchen, where the meal was ready. There was a high wind outside, and she liked hearing it at the corners of the house. It was like back home, in Glynmawr, the only thing still the same. The wind from the mountain, round the house, or the wind in the trees and the wires, the singing in the wind, walking the dark road. Myra remembered walking with Jack, down the Sun pitch, the night the ash was blown down on to the Pritchards' cottage. The dark and the wind, and Jack helping old Pritchard, who was half out of his mind, and old Amy Pritchard, crippled, they had to carry her out.

It would have been different, with Jack, staying there in the valley and the more people to be with. Like you knew, listening to the wind, how everybody was listening, and you could feel you were with them. It seemed almost to be talking, the wind, and you could feel the shape of your house, and the meal ready, and Gwyn getting home.

The side door was opened suddenly, and Kate came in. She had on her white raincoat, with the collar turned up into her hair.

118

Myra had known she was in, because she had heard the wireless for the news. And she had her slacks on and was dressed for the house, so why the raincoat, if she had only just slipped round? She couldn't be going out, not dressed like that.

'Gwyn not back then?'

'No, it's the overtime.'

'Yes, I remember. Harold said.'

Kate lit a cigarette, and Myra watched her, curiously.

'You been out, then?' she asked.

'No. Though I might, later.'

'You're lucky to get out so often.'

'What's lucky about it?'

'I know I can't, these evenings.'

'Why not? His meal's ready.'

'It isn't only the meal.'

Kate turned away, irritably.

'Yes, well we know your standards, Myra.'

'Standards?'

'Making a home, and so on. I know I can't compete with you.'

'It's not to do with competing.'

'Then if you do it because you want to, you shouldn't be so damned virtuous about it.'

'Did you come round here to tell me that?'

'I'm sorry, Myra. I didn't come to quarrel. Honestly I didn't.'

'Well if you don't, I shan't.'

Kate nodded. She was standing with her back to the door, her shoulders forward as if she was still cold, her hands pushed deep into the raincoat pockets. Myra looked at her for some moments. Then she asked, gently:

'What is it, love?'

'Nothing.'

'I can see there is something, but I don't want to push in. Only if you want to tell me. Whatever it is. You look worried to death.'

'No.'

Kate moved away from the door, and sat on a chair near the stove. Myra came and sat near her, still watching her. After a while she looked up, staring across at Myra. It seemed so wrong, the way it was all turning out. She looked at the brightness of Myra's hair, at the fullness of her body and the open sensuousness of her face. It was always wrong, this contrast between the real Myra and what she had been made to become. It was as if her

119

body was quite separate from her, shut out and ignored, though nobody else could ignore it. Kate's mind went to Beth, and then to Gwyn, and then back to Myra.

'Were you sorry when you knew you were having Beth?' she asked suddenly.

She watched the violence of the shock in the face. For once the reaction was part of the physical Myra. Then there was an immediate deadlock. Myra could say nothing.

'I'm sorry, Myra. I shouldn't have sprung it on you like that. But I really do want to understand this. I want to know how you felt, having a child before you were married.'

'I was married when Beth was born.'

'Yes, I know you were. But you were having Beth before you were married.'

'What if I was? I was engaged.'

'Were you, Myra? Or did that come after you knew about Beth?'

'It came before.'

'In the very beginning, I mean. When it all started.'

'Well yes, of course I was engaged.'

'And that made it all right.'

'Yes,' Myra said.

She was looking at Kate in a quite bewildered way, and yet the strength of her feelings was quite clear in her face. On her last answer, she stared at Kate.

'No,' she added suddenly. 'I wasn't.'

'You weren't engaged when it started.'

'No. Only after I knew about Beth. And then my Dad had to go to his, before it was settled.'

'That's what I wondered. Because I wondered how you really felt about it, at the time.'

Myra looked away.

'It was what he wanted, that's all.'

'Not you?'

'No, of course not.'

'Are you sure, Myra?'

'Of course I'm sure. It was for him.'

'And the same after you were married? Still only for him?'

'Who do you mean? Gwyn or Jack?'

'Was there a difference?'

'Of course there was a difference.'

'How?'

Myra looked at her again. The eyes were afraid and pleading, though the whole body was roused and intent.

'I can't talk about it, Kate. It can't be talked about.'

'But did you want making love for yourself? Or only for him? For either of them?'

'You can't make love for yourself,' Myra said.

'People do, Myra. Even women do.'

'More fools them then.'

'Why?'

'Because it isn't love, that's all.'

'Yet you say you do it for him. You mean he can want it, for himself, but you can't.'

'One sort of man will.'

'Jack?'

'No. Why don't you let me alone, Kate? You got no right to ask me all this.'

Kate stubbed out her cigarette, and at once lit another. She was very tense and insistent now, in the way she had learned in committees.

'I know I've got no right, but, honestly, Myra, it's important. And why, after all, should you be afraid of talking?'

'We've never talked much, Kate.'

'No. It might have been better if we had.'

'Not to talk about our husbands, it wouldn't.'

'It isn't right to give yourself to a man before you're married. But you did.'

'I know I did,' Myra said, and tears suddenly started into her eyes.

'But you're sorry you did.'

'I am, Kate,' Myra said, getting up. 'But you'd never understand why, not if you talked from now till tomorrow.'

'But how can you be sorry, for what gave you Beth?'

Myra looked down at her hands, helplessly.

'It's not that at all, Kate.'

'But it is, Myra, it was.'

'You don't understand. You don't start to understand.'

'I know as much as you,' Kate said quickly. 'Even if you have had two husbands.'

'It isn't from that,' Myra said.

'If he had to be made marry you, he must just have been after whatever he could get.'

'Jack?'

'Yes. You just said so. And you said it was only for him you did it.'

'Did I? You muddle me, Kate, talking too fast.'

'I'm sorry. Really. But if you knew how much it meant to me. And I've nobody, nobody, to talk to.'

Myra looked at her, carefully.

'It's how you talk. Not just who you talk to,' she said at last.

'I know.'

'I've tried talking to Beth.'

'Yes,' Kate said sharply. 'And in fact you've frightened her.'

'Frightened Beth?'

'Yes, Myra, and I wonder who'll forgive you for it. All her life she'll carry the mark of it, that she's been scared to death about her own deepest feelings.'

Myra turned back, and sat down.

'You know nothing about her if you think that. A girl doesn't have to be frightened, she starts frightened. All I've said to Beth is to help her.'

'Would it have helped you?'

'Yes, Kate, it would.'

'But in fact it didn't. You went your own way. And now you're punishing Beth for your own mistake.'

'You really think that?' Myra asked, stubbornly. In the last minute Kate had hardened, noticeably. She seemed to have come back to her ordinary self, though she had been on the edge of breaking down and showing a quite different woman. Myra was hurt and angry, but she wanted to face Kate on this; she wasn't going to be broken down.

'There are the sins of the fathers,' Kate said (why did her voice remind her, just then, of Arthur?). 'But look, for a change, Myra, at the sins of the mothers. Twisting and crippling their daughters because of their own guilt.'

'Twisting and crippling? You don't know what you're saying.'

'Have you seen Beth and Peter together?'

'Of course I have. They're all right.'

'I wish to God he'd leave her alone,' Kate said, getting up. 'I wish he'd clear out and find a girl who could make him happy.'

'Like that? You must be mad, Kate.'

'I mean a girl who didn't make him feel he was dirty.'

'Yes, because she was dirty herself.'

'Like you were, Myra. A girl like you were.'

Myra looked away. She wanted Kate to get out, never to see

her again. If it wasn't for Gwyn and Harold, it would have happened years back. She had taken more from Kate than she'd have believed possible.

'You won't make me angry, Kate, so you needn't try.'

'It's just the truth hurts, Myra, isn't it?'

'Yes, Kate, it does. Only let Beth and Peter alone, if you can bear to. I don't ask why you're trying to break them up. You think you're so different, not like the rest of us, but it's always the same. Your son's girl is never good enough. Why doesn't he leave her and find a really nice girl? And with a new one it would start all over again.'

'But you're so prejudiced, Myra, you won't even look at what's actually happening.'

'Beth's frightened, that's all, like most girls are. But part of her fright is about Peter. She says sometimes he's like a stranger, he can hardly remember who she is. And I told her to be patient with him. He's got his own ideas of how a marriage can turn out.'

'What exactly do you mean by that then?'

'A boy needs to trust a girl, just as much as the other way round.'

'Well, and if he doesn't?'

Myra smiled, crossing her hands in her lap.

'You look at the women he's been closest to.'

'Anybody except the girl, in fact.'

'The girl of course, when he can see her.'

'Would she let him see her?'

Myra looked up. Her smile had faded, and her face was intent and serious.

'Peter's her whole life, Kate, you know that.'

'Yes, isn't that just it? Like you said yourself, it's for him. Subservient and narrow, the two things at once. The woman's never there as a woman, as herself. She's just a bit of portable property, that he's going to take possession of. But of course, since she is property, she's got to bargain. She doesn't make herself cheap, because it wouldn't do to make property cheap. Let her sell herself dear, because selling is all it can be.'

'I don't know what you're talking about,' Myra said, getting up.

'No, Myra, you wouldn't. You still live in the eighteenth century, like all the women in this street, the women all over the estate. You're bits of property, and you've got your own cunning

123

about it. But you'll never consider a man on really equal terms. You'll never just go to him as yourself, for your own reasons.'

The wind had dropped a bit, outside, and there was the sound of rain against the glass. Myra thought of the pitch down to the corner, and the street lamps. It was time Gwyn was coming.

'That keeps a woman to her home, anyway,' she said, at last.

'Yes, dear, it does,' Kate said bitterly. 'And look what it does to her, look what it does to her children. This empty, narrow sort of half-life we've got here, and we deserve it. Does it look, walking round here, like living at all? And we've broken the men, taken the heart out of them with our narrowness. They go to work just expecting to be bored and cheated, and they don't know anything more they could really get.'

'Have you done that to Harold then?'

'I've done everything for Harold and you know it. I've kept him active enough to go out and fight for something better. He hasn't just given up, like the others.'

'But that still isn't enough for you?'

'What are you looking so damned pleased about?' Kate asked, angrily, for Myra was looking across at her and smiling.

'Just I thought this was about being satisfied.'

'Well of course Harold's satisfied. He gets tired, but he's glad to be doing it.'

'It wasn't him I was asking about,' Myra said.

Kate swung round, throwing back her hair. Her raincoat was still tightly belted, above the tight black jeans. She was now much more sure of herself than when she had come in. The strain seemed to have gone, and she was no longer pale.

'I've done everything for Harold,' she said again. 'I shall go on doing it.'

'All right then,' Myra said.

In the brief silence, the side-door was opened, and Beth came in. She was flushed and out of breath, her coppery hair loose and shining with wet.

'Has Peter been here?' she asked, hurrying into the kitchen.

'No,' Myra said.

'We were going to the cinema. We were to meet down there. I waited nearly an hour, outside, under the porch. Then I came home to see.'

'Take your things off and get warm,' Myra said. 'He'll know to come here to find you.'

'But I can't understand it,' Beth began, and then broke off.

'I must go,' Kate said, and walked across towards the door. Beth had pulled out a chair and was sitting with her arms on the table, her head down. Kate saw the shine of the rain in her hair, and that the bottoms of her stockings were wet and discoloured. As she watched, Beth broke down and dropped her face to her hands, crying bitterly. Myra went to her quickly, putting her arm across her trembling shoulders. Beth pulled away as soon as she was touched. She was crying now beyond reach or control.

Myra looked back at Kate. Her face was ugly with anger.

'You'd better go, Kate.'

'I am going,' Kate said, pushing her hands deep into her pockets. Myra stayed close to Beth until she heard the door shut, then leaned over her kissing her wet hair.

Back in her own house, Kate looked at Harold's supper in the oven, and turned the gas lower. She sat at the kitchen table and wrote a note saying she hadn't been able to wait, if she was to get to the meeting. Then she hurried up to her bedroom and got the newspaper and refolded it, putting it on the table beside his place. She found matches and cigarettes and put them beside the paper, then quickly took them away again and put them on the corner of the dresser. The stove was drawing steadily, and she opened the damper a little. The room was warm and she left on the light.

It was still raining as she walked down to the bus, and the wind was still strong, almost holding her back down the hill.

She hadn't long to wait. She stood back in the doorway of the empty shop, away from the glare of the lighted windows. There were big crossed keys on the empty window, in the space left clear of the whitening. Somebody had drawn a ban-the-bomb sign over the keys. Yes, she said to herself, feeling suddenly warm. Yes, really, we're going.

She thought of Peter, who must be somewhere in town. If she could only get him through, get him out and clear of the narrow habits, the breaking compromises, to which she herself would always have to go back. He would have to earn his independence first: that was the way of it. While you were still dependent, you could break the rules but you must pay for breaking them. The false liberalism, the inner hypocrisy, of the society. Anything could be done, for there were no absolute standards. But if you moved an inch outside your own set world, the whole pack was on you. You could only survive if you had somewhere else to go, something solid and negotiable you could take with you. Money or a qualification or a guaranteed living. Then you could live as you chose.

In her own case, nothing. So look straight at the risk, and accept it. Accept it but still be careful. Though in herself she was justified. It would be the final capitulation if she now drew back. For this, after all, was her last chance. If she rejected this, she would die in Goldsmith Street, knowing that all her life she'd been cheated and deprived. And she would have for company, in that bare street, all the other grey restless people; the shadows of what could have been men and women, the huddling survivors of a generation that had seen every chance of a new life deferred, and had acquiesced in the deferment. This was what it meant to have been born into the deferred generation: into depression, into war, into the slow collapse of hope. Certainly, if she exposed herself, she could expect no mercy from those shadows. The least stirring of life was an intolerable rebuke to them, and they would have to stamp it out.

She got on the bus and ran quickly upstairs. The windows were misted, but she rubbed a clear space with the back of her glove, and then wiped the wet glove, quickly, on the back of the seat. Through the wet glass, the street was distorted, especially near the lights. She watched the people in the street, indifferently. It was difficult, in the brief moment as the bus passed, to see them as real. We just accept the familiar shapes, and assume they are people, with a history and with a future. Perhaps that after all is the deception.

Sitting very still in the corner of her seat, pressed tightly against the window with her reflection jolting beside her, Kate was deeply conscious of herself and what she was doing. Her body was quite cold, but she had made her decision. It seemed, in a way, to cut her off from people. It was the conventions of their world she was rejecting.

She was smiling when the conductor came for her fare. He responded immediately, at once pleasant and easy. She heard him whistling as he went back downstairs. And perhaps that was the truth, in the end. The tension, the guilt, the fear, could be broken. The other life was very near, all the time; very near and simply waiting to begin. Everything in the street seemed to conspire to suppress it, but in fact the few customary gestures were made, to keep the street occupied and as it should be. Then people could step aside, in themselves; draw back, smiling, to where they actually lived. Let the street have what belonged to the street. In the margins people could live.

She hurried down the stairs, having nearly missed her stop. She folded the ticket into her pocket, still smiling. She walked quickly along the crowded pavement, still pressing the ticket between her fingers.

At the corner she nearly collided with a man in evening dress, who was walking with a heavily made-up woman in an unfashionably long fur coat. The man apologized and stepped aside. Kate was past him quickly, merely glancing at the woman. It was another second before she recognized the man as Robert Lane, whom she had seen only twice before. May Lane she did not know at all, except that Peter had mentioned her. She looked a disappointed woman, very unlike her husband's reputation. But so was the evening dress unlike his reputation. They were probably going to some college party: Edwardian ladies and gentlemen for the evening. Kate smiled again, enjoying her freedom, as she crossed the road.

In the hall, with its Edwardian furnishing, she panicked for a moment. It was quite irrational, this sudden breathlessness, but she had to slow down, climbing the stairs.

And the last thing I want, she thought, mocking herself, is to go up sedately. As if I were carrying a tray. You feel a fool knocking at a door with a tray in your hands. Before that bored, sleepy come-in, when you'd at last managed to balance it. Managing to twist the handle and pushing the door back with your knee or your elbow. Then the figure sprawled in the chair, looking up as if surprised yet not really surprised at all, quite confident that the tray would come.

She knocked, still smiling at herself. Coming to the door in an overcoat, she remembered. Or the uncle in the nest, doing his duty by Spring, which hadn't amused her at the time. When Arthur opened the door, she was almost laughing. It was strange to see him looking so set and anxious. What on earth had he got to be anxious about? He had his own life, and his freedom. Though perhaps even he had to make the customary gestures, to keep the world occupied and as it should be.

'I ran into Robert Lane in the street' she said. She took off her raincoat, which was wetter than she had expected, and folded it over the back of a high wooden chair. 'I suppose with his wife. One of those formidable university wives.'

'It would be a change if it was someone else's.'

Kate laughed, feeling warm and relaxed. She ran her hands lightly down her arms, smoothing the long sleeves of her jersey.

'Would it improve him then, Arthur?'

'I don't know. He's too good to be true. In any case, I often wonder, with those women, how the men know the difference.'

'The women would see to that,' Kate said, and went across to the fire. 'But is he really too good to be true?'

'I think he's a phoney, but a clever phoney. All that generalized idealism, at this date.'

'Yes, I notice he never does anything for the Party.'

'Exactly. He's got a new definition of politics, which lets him out of anything so limited as the politics the rest of us have to put up with. His idea of society is a rapt contemplation of the goodness, the fundamental goodness, of people. From a safe distance, of course.'

'Is he Welsh?' Kate asked, smiling.

'No, thank God. He's from some odd garden suburb. At least that spares us Wissdom.'

'Wissdom?'

'Haven't you heard them on mission, Kate? Wissdom, gootness.'

'I'm Welsh myself. That's stage Welsh,' Kate said, laughing. 'It's all an act, anyway.'

'Yes. I was just thinking about it on the bus.'

'If you'd phoned, Kate, I'd have brought the car.'

'No, I wanted to come on my own.'

'You've got wet, though.'

'I'm all right,' Kate said, sitting closer to the fire.

'Let me get you a drink.'

'No.'

'Really?'

'No, that's another thing I was clear about.'

'Well you won't mind if I do.'

He pulled the bottle towards him, across the smooth polished surface, and poured a large whisky. He drank about half of it, at the sideboard, and then walked back to the hearth. Carefully balancing the half-full glass, he sat beside Kate, looking into the fire.

'What do you mean, Kate, being clear?'

'What I said. I'm leaving no room for illusions or excuses.'

'Is that sensible? Or even possible?'

'I know it's not wissdom,' Kate said, and laughed.

'Yes,' Arthur said, rubbing his hand over his eyes. In the shadows from the fire he looked tired, and older than she was used to. But he was sitting easily on the edge of the sofa, holding his glass. There was no stiffness, no reserve, but the tiredness was there.

'What are you thinking about, Arthur? Tell me.'

'About you, Kate. Naturally.'

'You won't get it right, Arthur. You can't be my conscience.'

'Perhaps even my own conscience.'

'After all the arguments?'

'Kate, to a person I have a conscience. That's the trouble with the public moralizing. It prevents any real recognition.'

'Well then?'

He lifted his glass to his lips. She saw the reflection of the fire in it as it moved.

'You're refusing to bargain, Kate, is that the point?'

'Yes, I thought we'd agreed that. The whole apparatus of bargaining. The advance statements, the declarations, even the promises.'

'Yes,' Arthur said.

'I've thought it right through, Arthur. To live without bargaining, or at least to try to, is the only possible way. Otherwise it's all nothing. Or just ugly and mean.'

'It isn't easy,' Arthur said.

'I never supposed it was.'

'And it presupposes bargaining of a sort elsewhere.'

'Yes,' Kate said. 'I'm not in fact burning my boats.'

'In what way exactly?'

'Just that if we go through with this I shan't tell Harold. I didn't foresee it that way but now it's quite clear.'

'Or the bargaining starts, you mean?'

'Yes, the bargaining starts.'

Her face, in the shadows from the fire, was drawn and sad. Arthur finished his drink and put the glass down inside the fender. For a little time they were silent.

'You wouldn't want me to tell him, Arthur, would you?'

'That isn't really for me to say,' he replied, carefully, his expression quite open and frank.

'But don't you see I don't want to hurt him?' Kate said, excitedly. 'If I don't tell him he won't be hurt. I've gone over and over this, and I'm really sure of it. It's only an idea that says otherwise.'

'Maybe,' Arthur said.

'And in any case I can't tell him and break up my marriage. This isn't an alternative.'

'Isn't it?'

As he spoke his eyes widened, and she could see a line of white above the very pale blue irises. She stared into his face, certain that the edge of a smile was there, though his lips did not move.

'No, it isn't.'

'What then?' Arthur said. 'A sort of coexistence?'

Kate hesitated. For a moment she did not know whether she would laugh or cry. The sudden emotion had come unanalysed into her throat.

'We needn't use any word. I came for myself.'

'I'm glad you came, Kate. I'm very glad you came. I wanted you to come. I wanted you very much.'

Kate clasped her fingers tightly in her lap. The words had fallen quite dead in her mind, but as in the street, when they had been walking together, she was committed beyond the words. She waited, and felt his fingers touching her shoulder. She leaned back to him, looking into the low fire, her fingers still tightly clasped.

He kissed her neck and her forehead, and reached for a cushion for her head. She lay back, her face turned away. He went on kissing her and whispering into her cheek, but she leaned back, beyond him. He touched her breasts and she drew in her breath, sharply. Her eyes were still closed. Then he whispered to her again and she held tightly to his arms. He kissed her eyes, waiting, and then, as she lifted her head and kissed his lips, he drew gently away. He went across and locked the door, and switched off the light.

Kate undressed quickly, as if she were alone, and then pulled on again her long black jersey, which was rough to her skin. He came back and stood above her, looking down at her as he undressed. Her loose black hair was pulled forward, on either side of her neck. He could not see her face clearly, for she was turned away into the shadows. She lay quite still, and her legs and thighs were small and very white under the blackness of the jersey. When he came to her, she held him with a sudden fierceness. As she held to him there was a deep pain through her whole body, and she set her teeth against it. The pain and waiting of years seemed suddenly localized, in a centre of hurting that spread out through her body. He was trying to be gentle with her; she could

130

feel the effort, the quick caresses of gentleness. But she pushed past this, tightening her hold on him, to a different feeling. As she turned she could see his face, and the expression she had always known was quite gone; he was excited and uncertain and even rather stupidly frightened. She closed her eyes and opened her mouth, reaching up to him, and at last felt his body quite clearly and separately. Slowly, as he moved with her, she felt the deep warmth she had almost forgotten. She said his name at the back of her mind, and as she said it she told herself that nobody could judge this, in the ordinary coldness of the world. Within this touch and movement there was no judging and no accounting, whatever afterwards might be said or might happen. Suddenly, inside her arms, he went limp. She cried in protest and pulled him tighter and closer, feeling his whole weight. Then she cried again, in a sudden deep pain, and her head fell back and away from him. After a while she could hear him whispering to her, his lips very close to her ear. She lay for a long time without moving. She could not listen to what he was saying. At last he pulled away from her, lightly kissing her forehead. As he moved she felt a quick resentment. The cold and the emptiness were flooding back. But he stood away from her, and bent to put a log on the fire. She sat up, watching his fingers on the log. He lit a cigarette and offered one to her. She took it mechanically and let him light it. He was speaking again, but she did not listen. She reached back, without looking, for her clothes, and dressed quickly. Arthur brought her a drink and she took it, though she could hardly taste. At last, quite suddenly, she could hear his voice.

She got up and sat in a chair, pulling her legs up under her. She looked across at him, meeting his eyes, and he smiled. She acknowledged the smile, still holding the glass, and drank again. He came over to her and sat on the arm of the chair, gently stroking her hair. He went on talking to her, but she hardly listened. She sat forward, looking around the room. Her eyes had got used to the dim light, and it seemed that she could see the room more clearly than when she had come in. She remembered how she had once stood at the window, looking out over the roofs.

'I want to stay, Arthur. I know I can't, but I want to stay. I want to stay or it will be just what you said.'

'What I said?'

'Coexistence. Coexistence the way they talk about it. Peaceful competition and trading.'

131

'You can stay whenever you want, Kate. You can always stay.'

'Yes, but I can't, Arthur.'

She walked across towards the window, but turned aside and went to where her coat was folded. She touched it. The shoulders were still damp.

'Can you run me back?'

'Yes but not yet, Kate. You needn't go yet.'

'Yes, I want to go,' she said, firmly, picking up her coat.

He crossed to her quickly, and held her in his arms. She did not respond, though she let him hold her.

'I must put on my coat,' she said, at last.

'Really?'

'Yes, really.'

She was quite back to herself now, alert and confident. She smiled again as he helped her on with her coat. As she tightened the belt she walked across and switched on the light. Arthur followed her, taking the car keys from the sideboard.

They walked together downstairs, and got into the car. He drove her back to the bottom of Goldsmith Street, and they talked for a while before she got out. As she opened the door, to walk back up the hill, she said:

'If this redundancy crisis really starts, Arthur, you would help, wouldn't you?'

For a moment he was disconcerted, and did not know what to answer. The words flashed through his mind, in two or three possible interpretations. The switch of subject was so unexpected that he searched for some reason.

'Well, of course, I'd do everything I could, naturally.'

'They'll really need every ounce of help they can get. You don't know what that kind of fight is, when it comes.'

'I remember what Manning was saying.'

'Yes. Well not only Manning. The differences will all drop when this hits them. They'll be on the same side, inevitably.'

'When will it come?'

'Very soon,' Kate said. 'We've got very little time.'

In the next weeks, which were also the weeks of waiting, Kate and Arthur met regularly. She came more often, and stayed later, as if she had forgotten any attempt at concealment, though in immediate details she was always still careful.

More and more clearly, the balance between them shifted. It was Kate now who seemed sure of herself, and Arthur who was uncertain. After that decisive evening, she had almost naturally taken the lead, in most things they did together. Having seen her earlier tensions, he was continually surprised by this new ease and confidence, and by the absence of any sense of crisis. Still, when they talked generally, about politics and ideas, he took an easy lead, though she was learning to argue back, with real force. He was again surprised by the range of her intelligence. He had known that she was much more intelligent than her background would have led him to believe, and she was still limited by lack of training. But what he found increasingly—it was an odd admission to have to make—was an intelligence quite equal to his own, capable of the last surprising reaches and insights that couldn't be taken for granted anywhere. Yet when he tried to talk to her about their own relationship, it was different. There he felt no control, and could find no bearings. Usually, indeed, she would put him off with some joke. The only direct thing she said was that she wasn't a young girl, to be dreamy and overwhelmed; she was a woman perfectly capable of managing her own life. And in the link which most mattered between them this seemed, against all his doubts, unquestionably true.

It seemed true, indeed, over the whole range of Kate's life. At home in Goldsmith Street the change was very clear, though it was in effect only a return to the Kate of the earlier years, perfectly able to run a home efficiently and comfortably and to follow all her interests through.

She took immense trouble for Harold, in everything he wanted. He could hardly believe how active and cheerful she now was, and how the home seemed to grow again around her, like the very best he could remember. She was in charge, of course, and in a way he only fitted in, comfortably, to what she had made. But most good homes he had seen were like that; it was the woman's place. She was going out more often, but no more in the evenings. It was the afternoons she usually went into town, and she was on a new committee, but in any case she was nearly always back by the time he got home.

She could affect him so much, he realized in these weeks. When things were right with her, it was as if the world was right, or at least could be faced up to. She still kept to her own bed, as she had done after the quarrel, but they were both sleeping better, and she would come in to him in the mornings, with his tea. She had bought him an electric razor, out of her own savings, and persuaded him to shave in bed, before he got up, to ease the start of the day. And things were so bad at the works now, with the threat of redundancy in everybody's mind and tempers running even shorter than usual, that these quiet mornings, while she sat on the edge of the bed and watched him shave and drink his tea, and then the evenings with supper and the fire, were a real rest, that he was deeply grateful to her for. He remained grateful, even as he slowly recognized the real terms of the settlement.

Kate went in more often, now, to talk to Myra. With a little effort she became quite friendly with her again, responding to all her interests. She was even, at times, affectionate, as if there were some really deep tie between them.

Myra never encouraged this; she always started away from feelings she could not understand. But it was there, unmistakably, on Kate's side: a new tenderness and an instinctive sympathy. Myra would think about this when Kate had gone, and always she found herself setting hard against it, only to wonder if she was being unfair when Kate came again and was so warm and easy.

Kate's attitude to Beth had also changed. She made opportunities to talk to her about Peter; never pushing things too far, but letting Beth know that she was on her side. She gradually won a little of Beth's confidence, around the idea of marrying at Easter. His thesis would be finished then, and they could have their honeymoon before his examination.

She also talked to Beth about politics, and especially about the campaign against the bomb, in which Peter, since the meeting at the factory gates, was now more involved. At the beginning of December, Beth went with them on a protest march, to a bomber base. They went out in buses, and marched the last few miles. Beth had never been seriously interested in politics, but this kind of protest made sense to her. It wasn't the usual sort of argument, but just going out and showing you were against the evil that was threatening to destroy the world. You couldn't quietly marry and bring up children in the sort of world they were making, with their priorities for bombs and preparations for war.

The march was interesting, though nothing exciting happened. They just marched quietly past the miles of wire and the sentries, and this seemed to make its own kind of sense. What it did was to show how you felt yourself; that was always about the limit, and then see. To Beth the march was impressive, in just this kind of steady quiet, except for one group of students singing revolutionary songs as if it was anything to do with revolution and they ought really to have made a march on their own. Kate would have joined in the singing, given half a chance, but Peter walked straight and silent, and Beth felt right with him, and knew that in a way he felt right with her, though they took each other for granted, just being there.

It was cold that day, with the wind shifted to the north-east. When they got back to Goldsmith Street, Beth and Peter, without hats or scarves, looked as if they had been crying, at the corners of their eyes. Kate hadn't come back with them; she had dropped off in the town. She had the money to see to, she said, for one of the coaches. She was late back, but Beth and Peter sat with Harold, and Beth got supper.

Beth wasn't afraid of this house any more. She could feel her way into it. And it was one of the best times for months, just Peter and his father, and her getting the meal and them all talking a bit. You could say what you like about all the bad things in the world, and, of course, when you had to, you made it clear you were against them. But seeing life that way all the time; twisted by it into a sort of ugliness, really; finding the bad things everywhere. The real thing was to get your own life right, your own place, and then you had something to stand by, something good and worth making the effort for. One evening like this was worth a lot; just being with people you liked, where you knew you were wanted.

Chapter Eleven

PETER sat with the manuscript of his thesis, looking through the bad typing and the hastily scribbled corrections, in so many different inks. He was supposed to be revising again, following Robert's suggestions. But every page that he touched seemed to belong, suddenly, in a quite different life. He could hardly recognize his own words, which seemed a senseless jargon. For his own voice, his own words, were not in this work at all. These were simply the words that he had learned to rearrange and manipulate, that he had been paid for manipulating. The rewards were quite clear.

There had been two men, in his own year: each clever, each praised. Almost automatically, after their first degree, they had stayed on for research. Asher was already a poet, and had wanted to work on the dramatic verse of the last thirty years, as an accompaniment to his own intention of writing a play. He was now working on an edition of the eighteenth-century critic, Henry Home, Lord Kames (1696–1782), author of *Elements of Criticism* and *Introduction to the Art of Thinking*. His edition would be good, and he would get his fellowship. Then Morris, Asher's friend, who wanted a political career and had begun working on the history of the Popular Front movement in England in the late nineteenth-thirties. After eighteen months, he had chucked it, and was now a political correspondent on a weekly. He seemed always to know what had been said on an occasion at which, by definition, he could not have been present. The way he wrote it up was almost as interesting as a novel. 'And it makes sense, boy. It's not like Asher, dwindling back to Lord Kames. That was the trap, even with the Popular Front. At least, now, I'm in touch with my own time.'

Asher. Morris. Owen. Peter shuffled the papers, for the hundredth time. He was passing, he knew, from revision to reconstruction, and from that to rejection. Yet it seemed so daft, having to arrive at that. Two and a half years wasted; that would be too much to face. Wouldn't everyone tell him to make the best of a bad job, get the thing finished and the degree sealed, and then start? But start what? Would there be anything left then to start with?

He put down the pile of paper. He could not bear failure, at any price. This was a thing he had said he could do, and he would do it. You have to beat the system before you're in any position to reject it. Otherwise, what? Just the ordinary griping of the failed. The griping that filled England.

His mother, more than anyone, had said he could do it. A necessary training, for yet one more effort. Because history had nothing left to offer to the part-timers and the amateurs. They had failed, or, rather, had been beaten. It was time now for the professionals to take over. Except, perhaps, that they had taken over already.

The whole pattern was wrong somewhere, disastrously wrong. Peter could not explain to himself his increasing sense of this wrongness at the heart. The things he could name as wrong seemed quite inadequate, for so deep and frightening a feeling. To centre on the research, the pieces of paper around him, seemed as much a diversion as the research itself. It was the whole career he was now questioning: the whole giving of energy which had ended in this kind of frustration. Of course his mother had wanted this work for him. His father too had wanted it. Not only his immediate family, but in a more general way all his own people, had wanted this for him: it was the ordinary image of a better life. Whether in fact it was better he now radically doubted. The idea of learning was right, but its current world was so deeply alienated, so deeply shut off from any actual human need, that it contradicted the intention in the very process of seeming to realize it. He could not now do what his own people had supposed he would do. He could not learn in ways that would really change their condition. Yet they still seemed to approve, in an abstract way, the substitute activity he had been offered and had accepted. The education had dwindled to an end in itself, but was still given a quite mystical approval. But then what did this show of the condition itself, the condition in which this kind of change was conceived? Surely it was now so resigned that all it had actually conceived was a fantasy. People would rather see their own sons separated, going away from them into the rituals of another kind of life, than probe at all deeply into their own lives, where the important changes must come.

Anyone knowing the pressures of course also knew that the effort required, for the real changes, was almost beyond human strength. But there was no gaining of strength, there was only deliberate weakening, while this other pattern persisted. It was really as if, oppressed by an enemy, a people had conceived its own liberation as training its sons for the enemy service. And they would even boast how well they were doing, how much the enemy thought of them. What happened to the sons? This, now, always, was what he was asking. This, over the years, had been his quite physical shame. He had nothing to respect in himself, from the years of confusion. He had lived badly, in all his immediate relationships, and he wanted to redeem this. But he could not redeem it if it was seen, by others, as a simply personal inadequacy. The point of this, always, was the polite pretence that no enemy existed. Naturally the enemy said so themselves; they were just normal people, doing what needed to be done. But also his own people said this: the fact of oppression was always softened and rationalized; it was easier, that way, to survive. And after so long an agreement, so long a settlement, when the pressure on the sons became desperate, when they could not learn how to live under the weight of the facts and the comforting lies, no more could be said than that they were inadequate as people, that their troubles lay in themselves.

Still, this had to be lived, and in the actual living, the failure was his own, and there were real barriers to any close understanding. The man who had been made, by this social process, still contained the child, who had not really grown at all. The child seemed to beat on the figure of the man, who if he rejected the directions of others had nothing formed, nothing grown, to take to the demands of each day. The directed self acted, and the other, the unknown, merely disturbed and compromised, in a widening area of misunderstanding and damage. At the very time when he saw beyond the limits of the settlement, he was still a child of the settlement, and everyone in it was more capable of its kind of life.

Yet the disturbance in himself was in fact widening. He could feel it now, every day, in the bodies of others. It came through as pain, and there was then no separation: the pain of others was quite literally his own. He closed his eyes, and the figures flared in his mind: Kate, Beth, and with Beth, Myra. He felt an intense cold light through his body, and his fingers were clenched. He screwed up his face, as if to keep out the light, as he had seen a child doing. Yet no distortion of the flesh, no screwing of the eyes leaving the mouth bare and open, could exclude this light and this movement that were now dangerously close. He spoke Beth's name, first under his breath and then, consciously, aloud.

138

But though the name was spoken, he could still not see her as separate: the other figures, of Kate and Myra, were always there with her, part of her. The desire started, only at once to turn back on itself, forcing him yet again to tighten his body, to keep out what he must not see.

A door was opened and closed, at the back of the house. Hearing the noise, he sat up at once, rubbing his eyes. He heard the footsteps come along the passage, and then Gwyn was standing in the doorway. Peter stood up, surprised.

'Sorry,' Gwyn said. 'I've disturbed you.'

'No, Uncle.'

Gwyn had two empty sacks under his arm, and was wearing rubber boots and an old long overcoat. He went up every year, to High Wood, to get leafmould, and in earlier years Peter had gone with him.

'I should have mentioned I was going. Only I've left it late, it'll be too wet soon.'

'Well I'd like to come.'

'No, no, Peter, I won't disturb you. You've got your work to finish.'

'Finish? Does it look like it? I could spend a month and not get it right.'

'I expect it works towards it,' Gwyn said, backing away.

'I don't know. I've got five boxes under my bed, old cardboard boxes full of papers I daren't even take out and look over. And the months of time that went into them seemed good and alive then.'

'You can't get it right all at once, Peter. Not with your sort of work.'

'I still need some air. Hang on a minute, I'll get my coat.'

'And your boots then, you'd better.'

'Aye, all right.'

Peter hurried to the stair cupboard, and pulled on his coat and boots. As he walked back through the kitchen, Gwyn was staring down at the floor, seeming quite lost.

'All right then?' Peter asked.

Gwyn's effort to attend, to come back to ordinary consciousness, was quite open. For a moment he looked at Peter with a stare so frank and searching that it took Peter's breath away. Nobody, ordinarily, ever looked at him like that. It seemed more than any human being could stand. But perhaps it was only the reflection, the carry over, from that long silent stare downward.

They went out together, up the dark side passage. It was late evening, and cold. The lamps had just come on, along the street, but their yellow light was still confused with the failing daylight and nothing stood out clearly. They walked together without speaking. It had always been like this, Peter remembered, on these walks with Gwyn. But though in a way he was glad of the silence, it became steadily awkward and too close. As they turned in the last street towards the hill, he had to speak, though he did not care what he said.

'I never asked you what you thought of that meeting. When the Longton men came?'

'It was the usual.'

'Don't you approve of meetings like that?'

'Yes, they have to be.'

'But quite like that?'

'More or less like that. It's the speaking in public. It's very different, mind, when there's something real behind it, something that's happened to ourselves.'

'But ought it to be? Can't we get through to others?'

'It don't often seem to happen,' Gwyn said, and there was something in his voice that indicated a turning away.

'Was it right, what Dad said?'

'Yes, what he did say.'

'But it was just to get it back into his own hands, wasn't it? Into a smaller meeting, so that he could get his own way. As he has done.'

'He's given his whole life to it,' Gwyn said, after a pause. 'He knows more about it than all the rest of us put together. It's because of him that we've got what we have.'

They had passed the last street lamp, and ahead of them was the low stile and the path across the dark field.

'Watch it across the field,' Gwyn said, in a quite different voice. 'It's only the path is really dry.'

The wind blew from behind them. A dog was barking, some-where back in the town, and there was the revving of a motorbike, down the hill towards the works. The wind dropped, briefly, and from the wood ahead, going, away, there was the cry of an owl. If he had not been following Gwyn he would have had to stop and let his eyes get used to the darkness, which had thickened so sud-denly. For most of the way across the field he was merely follow-ing, just able to make out Gwyn ahead of him. But gradually the light seemed to come back, or rather a different light, more
140

diffused, more silent. He could see now where the path ran along under a tall, straggling thorn hedge. Very slowly, the world reformed around him, and he could almost feel with his body the shape of a field gate at the end of the path, with a thick old post at its hinged end, and above it a birch tree that seemed to curve in exact relation to the lines of the gate: not following the lines, but making a precise relation with them.

The gate was locked. It creaked and its chain rattled as they climbed over, looking up through the birch at the pale night sky.

'It's strange, don't you find?' Peter said, coming beside Gwyn in the wide track they were following. 'After the first minutes there seems more light than there was before. More light in a way than there was in the street, although that's impossible.'

'It's getting used to it.'

'No, it isn't only that. It's the different feeling when the light seems to come from everywhere, and not just from a few fixed points.'

'Yes, your eyes get used to it.'

'But what does that mean? I suppose there's some physical change, some change in the pupils. But it's the adjustment I don't understand, when the light is no longer some single thing.'

A gust of wind blew through the trees overhead, and within its dry rustle there was a sudden hard crack of a branch. He became slowly aware of a level of sound which was not the sound of any particular thing but of a whole area that surrounded them. He could still hear the echo of his voice, in that last question, but it seemed to come from a different part of himself, and he let it fade.

Along the broad track, overhung with trees, the ground was heavy and slippery, and his boots seemed to become heavier with every step, until he had to walk differently, finding a different balance. He stumbled over an old dead bough that lay half across the track, and felt the sharp cut of it through his trousers. The sense of enough light, from back at the gate, was gone. This was another darkness again.

'We're almost there,' Gwyn said, and the voice was harsh and startling, coming unexpectedly from the night.

They stepped in under the trees. Gwyn pulled a torch from his pocket and shone it back to Peter's feet.

'This'll do. If you'd just hold the sack at the top.'

He put down the torch, and in a quick movement bent his knees and found a light, easy balance. Peter took the first sack and shook it out, then carefully spread out its mouth. He bent over the coarse familiar smell of the sacking, while Gwyn, just beyond him, carefully brushed away the top layer of withered brown leaves. He cleared a space that was black and damp, and pushed his fingers down into the crumbling leaf soil. Then he cupped his hands and began scooping the black handfuls of soil into the sack. After a while he shook it down into the full length of the sack, and when it stood on its own he cleared a new space, brushing the hard layers of leaves carefully aside. Under the light of the torch the leaves curled back over his spread fingers, and he could feel their clean touch. When he pushed his fingers down into the damp soil he felt a withdrawal, back through his body, though the immediate touch to the fingers was satisfying. What had seemed fine and crumbling, in Gwyn's hands, he now found to be rough and uneven. His fingers felt husks, roots, fragments of twig.

'Will you sieve this then?'

'Aye, riddle it.'

'You didn't bring a trowel?'

'No.'

Peter scooped his first handful into the sack. He felt very strange and conscious, and wanted to talk, but his hands went on working.

'I expect you can buy this stuff, can't you?' he asked, moving to relieve the cramp in his legs.

'Aye, it's sold.'

'But otherwise just lying here?'

'In certain places they work it. Like with peat.'

'Or coal.'

Gwyn pulled the sack away to a new area, and again began clearing. In the new place, the layer of dry rustling leaves was much thicker, but also, underneath them, the loose black soil had a much greater depth. They finished the first sack, and Gwyn fetched the second for Peter to hold. All the area of light, the new area of sound, that he had got into touch with on the walk, had now gone. They worked in a close circle, in the light of the torch. Immediately below the glass of the torch the light was white and intense, glinting on the dry leaves. When the sack would stand, he began filling again. It was easier now, with more depth. He could even separate out the odd twigs and husks which came to his fingers. He felt a little warmth from the work, and was disappointed when the second sack was full.

'I'd got this bit more.'

'Aye, but you won't have the grip to carry him. The ears, as my Dad used to say. Get hold of his ears.'

Gwyn picked up the torch and put it away in his pocket. Then he lifted the first sack, lightly, to his shoulder. Peter followed his movements, but awkwardly. Some of the soil spilled out on his hair and neck. Gwyn led the way back to the path.

It took time to recover the area of light. He followed Gwyn, glad that the way back seemed shorter. The sack was not very heavy, but its bulk was awkward, and he had to walk with a curious twist and with his head bowed. There was a breeze from the field, and he could feel his forehead damp in it. They went on under the high thorn hedge, and then curved across towards the street lamps beyond the trees. They could see the glow of the city, farther out, in the night sky.

The weight and awkwardness of the sack seemed to increase all the time. As he carried, he felt that he was being touched, and was moving, in forgotten parts of his body, as if the weight was pressing right through. The smell of the sack was close to his face, as the field seemed to lengthen ahead of him.

Then, quite suddenly, they were back at the stile. When he had got the sack lifted again, he walked quite easily down to the lamps and the streets.

'A pair of burglars coming home, Uncle.'

'Aye, a bit early, though.'

'Yes, of course, it is still early.'

Yet it seemed that they had been away for a long time, and over a long distance.

'It seems odd, carrying through the street,' Peter said. He was making an effort to straighten up, and to walk with more possession of himself.

'Aye, I'll be glad for it in the country,' Gwyn said.

'You've decided then? You're going to Trawsfynydd?'

'Yes, we've started to settle it up. From the holiday. We'll go to the caravans as usual.'

'Dad and Mam are going with you?'

'So your Dad says.'

'And Beth?'

'She hasn't decided yet, Peter. She says it's a long time ahead.'

'Not to decide it isn't.'

They had reached the houses. Peter walked on to Gwyn's gate.

'It's all right, Peter. I'll take them on round.'

'No, I'll get it right home. And I must see Beth.'

He walked into the house, through the door from the conservatory. The room was dark, and he walked on to the passage.

'That you, love?' Myra called from the kitchen.

'No, only me.'

Myra came to the doorway.

'Peter? You've been out too, have you?'

'Yes.'

'She's in the front room. She's been washing her hair.'

The record-player was on, quietly. Beth jumped up from the fire as she turned and saw him. She was in a white dressing-gown and her hair was loose and wet. The hearthrug was littered with black cylindrical curlers, and there was a big black and white towel, spread in front of the electric fire.

'You look nice.'

'Like this?'

'Yes.'

'Like a dog in a thunderstorm, Mam says. Anyway, I've got to finish drying it, so come in and sit down.'

'I've been with Gwyn to the wood.'

'Yes, I can see. All your hair and neck, you're covered with it.'

'Damn.'

He pushed his fingers over his neck and through his hair. There were bits everywhere.

'Now I'm making a mess of your Mam's room.'

'Don't worry about that.'

'I get dirty and you wash. That's partnership.'

'Yes.'

She sat in front of the fire again, and let her hair fall forward. Peter sat near her. The wet hair was a quite different colour: a very dark copper, which made her neck look paler. He could smell the wet hair as he watched her, and he put out his hands to touch it. She moved quickly, and then held herself still.

'Do you mind being touched on the back of the neck?'

'No.'

'It scares me, always, yet I wanted to touch you.'

'It's all right.'

She turned and looked up at him. Her face was warm from the bath and the fire, and the skin, seen close, had a quite different quality.

'Like the flesh of a fruit.'

'Is it? Then what I wear make-up for, I can't imagine. This is the one look you're supposed to avoid.'

'Yes, it's naked, suddenly. I can see the blood and the cells.'

'Well, I can't go out like it. I'd be laughed to pieces.'

'I know. Blue eyelids, white cheeks, the cake on the lips. The face to be seen in the street. That's where you get your standard.'

'Not as bad as that.'

'It's all there, already, the actual colouring. But now so different. The whole face is alive.'

He leaned over and kissed her. The lips were different, less full but closer. She joined her fingers at the back of his neck, and held him to her. When at last she broke away she laughed, throwing back her hair.

'Will you marry me, Beth?'

'Yes, I've said so.'

'When?'

'When you want.'

'Tonight?'

'No.'

'Why not?'

'Because I'm drying my hair.'

She laughed again, and he touched her face and got up. He went across to the player and put on a new record, turning the volume up. It was a song they both liked: *Li'l Liza Jane*. Beth laughed as the singer started, in his hoarse, pushing growl. It was a sound beyond them. They could only listen to it on the player.

'Seriously though, when?' Peter asked, as the record finished.

'Your Mam said Easter,' Beth answered. She was suddenly very shy.

'One way or the other, it must be,' he said.

'Well yes. That's all right.'

'Is it? Have you talked to your Mam?'

'She'll be all right.'

'No, really, Beth, this is serious.'

'Well I know it is.'

'Then make her agree. Or shall I try?'

'No, Peter, please.'

'Then make her yourself.'

'I can't make her, Peter. But I'll ask her again.'

'Why ask? Why not tell her?'

'We've been over all that. But now your Mam says Easter.'

'Yes.'

He got up, and lit a cigarette. Beth wrapped the towel round her head, and stood up, with her back to him. He could see the reflection of her face in the mantelpiece mirror. It was very strange suddenly, with the hair vanished. She looked older and smaller, though the features were clearer, in the suddenly naked face.

The door opened, and Myra came in with a tray of coffee.

'Is it ready then?'

'Yes, near enough.'

'I'll help you fix the things.'

'No, Mam, I can manage.'

'Come on, got to get you looking nice.'

'She looks nice now,' Peter said.

'Now?' Myra laughed. 'No, but this is special. There's a party at the bank.'

'Not a party, Mam. Just a presentation. Mr Edwards is being transferred, to head office.'

'Well, that's what I said. And you're having drinks, aren't you?'

'Yes.'

'Well then, it's a party. Don't you say so, Peter?'

Peter leaned back, feeling his body stiffen.

'Yes,' he said, 'I should think so. Who is Mr Edwards?'

'He's been my boss. I've told you about him.'

'Billy?'

Beth laughed.

'Don't let him hear you call him Billy. That's just a name among ourselves.'

'Beth's got to make one of the speeches.'

'Not a speech, Mam.'

'Well, something of the sort.'

'What are you giving him?' Peter asked.

'An engraved pewter tankard.'

'Why not give it to his successor? It would do you more good. Since you seem to depend on these giants.'

'Peter, you're just being nasty.'

'All the usual inquiries made, I suppose. Married or single dark or fair, teeth or false, how many children?'

'Billy?'

'Hair or not, larky or not, four cylinders or six.'

'Oh, shut up, Peter. It's not funny.'

'Of course it's not funny, it's bloody serious. These twopenny-halfpenny tycoons have got it all their own way. Do you know there are men in this university working at the frontiers of knowledge in Victorian attics and writing their own letters in longhand, while these bloody bureaucrats sit in glass and marble with pretty secretaries filling their lighters?'

'That's nonsense, Peter.'

'Watching the way his moustache grows. Asking about his dahlias. Making his tea. Washing your hair to keep him virile.'

'I won't listen to you. You're horrible.'

Myra moved quickly, between them.

'Now sit down, look, love. Have your coffee.'

'No, Mam.'

'Peter, look, have your coffee.'

'No thanks. I must go. I've got work to finish.'

'What you two argue for, I don't know. You never used to.'

He nodded. He was watching Beth, who had unwound the towel and was now brushing her hair, slowly, leaning down towards the fire.

'I'll see you tomorrow, Beth.'

She did not answer.

'I said I'll see you tomorrow.'

She stopped brushing, and looked across at him. There were tears in her eyes, and she wiped them away, impatiently.

'Do you want to, Peter?' she asked, slowly.

'I just said so, didn't I?'

'All right then. Where?'

'I'll meet you for lunch. You were going to talk to your mother.'

He turned, abruptly, and went out. He wanted to get away before either of the others could answer. He went out through the front door, to avoid meeting Gwyn again. It might have been better if he had stuck with the thesis, for what it was worth.

He waited, next day, at the bank, for Beth to come out for lunch. He disliked meeting her there, but she seemed to expect it. The place seemed even worse to him, now, than before the alterations. The old high bourgeois mahogany had been replaced by cedarwood, formica and abstract mosaics. It was a temple he had never quite got admission to: Britannia Agoraia.

When he looked inside there was a queue at Beth's counter, but she saw him and smiled. For a moment he thought of joining the queue, to work his slow way towards her. Yes, I'm going to Italy. Yes, I need fifty pounds cash and fifty in traveller's cheques. Yes, on our joint account.

Except that it was no use, with Beth. She knew the real

situation too well, always. She didn't like playing around, and she didn't take to fantasy, except sometimes at a framed distance, on page or screen.

That was the trouble, really, with fashion. This air of fantasy now—in the hairstyles, in the gay dresses, in the glass and bright plastic colours—imposed too single a style. He watched the girls in the street, hurrying to the buses from the offices and shops. The elaborate hair, the brightly painted eyes, the short flaring skirts, the patterned emphasis of the tightly enclosed breasts and legs. But if the girls could choose, there'd presumably be every kind of variation. Skirt lengths would go up and down, with each individual, to every conceivable level.

He thought of Beth and looked again at the girls passing. Movement and quickness were everything, in this particular style. Movement of one kind, quite formalized, in the modelling walk and the poise of turning, to look and be looked at. Quickness in one clear convention, of reaction, understanding, assessment— this for this. The whole action of sex seemed formalized, now, in this bright public manner, as in the ordinary images of the hoardings and the magazines. These were the girls that men had created, to act a single role in public. It was all very pure and abstract in its single emphasis: the whole act of sex reduced to looking and being looked at.

Yet perhaps it was very little to do with them personally. He could never be sure. But there was one odd contrast. The other girls in the street, the students, looked a generation younger, though again not at all like Beth. They had the clothes and attitudes of peasant women, against these sharp town fashions. The faces were more naive and more practical, more sensible and more defenceless. They were at once self-contained and suspicious, as if they didn't yet know quite why they were living, apart from the books. They seemed not to notice the standard definition all around them, with its brightness and colour.

'I'm sorry you had to wait,' Beth said, coming quickly beside him and taking his arm.

'It's all right. There's always something to watch.'

'What, here?'

Peter laughed.

'Well, the money anyway. There's a reverence in the atmosphere of a bank, it's really very impressive. People come here knowing exactly what they're doing: this for this.'

'Well, there have to be banks, for goodness' sake.'

'Yes, it's very well organized.'

'It is really. Though it seems a bit chaotic, when anybody's away.'

'I suppose so. We only see what we want to see.'

They could not talk any more, along the crowded pavement. Beth held tightly to his arm, as they walked slowly through. Her walk, on the very high heels, was like a long stumbling fall, which only his arm seemed to prevent.

He looked at her quickly, and smiled. It was so easy to be deceived, by too early a pattern. She was dressed very smartly, with more make-up and colour than usual, and the bright hair was lightly lacquered. Why, always, should he separate Beth out? Why could he never be even ordinarily fair to her? It seemed to take him several minutes even to see her, getting past his own fixed ideas.

'I nearly came in and asked you for some Italian money.'

'You wouldn't have got it,' she said, smiling, as she curved close in behind him, passing a queue on the crowded pavement. They moved together to the roadway. They had to cross here, in the rush of traffic. People were moving among the cars, in every direction, as if in some mad game.

'I'm always afraid I shall stumble in the traffic, with these heels.'

'Hold on. But if it's like that why wear them?'

'Don't you like them?'

'Yes, they're very nice.'

'Well, there you are.'

'Come on.'

They made a risky way across. They first ran through a gap to the middle of the road, and then stood waiting while the double-lined traffic brushed past them, in each direction. They could feel the wind of the buses and lorries passing; and the fumes of the petrol were sharp in the moving air. At last, as the lights changed down the street, they got through again, but they had to separate. Beth caught the edge of her dress on the numberplate of one of the jammed cars, and bent quickly to release and straighten it. Several threads had been torn, and she bent to it again when she reached the pavement. Peter stood over her, waiting, while people pushed around, in the hurrying crowd.

'Mam told me not to put this on, but I wanted to,' Beth said, leaving it. Her hair had come a little loose at her forehead, and the blood was straining in her cheeks.

'It's all right, love,' he said, and took her arm again.

'Only it always happens to me. Like at the theatre . . .'

'Darling, don't worry about it.'

'All right. Whenever you say darling I know you want me to shut up.'

He laughed, and held her arm more tightly. She stayed very close to him, preoccupied by the accident to the dress. They reached their usual restaurant and went upstairs. The tables were so closely jammed together that though they found seats it was still rather like the pavement, except that the background of noise had gone and everyone was talking warily and defensively. They waited awkwardly until the food was served, and then gradually got to talking again. But the strain was still there, and in any case there seemed very little to say. Then near the end of the meal Peter asked quickly:

'Did you talk to your Mam about Easter?'

'I tried.'

'And got nowhere?'

'To the same as always. She seems to go nearly daft when it's mentioned.'

'Won't she say what she's afraid of?'

Beth looked across at him, and smiled. She looked still hot and flustered, in the heavy air of the restaurant, and her careful dressing seemed much too elaborate.

'She doesn't have to, Peter. It comes straight through without having to be said.'

'Yes, but still it's impossible. Really, At our age.'

'At our age is what she says.'

He turned away and called for the bill. Beth watched him carefully. In her eyes now there was a naked anxiety, that was very near tears. He looked so strained and ill, she thought. But it wasn't just the tiredness. Knowing him so well, she could recognize something else: the old, bitter withdrawal and conceal-ment. In plan or in fact he was already moving away elsewhere, and if he went again he wasn't likely to return.

'You ready?' he said sharply, leaving the money and getting up. She got up quickly, embarrassed and frightened. It could surely not happen here, not yet. But there were things he was not telling her, suddenly, just like three years back. She thought of what her mother had said, that she had not passed on. 'It won't hurt you to wait till the summer. By then we'll know what's going to happen to that family. You don't know how it'll affect him.' Only it was always like that, from her Mam: confident, menacing, vague. It was almost certainly Kate, but there was nothing definite. And probably Myra knew no more, but she was like that about people, sharply but never precisely intuitive. 'Like an old woman in a booth, with no mind at all, but so stupid she notices the obvious.' That had been Kate on Myra, several years back. Beth had overheard it on her way into the house, returning something. She had gone out, guiltily, and never again walked unannounced into the house as she had through the long years of growing up.

'You're all over the place, aren't you?' Peter said, as they walked down the stairs.

'What do you mean?' Beth said, anxiously, looking down first at her dress.

'Sorry,' he said quickly, and looked away.

The street was cold, and he did not take her arm. They walked back through the crowds and the traffic, and he left her at the doors of the bank.

'You're going back to the library?'

'Yes.'

'I'll see you tonight then.'

'Sure.'

'I shan't be long at this do. I'll be home about six.'

'Sure.'

He had meant to work in the library, but he could not go. It was one kind of moving away, into the religious silence of the high white room, with the worshippers at their booths, reading through the long hours. Some one man there, indistinguishable, might this afternoon find the one book, the one sentence, that would start suddenly into new life in his mind, and go on past the ordinary limits. But mostly, one had to read because others had written: a long compulsive activity which in the end was a deformation, though sometimes valuable. Walking now in the crowded streets, it seemed very strange that academic man, of all human possibilities, should have been selected above all others as an example of intelligence. It was mostly clerical work, in the strictest sense: shifting words from manuscript to print, from print to manuscript, from manuscript back to print again, almost regardless of their value. And there were endless keepers of the files and records: a priestly caste with its own decisive rules, and with jobs to offer. Intelligence, here, was neither being nor doing. It was mostly a long, careful keeping of records, in the quiet rooms with the chaos of the city around them.

Yet every course open to him was also moving away. He wanted to get out of these maelstrom streets, but in the quieter streets, at the edges, all the doors were shut; in the last straggle of the city, down by the canal, there was waste ground and uncleared rubbish; and in the country fields beyond there was only a different vacancy. Everything he saw, now, played back into his own negatives. The observer was finding the images of himself, yet the reality of these images was objectively much the same. If only something could come to challenge his mind: some other rhythm, some particular flame. For to feel like this was a kind of death, and only the dead could accept it complacently. To perceive the condition, now, was to confirm it. All that mattered, all that could matter, was the break, and yet to break from death into life was always impossible. He remembered a picture of the new kind of artificial respiration, the bringing back from death by mouth to mouth: the breathing lips on the unbreathing lips, and the rhythm of breathing until the inert body stirred. How many, now, could kneel and do this? Kneel by the body of a stranger, and breathe, widening the mouth, over the cold lips. A man who could kneel and do this, to anyone, was alive in some different dimension, old or new. To be able to do this, not technically but wholly, seemed the only living worth trying for. Breathing another to life, or taking the breath of this stranger, and the body moving again.

He had walked far out along the river. He looked out at the line of poplars, to the west, and the range of high clouds in the open sky behind them. Turner and Constable: breath to breath, and the body moving, in the shape of the landscape. He turned back, by a different path. The walk had quickened him; he could feel a different liveliness in his body. But it was still enclosed and contained, except in the passing connections with trees and water. Back in the city again, he would not have moved.

He was walking, head down, along the last street before the centre. But he had nowhere to go, except to walk. This was supposed to be freedom, and it was certainly very different from the organized life in which all the others were now engaged. Yet, if it was freedom, it seemed numb and cold. Any task set would be hard but confirming. There would be some use for the body, beyond this aimless walk.

He heard his name called, from the other side of the street. He looked up to see Rose, getting off her bicycle. He had almost forgotten her.

'I'll come across,' she shouted, and got back on the bike to turn.

As she moved, he remembered her, beyond the simple recognition; remembered her with his body, from years that had seemed forgotten. Two lorries and a bus were passing, and she had to wait before she could cross. He stood, confused, feeling the memory coming back. Each time he lost sight of her it was as if she were only a name again: a name for a set of fixed and half-forgotten experiences. But each time he saw her she seemed suddenly close: a whole possibility of his life, that had seemed to be over but was in some ways still active. When at last she came across, and stopped beside him, he smiled, almost against his will. Her long sandy hair was very dry and loose, and the face was still very young: clear pink cheeks and full childish lips; an unformed face, with hardly any mark of experience on it, except perhaps in the amused very light blue eyes, which she always widened, childishly, when she spoke.

'There, Peter, it was all looking homey till I saw you walking along.'

'Homey?'

'Yes, this place seems more or less nice till you turn up, haunting the streets with that sort of accusing walk.'

'Don't dramatize it, Rose.'

'Anyway, why do you have to walk on your own? Haven't you got a girl friend?'

'She's working.'

'Beth?'

'Yes. She's still at the bank.'

'Why don't you break in? Rob it or something?'

'What would I do with the money?'

'For God's sake, Peter. What we all do with it.'

He looked away. Rose leaned over her bike.

'No, but seriously, Peter, how are you?'

'All right.'

'You don't look it, darling.'

'Don't I? Or do you still call everyone darling?'

'Sorry.'

'And this old line, Rose. You're ill, you're strange, you're not a man but a ghost. Does it still work?'

'Evidently not.'

'Have you learned no others?'

'Yes.'

He stood back, and laughed.

'Come on, I'll give you some tea,' she said. 'I live just round the corner.'

'No, really, I'd better get on.'

'Damn, now I've embarrassed you. Tea, Peter, tea.'

'I don't know, Rose, really. I said I'd meet Beth.'

'Not yet. You've got time. You can watch the clock.'

'Won't you ever grow up?'

'I have. Didn't you notice? I'm a married woman.'

'And that's quite incredible.'

'Quite real, too. I'm a good wife. You should see my kitchen.'

'Is that what counts?'

'Come and see.'

He took the bike from her, and wheeled it along by holding the saddle.

'You can still do that?'

'It seems so.'

Milner Close, which they had entered, was a terrace of nineteenth-century cottages, originally built by a college for the families of its servants. Under the high spire of St Mark's, its attractiveness had steadily grown, since the war, and it was now entirely occupied by young university families. The cottages had been colour-washed, and the low front doors along the narrow pavements were painted in a series of yellow and blue and red.

Rose and Michael lived in Seven, on the west side near the church. Their rooms were sparsely furnished, in Rose's deliberate style. 'Like a cross between a nursery and camping,' Peter said when he saw them, but Rose was much too confident to care. 'I mean it's living-space, primarily,' was all she would say. There was indeed hardly any pressure of objects, defining a way to live.

Rose went out and made the tea: two yellow cups, without saucers, but good tea. It was getting dark outside, and the only light in the room was from the big stove. Rose took his cup, but again did not speak. He sat, tired, in the deep blue chair by the stove. He had his eyes closed and had almost forgotten where he was. Rose was kneeling on the green and white rush mat in front of the stove, by his outstretched legs. When she had to make up the stove, she pushed at his feet, and he sat up.

'Sorry. I was nearly asleep.'

'That's all right.'

She lifted the hod of anthracite, and filled the stove. She was wearing an old white glove, and he watched her throw it down, when she had closed the stove again. She had opened the air vents at the bottom, and the stove began to draw quickly and was soon burning fiercely. She sat back on her heels, her face reflecting the flames.

'Rose, I feel guilty, you know, sitting here. But I also feel tired and very reluctant to move.'

He leaned back. They were silent for some time until Rose said, suddenly:

'All right, tell me about Beth.'

He sat up, frowning. She smiled at him, running her tongue along her lips. As he still hesitated, she leaned across and undid the laces of one of his shoes. She looked up into his face, still teasing his frown.

'I know it isn't the moment, when you've come to see me. But it's a factor, isn't it?'

Peter smiled back at her.

'She's too good to talk to you about.'

'Too good may be the point.'

Outside, in the narrow street, a child was crying frantically, in the first paroxysm of despair. Rose got up and went to look from the tiny window. A door opened and a woman's voice broke through the child's crying. The crying did not stop but receded gradually, until the door slammed and the street was silent again.

'I don't accept failure that easily,' Peter said as she came back.

'You mean with Beth?'

'I suppose so. Though I was thinking of your failure too.'

'It's absurd, of course, that you're both still living at home.'

'Well yes. But people do.'

Rose leaned forward, turning over the book she had been reading.

'All I really wonder, you know, is why historians make out that the Puritans lost.'

'Both sides lost,' Peter said. 'That's the whole point. After that there was nothing. Only this long deadlock.'

'Except, you know, that we have to re-elect it, you and I and the others, in each new generation. We could go our own ways.'

'Yes, I get that all the time from Robert. Change and process and growth and generation; he seems not to know any other words.'

'It may still be true, even if he says it.'

'No, it's a middle-aged fantasy, all this about the energy of the young. What energy we've got feeds back into a personal struggle, that by his age has been forgotten. If anybody's relying on us for spare energy, they're going to be badly disappointed.'

Rose smiled, her lips curving and resting. The stove in front of her face was now red-hot, and she put on the glove again to close the air vent.

'Peter, we're making all the same mistakes as they did. Because we're still living on their terms.'

Peter smiled, in the reflected warmth.

'What's a mistake, though? It can be rubbed out, isn't that the idea? You grew up used to divorce, didn't you? You knew about divorce when you married.'

'Not that it would happen to me. Why should it?'

'Just that it needn't mean much, marriage, in your world. The dance can go on till quite late.'

Rose laughed. She was still wearing the glove that she had used for the stove. She curved her fingers inside it, and then slowly took it off. She threw it down by the anthracite, and then sat again, very close to the stove.

'I'm so cold, Peter.'

'Are you?'

'We've let it close in on us. We saw all the mistakes and then we went and made them.'

'Perhaps they're unavoidable then?'

'No. Why should they be? They frighten us so easily.'

'About what?'

'About ourselves. About everything that's outside their precious little system.'

'Meaning love?'

'Yes, Peter.'

'That comes in all forms.'

'And is good in all forms, don't you think?'

'I don't know.'

She smiled, and leaned back.

'All right, darling. Forget it. You ought to learn to forget. I mean, in two years, you hardly seem to have been living. You're so much your history and so little yourself. You feel everything, now, through a whole fence of the past.'

'Isn't that inevitable?'

'It needn't be. If ever the present were worth it.'

'What sort of present?'

Rose turned and looked across at him. He sat forward and put his arms out to her shoulders. He held her, lightly, at arm's

156

length, looking into her face. She smiled, opening her lips, and stayed still.

'I'm sorry, but I still distrust you, Rose.'

'Yes, I know. I wish you didn't.'

'Yet if you knew how much I want my life to be different.'

'It can be, Peter. It's all much easier than you think.'

He dropped his arms from her shoulders, but stayed sitting forward.

'Will you tell me how?'

'No, we tried that. We played the game right through. I was always the alternative. When you were confused or frustrated you had me to fall back on. And I could have stood that, but it wasn't just me, it was me in my world, your idea of my world. You used to say it so often. The enlightened minority, that you didn't like. All the relaxed disintegrated people, who'd even substituted sleeping around for adultery. The hours of all that, don't you remember, Peter? And I just belonged. I was an example of it. I wasn't a person, I was just this class in your head. When we were going to get married, it wasn't a girl you were taking, you were just moving out of your class.'

'And what should I have done?'

'When you were nineteen, Peter, after your first year, you were so lively, so full of yourself, so wanting to live. But every new term, it had to begin all over again. After a week with me you were yourself again, but you didn't think it was yourself, you thought you'd just pulled up your roots—always those same bloody boring roots—and you were guilty about it. Guilty about being excited. About just being alive and not being political. About dancing and being together. About everything we were doing and were going to do.'

He lay back in the chair, and covered his face with his hands. Rose sat quite still, for several minutes, and then quickly leaned over and re-tied his shoelace. He uncovered his face and looked down, watching her.

'Well?' she said, smiling.

'You said about guilt. But when I ask myself why I came, why I came then and why I'm here now, I think of something quite different, not in your explanation at all.'

'Yes?' Rose asked, withdrawing a little.

'I don't know. I'm probably wrong. But with you, all the time, the issues have been put into words. I think I came because I could talk to you, and because you were willing to talk. With you

I wasn't alone in the dark, with things that couldn't even be named.'

'Because it was straight, Peter. Because we weren't afraid. Because there was nothing we could do, nothing between us, ever, that we were really afraid of. It wasn't the long melodrama, of virginity and bargaining. It wasn't that endless nagging, about money and the future. I was an equal, Peter, and we could do what we wanted.'

'It seemed not to be that, Rose. It seemed, in the end, to be only words. I had come for words, and I had got words. The talk was easy, but the loving was hard.'

'You made it hard, for yourself.'

'How do you know, Rose? Perhaps it was only the talk that I wanted.'

'Still, Peter?'

'Yes, I think so.'

Rose moved and turned away. She picked up the glove and began straightening its loose blackened fingers. Peter watched the dust falling from the glove, in the light from the fire.

'Only did it ever occur to you,' she said, looking up, 'that it was very little to offer.'

'Of course it occurred to me. You made it perfectly clear.'

'But still that's all it is. The same bad bargain.'

'Not bargain'.

'All right, I mustn't say bargain, I mustn't ask the cash value, I mustn't ask whether a thing pays. All right, I'll change the language, if you'll admit the terms. I mean admit who you are, what you want, what you're actually doing.'

He sat forward, rubbing his hand over his face.

'I'm trying to, Rose. Honestly. It's just that I can't go on much longer.'

'No, that isn't true. You are going on.'

'In what way?'

'With Beth.'

He smiled and turned away.

'Always the same thing?'

'Yes.'

'Like you with Michael, I suppose?'

'Yes. Perhaps.'

'But with one important difference.'

'What difference?'

'That you sleep together. Isn't that a difference?'

158

'Not necessarily. Not at all necessarily. Why should it be?'

'Then I don't understand it at all. I don't understand the first thing about it.'

'As much as the rest of us, I daresay.'

Peter looked back at her as she spoke. She was still very calm and settled. The very young-looking face seemed quite unmoved and untouched. He saw the sandy lightness of her hair, the ease and fullness of her body as she sat looking up at him.

'Now I know you're lying,' he said, getting up. 'Everything you say is calculated, to create some situation you want.'

She did not answer. She smiled, looking up at him. He saw that her lips were wet.

'I know this anyway,' he said angrily. 'I know the talk I came for and valued is just a nullity like the rest. What you say is convincing, until I see it has no connection with what you really are.'

'You said calculation, didn't you?'

'I meant nullity. Do you wonder you've no child?'

He watched her face change and her whole body tighten. It was as if he had hit her, with his full fist, and her whole body was numb.

'To get a child needs love, can't you see, Rose? But do you even know what that means? Have you any idea? You've got no child because you've denied love. You're not capable of it. You just explicitly denied it.'

She got up, impatiently. Her face looked changed, older and harder, as if under a sudden strong light.

'Peter, it wasn't love we were talking about. Or don't you know the difference? And it isn't my failure. I haven't denied him.'

'You must have, Rose. You must have, whether you know it or not.'

She turned her back to him. Her dress was tightly drawn across her hunched shoulders.

'No, Peter. These are physical things. You know nothing about it. In fact we've been to specialists, we've tried everything.'

'Not everything,' Peter said.

Rose did not answer for some time. Then she went quickly across and put on the light.

'You'd better go now, Peter.'

'All right.'

He got up and buttoned his coat. She moved to him, and

159

pulled the collar more tightly around the neck, buttoning it at the throat.

'Haven't you got gloves?'

'Yes, somewhere.'

'Do you want to come again?'

'I don't know. Everything I touch goes wrong.'

'You don't touch anything. Isn't that the trouble?'

When he got back to Goldsmith Street, there was a letter from Robert. A sociology professor, from California, was visiting for two days, and would like to meet him. Robert had taken the liberty of describing some of Peter's work, and the professor was interested. Would he come for a drink, in college, that evening?

Peter read the letter again and again. It seemed impossible that anyone should ask to meet him. And what, in any case, was Robert trying to do? He couldn't even get this work right, let alone do anything for the future. California, like all the rest, was just a name in the book.

Beth was due back, from the party, but he had better go. He scribbled a note and pushed it in next door, then hurried down to the bus. It was absurd, really, to be so excited, but he was excited: the break had to come somewhere, and perhaps this was it.

He turned into Robert's college, and went through to his rooms. The small white letters above the door, *Dr Lane*, seemed remote and strange. He knocked, expecting the vague distant voice, the tutor's call to go in. But the door opened suddenly, and Robert stood there, smiling.

'Peter, I'm glad you could come.'

'Yes, thanks.'

It was so absurd, being welcomed like this. Even when you knew it was an act. A man was sitting in one of the low chairs by the big coal fire. Why were no other fires like college fires: that great bank of glowing red coal?

'Professor Kissler, Mr Owen.'

Kissler shifted his glass to his other hand, and got up. He was a very small man, in his fifties. His grey hair was cropped so close, and the cheeks were so hollow, that the head had the clear lines of a skull. But the voice was deep and warm, and the handshake strong.

'Mr Owen, this is a pleasure.'

'How are you?'

'Now sit down, Peter,' Robert said. 'Madeira or sherry?'

'You make me feel bad, drinking whisky,' Kissler said.

'Not at all, please.'

'Dr Lane's a very hospitable man,' Kissler said to Peter.

'Not after your hospitality to me,' Robert said, smiling. 'I tell you, Peter. But never mind, you'll experience it yourself. The American people, without exception, are the best hosts in the world.'

'Without exception?' Peter said. 'That makes a lot of whisky.'

'Sit down, Peter,' Robert said, and smiled again, with a geniality insistent on getting its way.

'Mr Owen,' Kissler said, 'you're doing some extremely interesting work. Dr Lane's being going through it with me, in some detail. I think you've made real progress, in one of the most difficult fields.'

'I think I've made no progress at all.'

'British community studies usually leave that impression,' Kissler said. 'But then it's precisely at that point that your insights have value.'

'What, that there's nothing?'

'Mr Owen, have you read Schachtel?'

'Yes.'

'When you remark, as you do, that nostalgia is a primary posture in British community studies, do you relate that with Schachtel?'

'It's relevant. To several things.'

'Right. And have you read Kardiner?'

'Yes, I liked the title.'

'You've used two concepts, in your account of the gaps in British community studies: the psychosocial moratorium, and identity diffusion.'

'Yes. They're not mine, of course. I took them both from Erikson.'

'Right. But your application of them is new. You point out, in effect, a wholly silent area in British social thinking. Do you relate this, ultimately, to psychological distortions in the observer? In a whole class of observers?'

'Most professional observers. Though the novelists know about it.'

'Novels are fantasies, Mr Owen. You agree?'

'No. Though because they are fictions, the dimensions are different. They negotiate feelings, they are not reports.'

'We argued this for weeks,' Robert said, trying to get back in. Kissler drained his glass, and let Robert refill it.

'Mr Owen,' he asked, 'how do you see your own career?'

'I don't, I'm afraid.'

'Not even in outline?'

'No. One arrives at a nullity, and one arrives with a nullity. I've been trying to explain this to Robert.'

'You have explained it,' Robert said, kindly.

'The society and the individual are kept rigidly apart. They are assigned, by distortion, to different schools. Do you agree, Mr Owen?'

'I've said so.'

'Right. But then that is the insight, into your own society. Into a limit of your society, isn't that what you're arguing?'

Peter leaned back, closing his eyes.

'It's just that we're afraid to put mouth to mouth.'

'I don't get the analogy.'

'So am I afraid,' Peter said, looking up. 'I discover a barrier, and I discover it is my own barrier.'

Kissler brought his fingers together, just touching his throat.

'But then analyse this with your concepts, Mr Owen. The limit on you is a social limit. A suppressed limit, for the society has to suppress it. It reappears, in practice, as a supposedly individual guilt.'

'Not supposedly. It becomes so in fact.'

'While you are within the society.'

'I don't know. I haven't been out of it.'

'Right. But theoretically, you can conceive this.'

'I don't know how. It doesn't quite fit.'

'That is why I say your work is important. That you've reached the barrier you were trained not to notice. You've reached it and insisted that it is a barrier.'

'Then bust,' Peter said, and laughed.

'I don't think so, Mr Owen. You are a free man.'

'No.'

'There are opportunities for you to continue this work. I think it is crucial, and Dr Lane agrees, that for some years you continue it outside the society that has trained you.'

'No limits elsewhere?'

'Different limits. Differently structured. The United States and Britain are complementary societies. The weaknesses of each are the strengths of the other.'

'But on this particular point? Are you serious?'

'I'm entirely serious, at least to the point that you should come and try. And there are people you can meet, making this precise inquiry, whom you won't meet here.'

'When I've got my degree, I suppose?' Peter asked, taking a drink for the first time.

'Dr Lane and I have discussed this. Yes, formally, that would be the easier way. But the other way is by no means ruled out. Because from what you've said, it seems perfectly possible that you won't finish your degree, at least at a level that is at all important to you. I consider it vital that, at this stage, you do not relinquish the decisive insight.'

'You make it sound much bigger than it is. It's just a vague idea.'

'I don't think so. And so, if it doesn't conflict with your career idea, the opportunity can, I'm certain, be given.'

'You mean now?'

'It would take a few months. By April perhaps.'

Peter sat back.

'What do you think, Robert?' he asked, suddenly.

'I'm trying not to think, Peter. I don't want to lose you.'

'But if you did think, you would?'

'So far as I understand it, yes.'

Peter lay back in his chair, staring at him. Kissler again emptied his glass.

'On the financial side, there should be no problems,' he said. 'I mention that specifically because I know it's not British to talk money.'

'It is,' Peter said. 'It used not to be, when it came in quietly and regularly. Now that it has to be asked for, it's asked for.'

'I made the remark as a courtesy,' Kissler said, and for the first time smiled.

Peter sat forward, and laughed again. He had drunk hardly anything, but he felt the exhilaration of drink, the sudden release and well-being when a burden is dropped.

'I'll have to think it through,' he said cautiously. The remark reminded him of someone, pink-faced, at a party, saying he mustn't have any more while he watches his glass being filled.

'I'll write you, Mr Owen,' Kissler said, and got up. Peter remained sitting, for some moments, but then got up and shook hands. As he turned away, he looked across at Robert and grinned. They talked for a while longer, and then Peter went.

He skipped, several times, going back under the high towers to the street.

He didn't go home until late. He was actually waiting for the bus, to Between Towns Road, when he looked across the road to a cinema, and suddenly left the queue. The film was an American musical, a very big and successful production. Before going in he drank several whiskies, and sat alone and happy, watching the dancing and liking the loudness of the music. When he finally got home he went straight to bed.

The next afternoon he went again to see Rose. She came to the door wearing a bright blue jersey and jeans, with a yellow scarf knotted in her hair. Her hands were yellow with paint, and there were one or two flecks on her cheeks. Peter could smell the fresh paint in the house from where he stood on the narrow step. As she smiled he reached out and touched her scarf, which was soft and transparent, bringing out the fairness of her hair.

'So you've come again?'

'Yes.'

'You look happy suddenly. Have you won the pools or something?'

'I got an offer. To go to America.'

'Really? What sort of offer?'

'I haven't got the details. There's a man called Kissler. Robert showed him some of my work.'

'That often comes to nothing.'

'Not this one. He was pretty definite. A post-graduate fellowship, to do my own work.'

'Well then, that's marvellous, Peter.'

'Yes, Rose, it is.'

She smiled, and touched his hand.

'It makes a change, Peter, when anything at all happens.'

'Yes.'

'This is such a bitty life here.'

'So you said before.'

'I'll try to think of a new way of saying it. It's still true.'

He smiled again, and moved on. Rose picked up a rag and started wiping the thicker paint from her fingers. Peter stood looking at the sitting-room door, where the paint was wet and half-finished.

'Are you going to finish it?' he asked.

'Sure.'

'Now?'

'Yes, I feel like finishing it.'

'All right, I'll watch you.'

'You can help if you like.'

He didn't answer, but went carefully past the door and sat in the deep blue chair near the stove. He bent down and adjusted the setting, then raked out some ash. It began drawing fiercely, and the little mica windows went red and then orange in the heat. He took off his jacket, and sat back. At the open door, Rose was sitting with her legs apart and the pot of paint between her ankles, leaning forward and painting one of the lower panels.

'How's Beth?' she asked, while he was still crouching at the fire.

'All right. I've hardly seen her.'

'You went on that march with her, didn't you?'

'Yes.'

'I should have gone, Peter.'

She was leaning even closer to the door and jigging the end of the brush into a line of narrow moulding.

'Because I'm against all that, as against as anybody could be. It's so foul and dead, this sort of war as an institution.'

'But you didn't go?'

'No, I went with Michael to a party. Is that so terrible?'

'No. The will has to be kept up, somehow.'

'What does that mean, in English?'

'Just that you stand six inches from somebody and force your stomach to talk to them. And the stomach obliges while the alcohol lasts.'

'Is it really like that? You said once it was just talking from the top of the head.'

'It would be better if it was. If I said it, I was just repeating the jargon. This is something much grosser than casual conversation or intellectual chat. All that fake intimacy, as the drink takes effect. You only have to stay sober to see it quite clearly. It's a real half digestion and eructation. Even the sex-talk has the smell of it.'

'Oh yes. Quite. To our Peter the Puritan,' Rose said, smiling. She was painting more easily now, with the paint dripping from her brush on to the long clear panel.

'Look, I'm past being shut up by that.'

'But not past dramatizing yourself. Don't you always suspect these fierce and sort of slangy denunciations? You can feel *them* being worked up all right. And it isn't as if they were really about anything. They've just learned to do it for chips.'

Peter didn't answer. He had gone across to the window and was staring out. In the brief winter sunlight, the shadow of the spire was grey and blurred.

'I know I do it myself sometimes,' Rose said. She got up and went round to the other side of the door, holding the tin carefully in her wet paint-covered fingers. 'But I listen to it. Like you say the sober man at a party. And in fact *anybody* can do it, Peter. One long slangy denunciation coming up, sir. Always willing to oblige. What I can't understand is why people want it.'

'Perhaps it makes enough noise to prevent anything else being said.'

There was nothing more said, for some time. Rose went on painting, and Peter went back to the chair by the stove, and took up the book that lay open on the mat beside it. He read as had become his habit, leafing backward through the book as if reluctant to commit himself to it and in a way suspicious of what he might find there. Only a few books seemed straight enough to read from the beginning.

'Is that Arthur's book?' Rose asked, as she got up again.

'A. L. S. Dean,' Peter said, turning over to the cover.

'Don't you know him?'

'I've heard of him.'

'We see quite a lot of him. He's one of the few tolerable people.'

'Yes, of course, he's in the same college as Michael.'

'He's very nice, really, but a bit queer.'

'Queer?'

'Not that queer. Odd. Especially since his wife left him.'

'Did she?'

'Yes, she ran away with some scientist, who already had a wife and four children.'

Peter laughed.

'Well?'

'Nothing. I was just thinking when you said she ran away. It's such an odd old-fashioned way of putting it, now that we have these very smooth take-overs. It gives this scene of ex-husband and ex-wife racing off like mad in the moonlight, with their bundles of clothes. Not our clear, organized procedure: the hotel-room, the letters, and the removers coming round.'

'Yes, it's funny,' Rose said, watching him as he went on laughing. 'Though I'm surprised you can laugh at it.'

'Why?'

'Never mind. Life's full of surprises.'

166

Peter looked down at the book.

'You were saying about Dean?' he began again.

'Yes. It hit him very hard. Especially since he's what you called one of the middle-aged kids. You know, the great enlightenment.'

'I can see that from the book. It looks completely phoney.'

'Yes, but he isn't phoney. It was almost a religion with them, you know.'

'A religion? What?'

'Sex,' Rose said, pouting her lips over the word.

'I don't see any sex in this.'

'All that at the end, about the sexual radicals.'

'Quite. That's what I meant. That's what somebody called the Home Office issues.'

'What are they?'

'The laws on homosexuals, the laws on divorce, the laws on obscene publications, the laws on drinking hours.'

'Well, they're to do with sex. Most of them.'

'No. They're just the Magna Carta of the middle-aged kids.'

'Are they? But from what great heights of maturity are we looking down on them?'

'If they think that sex is a Home Office issue.'

'Interference with it is.'

'Sex is between people.'

'Yes, that's what they say. And that the law should keep out of it.'

Peter threw the book down, and walked across to the window.

'It's what people won't put up with that matters,' he said.

'Yes, and then that's private morality.'

'There isn't a separation, Rose. There can't be. The law has to be the common morality of people.'

'Exactly. That's what they say. And that the old-fashioned laws should be brought up to date.'

'What they say in fact is that a sexual relationship is private, and that nobody from outside should interfere with it. That's absolute rubbish.'

'Well, on seduction and things like that. But between adults it's right, it is a private affair.'

'It isn't, you know. There are always more than two people involved.'

'In certain cases, perhaps,' Rose said, getting up and wiping her hands.

'No, Rose, not just adultery. All the time. Marriage is a social

167

fact, it's bound to be. It involves children, and so another generation. And adultery is a social fact, a disturbance of relationships over a very wide area. Even fornication is a social fact. Either the parents are involved, or the relationships each might go on to are affected. One way or another, what starts as a personal relationship becomes social. Other people are affected, and so law is relevant.'

'Not bad laws, though.'

'No, not bad laws. But you'll only get more bad laws if you think that sex is private.'

'I suppose you're right,' Rose said. She had moved across to the stove, and was carefully cleaning her hands. 'It did sound too easy, what you call the middle-aged kids. But it had, don't you think, some warmth in it? Of a kind?'

'It was often pretty cold in practice.'

Rose put away the cloth, and sat by the stove, looking up at him.

'I've heard more of it than you have, Peter. Sex is just getting into bed when you honestly feel like it: that's what they all said, really. The only mistake, it seemed, was that people made altogether too much fuss about it. Because sex is fun, don't you remember? A civilized game that you can learn to play well.'

'Yes, that's what they said.'

'They may be right after all. What happens to people who don't get into bed when they want to? Don't they just die, Peter? However respectable they may look?'

'Yes. They die.'

'And in a good society the effects could be carried. In many societies they already are. It's only in this sort of nagging society they can't be. There could be more tenderness, more natural loving, and the society could grow from that.'

'It could, Rose, but we're living now.'

'But the way is still there. People can love and marry.'

'Or marry and not love.'

'I expected you to say that. But then it's all still open, if we're serious about it.'

'Not if there are children it isn't.'

'But if there aren't.'

'Then one asks why.'

Rose looked quickly at him, and at once got up, pushing her hair back into the blue knob of her scarf.

'Don't start that again, Peter. You're a devil, really a devil, to taunt me with that.'

'I'm sorry.'

'No, you're not, Peter. Not really. You come back to it too often.'

'Perhaps you shouldn't have told me.'

'Of course I shouldn't have told you. It's between me and Michael.'

'Yet you did tell me. And you knew quite well what you were doing.'

'Yes, I thought I did. I thought you would know what I was telling you. But you don't give a damn, do you? You just sneer at any actual desire, because you're twisted and frightened.'

'I've given you my own confidence, haven't I?'

Rose straightened up suddenly, brushing her fingers against the front of her jersey.

'You've talked about Beth,' she said.

'Isn't that the same?'

'I don't know. I doubt if you've told me the beginning of the truth about her.'

'I don't know the truth about her. We've been too close for too long. It's been like a marriage, in that way. Just as you can tell, sometimes, when a couple come into a room. It's quite unemphatic, but still real and unbreakable. Without effort, it simply excludes others, from that centre.'

Rose looked at him, pulling the edges of her jersey tighter over her waist.

'Yes,' she said, 'I've seen it like that. Once or twice.'

'Except that with us,' Peter said, 'there isn't a centre. Not really.'

'It's the consequence without the relationship. Isn't it? With you and Beth.'

'Without that relationship.'

'And then one asks why,' Rose said. Her smile had come back, the lips curving and resting.

'Well,' Peter said, 'Beth's idea of marriage.'

'No, darling, don't be stupid. Would that survive five or six years of being constantly together? Five or six months perhaps, but years. It's completely incredible, between normal people.'

'You're saying not normal, then?'

'Well, I think you're either incapable of loving, or incapable of loving her.'

'Are you too polite to say which?'

'Not too polite. I don't know. In my own marriage it's the same question, and I don't know the answer to that either.'

As she spoke, she moved right away. She stood looking at the newly-painted door, almost as if she were alone. When she spoke again, her voice was very quiet, so that he had to strain for the words.

'All I thought I knew, Peter, was that once I wanted you. I wanted your child.'

He looked across at her, but didn't answer.

'Well, Peter, there—it's said.'

She bent and picked up the paint tin and walked out with it to the kitchen. He closed his eyes, and lay back. When he opened his eyes again, it seemed a long time since Rose had gone, but he was too tired to move. The house was very quiet, and there were no sounds from the street, though he could hear, when he tried to, the distant noise of traffic from the centre. The clear bell of St Mark's struck three o'clock, and he opened his eyes. Rose had still not come back. He stood up and looked around.

'Rose.'

There was no answer, and he called again. He went to the passage and again called. The house was very quiet, as if there was no one in it. He walked along to the kitchen. The rag and the bottle of spirit lay on the table, but there was no other sign of her. He went back along the passage, and called again. Still there was no reply.

He stood at the foot of the stairs, looking up.

'Rose.'

There was no answer. He went quickly again through the small ground-floor rooms, and then back to the foot of the stairs. He called, more quietly, and walked slowly up. The door facing him from the tiny landing was ajar. He pushed it open.

Rose was standing watching him enter. She had just slipped off her dressing-gown and was standing naked. She smiled as he stopped suddenly.

'You took your time coming,' she said.

'Yes.'

He was looking at her, though he still did not move. It seemed, as he looked at her, that he had never seen anyone so lovely. She stood very still, with her fingers lightly linked over her thighs. Her yellow hair was loose, and drawn forward over her shoulders.

'But now you're here,' she said.

He looked away and felt for a cigarette.

'No, Peter. No more delaying.'

'Am I delaying?'

He looked at her again, and then moved towards her. As he reached out to touch her she caught his arm quickly.

'No. Undress, darling.'

He was close enough now to feel the scent of her body. It seemed very dark in the room, though the drawn curtains were very thin and let through a good deal of light. He released his arm and again looked at her.

'You keep saying no. Did you notice?'

'I don't want to say anything, Peter.'

He caught her suddenly, and held her close to him. He kissed her hair and her neck, feeling the warm scent of her body. She stayed for some moments, and then turned and went to the single bed under the window, and sat on its edge. He moved to her, and put his head in her lap, kneeling below her.

'No, darling. Come as yourself,' she said quietly, and lifted his head.

He looked at her quickly, and then bent to take off his shoes. He took off the rest of his clothes, slowly. She smiled as she watched his often awkward movements. When he again came to her, she kissed him on the mouth. He returned the kiss, but then moved a little away.

'This is wrong both ways, Rose. Because we're both committed.'

'All right, Peter. Then we'll re-commit.'

She smiled, and linked her fingers behind his head, drawing him closer.

'Yes, I want to come to you, Rose.'

'Then come, darling.'

'I've waited so long, I hardly know what I'm doing.'

She moved back on the bed, her arms lying loose at her sides. He placed his palms over hers, and moved forward to kiss her. His eyes were closed, and the long delay was suddenly broken. His whole body came into sudden violent life, and he was beyond knowing himself, beyond consciousness. Rose lay with her eyes open, completely relaxed. She smiled as his lips moved down to her neck, and continued to watch him. At the climax he shouted, and she jerked back her head in an easy and silent laugh. She released her hands and held his shoulders tightly. She kept him close to her as he lay breathless.

They got up an hour later. Peter had slept deeply and Rose lay beside him, watching him. Then she went down and made tea, and woke him, gently. He opened his eyes and smiled, then looked strangely down at himself. When he looked at her again there was still strangeness and surprise in his eyes. Rose leaned forward quickly, and put her hand lightly on his lips. He kissed her palm, and again closed his eyes.

She went down before him, and left him to dress. When he came down she had put on her coat, and they went out together. They had tea in a café and then went to a cinema. Afterwards, he walked back with her to the end of Milner Close. He had been wanting to talk but she had avoided it. Now she lightly touched his hand, and turned to go.

'No, wait,' he said quickly.

She looked back and smiled.

'Not to worry, Peter,' she whispered. 'No problems.'

Then she hurried on to the house, and he turned as she disappeared. He walked back to the centre and caught the crowded bus home.

Beth came round that evening. Kate and Harold were out and Peter was sitting, reading the papers, by the stove in the kitchen. He stood up when Beth came in. She was wearing a green leather coat, over a yellow jersey and slacks. She was without make-up, though her bright hair was elaborately waved.

'Don't let me disturb you, Peter.'

'You're not disturbing me.'

She went to the other side of the table and drew out a chair. She sat facing him across the table. He kept away from her. He was still remembering Rose.

'I want to talk to you, Peter.'

'All right.'

'I haven't seen you for two days.'

'No. Not since the lunch.'

'I don't mind where you've been. I don't want to know. But I want to get straight, in myself.'

'Nobody gets straight, Beth. What's the use of talking?'

'That's stupid.'

'Well all right then, Beth, I'm stupid.'

'You say that expecting me to deny it.'

'No.'

'You're so sure, aren't you, Peter?'

'Sure?'

'That you're not stupid. That you're very intelligent. Because you've passed your exams.'

'What does that prove?'

'Look, I'm not against it. I've always wanted you to go on. But what you've gone on to isn't what you're living. In that you can still be stupid.'

'That may be true, Beth. But where does it get us? I have to live as I am, there's no choice there. I have, even, to make my own mistakes.'

'What do you mean, there's no choice? There's every choice.' She was gripping the edge of the table, and her face was hard and strained. Peter had never before seen her quite like this: a whole new layer of herself was uncovered and active. Her voice was hard and urgent, suddenly, and she was very pale under the tightly waved hair. He particularly noticed her hands: strong hands, and graceful, like Myra's. He remembered Rose's fingers, untying his shoe.

'Well, there is. You're choosing, aren't you?' she insisted.

'It doesn't feel like it.'

'Then you're even stupider. Don't you know you're choosing?'

'Yes, perhaps I am. Perhaps I didn't want to tell you.'

'I don't want to know, except as it concerns me. I've a right to know that, Peter. I've been waiting for years, and I've been glad to wait, but only because I loved you and because I thought you loved me. If you don't want me, say so. Don't keep me hanging around. Because I shan't, Peter. I shan't hang around for the rest of my life, while you take your pick.'

'Don't nag me, Beth, please. This is like our . . .'

'Nagging? Has it gone that far? When you can cut out a whole world by calling it nagging? When I say what I have to say, and you call it nagging?'

'I call it what it is. It's been always the same, in this street.'

Beth got up, and stood holding the back of the chair.

'Yes, Peter,' she said quietly. 'You have chosen. Only don't think, now you have, you can come home to me, telling me what you've been doing. I don't want to know.'

'I've been seeing Rose.'

Beth smiled. She had opened her coat, and he could see the fullness of her breasts under the bright yellow jersey.

'I'm lucky, aren't I?' she said. 'Very lucky.'

'I don't know what you mean.'

'Oh, you're a fool, Peter. Such a fool.'

'Look . . .'

'Rose again. Rose! All that endless talking and giggling you used to go out for. Not again, Peter? Really?'

He looked away.

'You don't know much about her, do you?'

'Enough. She's married, isn't she?'

'Yes. She's Mrs Michael Swinburne.'

'But likes to keep up with her old friends. That's what I mean, Peter. You won't get anywhere with her.'

'Get anywhere? Who taught you that beautiful phrase? Billy Edwards.'

Beth laughed, looking across at him.

'Peter, you treat me as an innocent. It's how you think you respect me. But I'm twenty-four. I've been working six years. And day in day out I hear people talking, hear girls talking and what the men have been saying to them. I know what happens, Peter. I know quite well what happens.'

'Except here.'

Beth turned away, tipping the chair on to its back legs and looking down as it balanced in her hand.

'Yes, Peter. When I marry I marry. When I give I am given to. When I am loved, I love. When I say keeps, I mean keeps.'

'I know, Beth.'

She looked across at him. She straightened the edge of her jersey over her tightly-drawn waist.

'You could even sleep with her and you still wouldn't get anywhere. What do you think loving is? Is it all separate from living?'

He pushed back from the table, angrily.

'Look, Beth, living isn't something patented in Goldsmith Street. There are other ways.'

'Yes, Peter, and where there are, there are people. People who mean what they do.'

'All right, but then different actions, different meanings.'

'Some for keeps, some not, Peter.'

'Is that all that matters?'

Beth smiled and looked away. She ran her fingers quickly inside the neck of her jersey, as if a necklace were there.

'It's seemed, always, that girls are like strangers to you. You don't see them, Peter, as people at all.'

'Men are reduced too. Isn't that relevant?'

Beth smiled, and put her hand to her hair.

174

'Yes, Peter, you're right, men do get reduced. I've told you before. I've lived, for years, among girls talking. It happens both ways, through all the early years. But then at last it comes honest, between two actual people, and that is for life.'

'Always for life?'

'A good many fail, Peter, but more succeed. That isn't the question. There are some who don't even try, who live their whole lives on the first narrow lessons. What you do to get men, what you do to get women. And you know what get means.'

'I know what it usually means.'

'Get, get, get. You can get a hundred, and you're still with nobody.'

'How do you know, Beth?'

'Because I'm alive.'

She tipped the chair again, and then set it back on its legs. She sat down, looking across at him. She was suddenly very like Myra again, but a much younger Myra.

'You say about Edwards, and the men at the bank. Yes, we all know the traffic. I could play it, quite easily. I know the things to do.'

'Why don't you, then?' he said bitterly.

'I could do with you in the back of a car. Yes, it takes drink to get quite that open. But there's usually drink. We can all afford it.'

'Only drink? You're so wrong.'

'And the knickers in the handbag. Making up, after him, in the car mirror.'

Peter stood, abruptly, and kept turned away.

'What's the matter, Peter? Mustn't I talk like this? Isn't it like your Beth?'

He didn't answer.

'It could all be nice, Peter. Being loved is nice. Being made a fuss of is nice.'

'Yes,' Peter said.

'And if it's all to make, then it's the more to get. Nice and nice and nice.'

He turned and faced her. She was very excited, and the blood had come up in her face. She was holding her coat open, pulling tightly down on it.

'I've been asked, Peter. Not just by you. By others. And it's always open. I know how to do it. I could do it tomorrow.'

'That isn't what I asked.'

'It's the answer, Peter. Do you think I've never wanted to? Do you think there aren't better evenings than watching for your light?'

'You'd better take them if you want them,' he said, leaning across.

'I have wanted them. I've felt nice, being asked, and they've been nice people. '

She stood up, and carefully replaced the chair under the table. She was near to crying, but she managed to control it. Her shoulders were limp, and she had pushed down her hands into the pockets of her coat.

'You were right at the beginning, Peter. It's no use talking. You'll have to learn it yourself.'

'Learn what?'

'Never mind, I won't nag you. Have it your own way.'

'I want to get straight, Beth.'

'Yes, but I can't help you. You must feel it yourself. Only one thing perhaps, where it's easy. The ones who sleep around, who make it easy, not these nagging domestic hens. Just watch, if you can, where the sleeping takes them. No awful materialism, naturally. It's only hard cash on the streets. But still their feelings, their generous feelings, happen to profit them. Just watch and tell me I'm wrong.'

'Beth, listen,' he said, moving round towards her.

'No, Peter, I'm going.'

'But you must listen.'

'No, Peter, I'm finished. You and I are finished.'

'But at least . . .'

'As a friend, Peter? No, not on this. Yes, I'm the girl next door, you've known me for years, we're still bound to meet and why not? Only the other is finished.'

As she spoke, she opened the door, and then as he followed her she slipped through, and closed the door in his face. He opened it again, but she was running along the entry, and as he stood at the door in the light rain he heard her get back to the house and the door closed. As he stood in the rain, listening, his father's car turned in at the front, and his mother was with him. They came in and made supper, and Peter went early to bed.

He had a letter from Kissler, by the next morning's post. It confirmed the offer made, but in rather more complicated terms. If he went in April, an intermediate grant of 120 dollars a month could be made until October, when he would become eligible for a more regular grant of 200 dollars a month. Alternatively if he first took his degree, and came over in October, he would be eligible for a fellowship of 4,000 dollars annually for two years. In either event, the ordinary channels of application would have to be followed, except for the special case of the intermediate grant, but Kissler would do all he could to help. He still felt that, in relation to the work, the former course had the balance of advantages.

Peter read the letter over and did the necessary sums. It was all right, either way, he decided. The first excitement had undoubtedly faded, but the whole idea was still very attractive. He didn't believe what Kissler had said, about making more progress with the work itself. That could be done, or rather not done, anywhere. But the prospect of getting away, to a new country and a new situation, was almost overwhelming. He felt that this chance was what he had worked for, through all the long years. At every point where he now found himself blocked, this move opened up wholly new possibilities. And it was right, after all, to be able to use the results of his own work. Mother England thought she was so clever, with her complicated system of controls and adjustments, bringing people inevitably to certain fixed patterns. But she wasn't, finally, clever enough. Just a piece of paper, a letter to Kissler, and he could walk out from under the whole system and its pressures. For in any case he was finished here. The pattern he had tried to live to, with his parents and with Beth, was certainly broken. He had made the final break himself, and, though still anxious, did not regret it. When a people has missed its opportunities to change, indeed not only missed by rejected them, it can hardly expect to keep everyone under the shadow. Those who have the chance to go will go. All the rest of the world knew the English stalemate, and marvelled at it. What possible service could it be, to anybody, to stay and go on being diminished by every frustration and postponement it so powerfully bred? Nostalgia alone might keep him: a general love of England, and of English people, that was always accessible as a memory. But he had dealt with nostalgia: first, intellectually, and now, in these last days, personally. For it was a fact, whatever Beth said, that you could simply walk through the English prohibitions. If you got your nerve for life, you could simply disregard them, for they were only dead shells; they had no power behind them now, as they had once had. Stand up and challenge the English network, and it wasn't the steel ropes you had been brought up to believe in; it wasn't even a network, just an old spider's web, glistening on a bare hedge. A few, in each generation, had realized this: Lawrence, most powerfully, in modern conditions. The others might say what they like, drum up the usual phrases, but they didn't count any more; reality had moved away from them. Even here, in one of the last protected institutions, the emptiness at the heart was quite clear. They had begun, these English classes, by despising each other, and they had ended by despising themselves: at first secretly and then more and more openly, until now illusion and disillusion were so tightly tied together, in the English mind, that no break was possible; it was a drowning grip. And it wouldn't be that anywhere else was perfect. This recognition, undoubtedly true, was the last string they held you by. The vital point was that you could get away from your own pressures, which are always worse than anybody's else's. An exile may be disappointed by his new country, may come to be exasperated by it, but he is at least free of what drove him into exile, and that, inevitably, is the most important thing in his life.

He folded up the letter, and dressed and went out. It seemed, walking down to the bus, that he was suddenly free of this place, that had seemed so permanent. He could get away from it, get beyond it, so simply now. This feeling gave him a new confidence, a sense of direction and strength which had always been latent but had always, till now, been blocked. For it is in fact true that you can become a new man. The pressure that has been destroying you is never fully known until it is lifted, and then every part of the self comes newly and powerfully alive.

He got off the bus, and walked along to Milner Close. This, too, was ridiculous: this playing at cottagers, with the whitewashed terrace, the windowboxes, the bright front doors out of some fishing-village print. This, too, was a place to get out of: this shrunken gentility, this playing at housekeeping, these children setting up in the lodge. If Rose was still childish, in some ways, it was no real wonder, in the Close. A few more increments and then a red villa like Robert's: the Norwegian jersey, the pipe, and growing peaches that don't and can't ripen, in an English summer. Children playing the immemorial game, having learned their Latin early and well. Still the same exercise, the object of the exercise, a correct deponent so that the wine will be poured, the bowler hats lifted, the young men produced, on so beautiful

178

an assembly line, that had once had a market: Nigeria, Burma, Kenya. And the people of England, still happy to serve it: just an occasional haggle about the percentage on servitude, and the intermittent memory of words that had promised to reshape a world.

He rang the bell, and Rose came. They went into the sitting-room, and he sat again in the blue chair. Arthur Dean's book was still on the arm where he had left it, but it was lying at two pages further on. Rose was different today: more tense, more careful. He took out Kissler's letter, and handed it to her. She read it carefully, and then handed it back to him.

'Well?' she asked.

'I'm accepting, of course.'

She smiled and got up, moving lightly. She fetched a bottle and poured two glasses. Peter saw that it was college sherry, and hesitated.

'Go on, darling. Drink up. To America.'

'In sherry? In college sherry?'

'Why not? The college has done it for you. Your thesis will be finished, you'll get your degree in July.'

'On that option, yes.'

'But Peter, it's the only option.'

'It isn't, you know. The other is much more attractive.'

'Is it? The two of us, in the States, on a hundred and twenty dollars a month?'

'You can't be serious, Rose.'

She refilled her glass, and then sat by his feet. She rested her head on his knees, looking up at him.

'I am serious, darling. The divorce itself will be expensive enough.'

'Yes, maybe.'

'And even in the autumn, on two hundred a month. When you could get nearly three hundred and fifty by just waiting here for your degree.'

'Sure. The money would be better. But that isn't the point.'

'Of course it isn't, but it comes in, Peter. Look, I hate this calculating as much as you do, but we'd have to, wouldn't we, if we were serious about it.'

'Sure.'

'And you remember I said I wanted your child.'

'All right, but what's the alternative? We should have no more if we stayed till the autumn.'

'I know, darling. That's what I'm trying to say.'

'I couldn't start a family on my grant here. Or rather I could if we were married, they'd increase the grant. But we shan't be. Not by then.'

Rose looked up at him, holding tightly to his knees.

'I know,' she said. 'I've been working it out too.'

'It's a bastard,' he said angrily.

'No,' Rose said, laughing and getting up. 'No, Peter.'

He saw what she was laughing at, and laughed too, desperately. She held out her hands to him and pulled him up.

'We're making the same old mistakes,' she said, holding him to her. 'Hurry, hurry, get it all on paper.'

'Maybe.'

'We were wiser yesterday, when we didn't calculate at all.'

'Yes, I suppose so.'

'There's no rush, Peter. Look at what it's doing to us. We go to bed once, in, what, the five years we've known each other. And within twenty-four hours we're doing sums on back of envelopes: dates, dollars, divorce papers.'

'I know.'

'That's letting them win, Peter. Letting the grey ones take over.'

'You've done more sums than I have.'

'Sure. I'm ashamed of myself. I lay awake last night, doing sum after sum. I didn't know I felt guilty, until I caught myself at it.'

'Do you still feel guilty? Tell me honestly, Rose.'

'No, Peter, no. Not a bit in myself. And why should I, darling? I loved you and you came to me: is that so terrible?'

'It wasn't terrible, at the time.'

'It was wonderful, Peter, and we must hold on to that. Don't let them destroy us.'

'We're doing the sums ourselves.'

'Yes, the sums that they taught us. They've built the pattern right in. But we can break it, Peter.'

'How, exactly?'

Rose laughed.

'You're a big boy, Peter. You know perfectly well.'

'Don't tease me, Rose.'

'Tease you? Look, I'm the one person that never has teased you. When you wanted to come, you came. I made no conditions.'

'And still no conditions?'

'Of course not.'

'Sometimes it's only a show, the first time. The conditions come later.'

Rose pushed him away at once, angrily.

'Don't say things like that, Peter. Don't ever say things like that.'

'Why not?'

'Because they're obscene, beastly.'

'And true?'

'No, not true. Look, who have you been talking to? Is it Beth?'

'No.'

'It is, I can see, Peter. It was always like this, in the old days. While you were with me, you could grow as yourself, but when you went back to them they had their story ready: the awful woman, the immoral woman, leading innocent Peter astray. That's what they told you, wasn't it?'

'No.'

'Look, I know it was, Peter. I can see that smug look when you come out with one of their prepared defences.'

He went back to his chair, and she sat opposite him.

'Look, I want to go, Peter, and I want to go with you. I think I should like America. Anyway, we can see.'

'So?'

'So finish your degree. Write and say you'll apply for the autumn. That gives us six or seven months, to get it all cleared up.'

'The divorce?'

'Yes. I'll tell Michael, but not just immediately. We don't want you involved in a scandal, with your degree coming up. And then in May or so I can move away, anywhere. He can start the divorce and we can be clear by the end of the summer.'

'Why wait till May?'

'It would be more civilized, don't you think? After all, I must talk to him, give him time to adjust.'

'But by May we could be there.'

'Without your degree.'

'You mean with less money.'

'No. Why should you waste all your work, when it's almost finished? It will be important, you know. I mean, permanently.'

'I see. And meanwhile?'

'As we are, Peter. Isn't that agreed?'

'What do you mean, as we are?'

'I shall be here, and you'll come to see me.'

'The old shift system, you mean? Me the afternoons, him the nights.'

'Not him the nights. I shall tell him.'

'When?'

'As soon as I decently can.'

Peter stood up.

'No, Rose.'

'No to what?'

'No to this way of doing it. Damn the guilt, damn the sums. It's happened between us, and we must simply accept it. We must live it straight, whatever it costs us.'

'Well yes, Peter, of course.'

'There's only one way. You tell him at once. I've already told Beth.'

'You haven't, Peter?'

'Not everything. But enough. It's finished, anyway.'

Rose smiled, keeping her lips closed.

'Really, Peter?'

'Yes. I've said so.'

'Then why do you look so miserable when you say it?'

'Do I?'

'Perhaps, after all, I'm still only the alternative.'

'This is just avoiding the issue.'

'It's connected, isn't it, Peter? Why won't you wait? Are you afraid to wait?'

'It isn't just waiting, it's deceiving and lying.'

'You won't be lying to Beth. And shall I tell you why, Peter? Because she's the real one, and you want her to know that you're breaking away. I'm just the one who gets used, in your fight with her.'

Peter sighed and turned away.

'No, Rose,' he said. 'If it were so, I should be asking to wait. When in fact it's you.'

'Afraid of your own resolution, perhaps?'

He looked back at her, and then walked across to the door.

'I'd better go, Rose. This isn't getting us anywhere.'

'Where do you want to get?'

'I've told you, Rose. And you've simply refused.'

'To go away at once?'

'Yes. Will you? I'll write to Kissler tonight.'

'Even he says April.'

'We can manage till then. Will you come?'

She followed him across, and put her arms round his waist. She held him very tightly, and smiled looking into his eyes.

'Yes, I want you, Peter.'

'You'll come then?'

'Yes, of course. Did you think I'd refuse?'

'I didn't know. We didn't talk yesterday.'

'That was right,' she said, and leaned up and kissed him.

He held her close, but did not answer.

'Come with me, Peter,' she said quickly.

He hesitated, watching her.

'I asked you to come with me,' he said, at last.

'Yes, of course, darling. Now come, quickly. No more silly arguing, we've got our whole lives.'

'Not here,' Peter said.

'Yes, Peter. Until we can go.'

'I said no, Rose.'

'Yes, darling, yes.'

She moved against him, while he still held her close. His whole body was excited, but he still could not move. There was a coldness, a prohibition, somewhere far back. As she moved in his arms he seemed to feel her desire, but when he looked down at her he was doubtful; she might still be acting.

'Come up in a minute,' she said quickly, and began moving away.

'No, Rose,' he said firmly.

He watched the anger cross her face. She stood right away from him.

'What is it, Peter?' she asked, her voice strained and harder.

'I've said, Rose.'

'What are you, Peter? What kind of man are you?'

He smiled, looking down.

'Don't you know by now?' he said quietly.

'I know two men, Peter. You and the other, the other that's been made in you.'

He did not answer.

'From the beginning I wanted you, Peter. I wanted your hair, your skin, the man I could see and touch. But it seems, sometimes, that you're not this at all, that the actual man is a sort of parasite on it, a canker inside it. You denied yourself, Peter, and now you deny everything.'

'If you think all that, then why bother?'

'Because I want you, Peter. I still want you.'

She hesitated, and then put out her hand to his. She turned, holding his fingers lightly.

'Will you come away?' he repeated.

She let go of his hand.

'Yes, but to what, Peter? I've had one empty marriage, I don't want another.'

'Empty? Is it that you're afraid of?'

'Yes, Peter. Because what I think you want, what you really want, is something so perverse no woman can give it to you, no normal woman. You want to force the offer, so that then you can refuse. You'll do anything, Peter, to get to that point. Because that's all the sex you're capable of. That's your pleasure, and when you refuse it's the consummation.'

He put out his hand to the edge of the door, and held on to it tightly. As she spoke he seemed suddenly lost, and he closed his eyes. It was as if her voice was overwhelmingly stronger than his sense of himself. It was so strong that all relation and proportion seemed obliterated.

'And I won't have you, Peter, I won't go with you, on those terms. Beth won't have you, how could she? It's not a man at all, it's a child.'

He did not answer. He could feel a distant source of strength in himself, that he could not endanger by speaking.

'Adultery, afternoon visits, the shift system: any phrase will do, any words in your mouth, to avoid the truth: that you're not a man at all.'

He opened his eyes and looked at her. She seemed suddenly frightened, but she was also angry; she was not acting now. She lifted her hands, made an effort, and smiled.

'It's really not so terrible, darling, just waiting a while. You see, you come when you want. And by May we'll make it, we can be really married.'

He went back and sat in the chair by the stove. He stretched out his legs and put his head back, closing his eyes. She came and sat by him, holding his knees. After a while he opened his eyes, and sat forward. She stayed very close to him, and he put his hands on her breasts.

'We'll get this out of the way,' Rose said, moving the book, which was still lying on the arm of the chair. He took no notice, moving his hands inside her jersey and touching her breasts with his fingers. The book dropped to the floor.

'What was that?'

'Only Arthur Dean's book. Don't worry about it.'

'I don't. Why should I?'

'You ought to meet Arthur. Would you like to?'

'Not from the book.'

'He asked about you. He asked me about you.'

'Why? He can't possibly know me.'

'It's not really you that he knows. It's your mother.'

He pulled his hands away at once. Rose turned and stood up.

'Don't look so startled, darling. It's only the Labour Party. Committees or something.'

'You want this, Rose,' he said, getting up and facing her. 'You want this to break me.'

'Want what?'

'Why did you mention my mother?'

'Because we were talking. About the politics.'

'About Dean.'

'Yes, about his book.'

'I don't see the connection.'

'Then don't, darling.'

He turned and moved away from her. Rose waited and then followed him, putting her hands on his shoulders from behind.

'Honestly, darling, there's nothing. Honestly.'

'You'd better tell me what you know, Rose.'

'But I don't know anything.'

'Is this what it's all been about?'

'All what, Peter?'

He turned and held her wrists. She stayed facing him, keeping deliberately close.

'Because if I thought that, Rose, I'd kill you.'

'Go on.'

'It's for you to go on.'

She freed her wrists sharply and turned away.

'God damn you, Peter, God damn you.'

'No, Rose. Tell me.'

'I said a child and I meant a child. Don't you know anything, anything?'

'I don't understand.'

'Coming here and coming to bed with me, keeping me on a string for the next time, and all the hypocritical talk, the big words.'

'It's not hypocritical talk.'

'Yes. Why don't you face the truth, Peter?'

'What truth?'

'What actually happens. What people actually do.'

'Which people?'

'You come here with your trained speeches, your bits of cant about sex. You learned them at home, I suppose. You'll come and tell them to this immoral woman.'

'Why do you think it's cant?'

'Because we're all in the same boat, Peter. I told you before.'

'Told me what?'

'Your mother and Dean. Don't you know? Are you blind?'

Peter stood quite still. He looked away, past her, to the window.

'I think I would rather be blind,' he said slowly.

'It's their own affair. The way people love is their own affair.'

'Love, Rose?'

'Yes.'

'But how do you know? How can you possibly know?'

'Look, for a married woman it's different. It has to be love, the risks are too great.'

He looked at her carefully. She had controlled her open emotion, but she was exhausted by it. This was not the young face, with the quick smile, that he had always known. Despair and calculation, the bitter lines of resignation and watchfulness, had grown together, deep in the flesh.

'And so we come full circle,' he said.

'Yes, it seems so.'

'I have to go, Rose.'

'Where?'

'I don't know. This is a different world. I don't know where.'

'But away from me?'

'Not from you. From myself.'

'But in fact from me.'

'In fact from everyone, now that I know the truth.'

'Is it your truth, Peter?'

'My truth and my lie, in a single action.'

'But they are other people, quite separate people.'

'Not separate, Rose. What I knew intellectually I now know directly. I can't face it, but I have to face it.'

'By running away?'

'Not running.'

He walked to the door. Rose stood, watching him. She did not move; she would not humiliate herself again. She had made the worst mistakes, at the points where she had thought the control was complete. When the contempt had entered, she had known it was finished, but she supposed that in a way it had been there from the beginning, in them both. It had all been easy, except for the actual people.

He turned and looked back from the door. She met his look steadily: as an equal, a distant equal, with full consciousness between them. This was not feeling but statement: a final statement. Peter nodded and went out.

Chapter Twelve

NOVEMBER, as always, had been the decisive month. Slowly, but absolutely, the world had changed around them. What had begun in a mild light, with the colour of leaves on the trees, had ended barer and colder in the familiar emptiness of winter. As the weeks passed, the wind stayed in the north-east. The cold persisted, with unusual severity for December. For several days the frost hardly broke, even in the afternoons when the sun was big and red and the high skies over the city were strangely coloured, with mauves and greens. The water in the gutters stayed frozen, even when the ice had been broken. It was there to pass every morning, in the short-stepping walk down the hill, and to see again coming back in the evening, grey with a little shine under the yellow lamp, in the darkness that regularly set in before anybody could even think of leaving work.

On the Friday, the coldest day of that week, the expected statement on redundancy at the works was at last made. Kate heard it on the news at one, just before she was due to go down to Arthur: it was one of their regular afternoons. She rang Arthur at once, and put off the visit. In a way she needed him, needed him all the more because the release, the difference, had become habit. But now, suddenly, the excitement, the need, had changed.

She sat alone that afternoon, quite still and inactive. She went over everything again, but it was as if it were layered too far back in her mind. She could make no real connection with it, and though she sat steadily thinking, it seemed, when she got up, that she had thought nothing at all.

She decided suddenly to go to meet Harold. She went down the hill, in the dark, and round to the works gates. Harold was surprised to see her. As they met she looked at him intently, her heavy cheeks very pale in the cold air. But when she got in the car she was lively and talkative again.

They were driving in the ordinary end-of-day rush of cars, motorbikes, scooters, pushbikes, buses. They were locked in the dark movement of traffic, with lights pushing through it at many angles and speeds, and petrol fumes heavy in the still air. It was always remarkable, this sudden overflow of energy, as if of one man, one body, from the ordered work lines. It was in each dark figure, seen ahead: waiting at the wheel of a car, or heavily dressed against the cold on the motorbike moving up the line, or leaning forward over the bars of the pushbike, or queuing under the silver sign for the bus, with a dark crowded patience. Each figure led back to a single feeling, that crowded in on them both in the car.

'Where are they,' Kate said bitterly, 'while the rest of us are here? Where are they, the people who make these decisions and announce them as if they weren't about human beings at all, but just percentage reductions in the labour force? Where are they, that they don't feel what it's like, here with us?'

'They learn like that,' Harold said.

'It's so blind, isn't it, you could hate it. If they looked at us now they'd despise us. Just a black crowd rushing home.'

'It's us going home,' Harold said.

'No, they come to their bits of waste ground, they draw their lines in the dirt, and then they can run us, run our lives to the limit.'

'It's given the employment.'

'And now it's giving the unemployment. It's the same thing, always. It's just accidents to them, that there are men will take their work and then men they can lay off. They've just cut themselves out from people and society altogether, and yet they control everything, the people and the society.'

'They do as the market tells them,' Harold said, bending forward and rubbing the windscreen as the traffic moved again.

'And in the end it isn't a market at all, it's this. I can't understand how blind they are. They do a thing and never realize how wide its effects will be. They start what makes sense on their bit of waste ground and they find they've altered the world.'

'We're all a bit like that,' Harold said. He had spoken with no particular emphasis, and he was surprised by Kate's immediate denial.

'No, Harold, we're not blind. I won't ever accept that. I won't let us be blind.'

'I know that, love,' he said, soothing her.

Kate didn't answer. She was silent for so long that he turned and looked at her, as soon as he safely could, when the traffic began to divide into separate streams past the roundabout. He saw her staring forward through the windscreen, her prominent

189

eyes unusually open and clear, though it seemed for a moment there was an edge of tears in them.

'It's all right, love, we know how to fight,' he said. He was gathering confidence as the car gathered speed, on the less crowded road.

'Do we, Harold? When I heard on the wireless, I wanted to smash something. Only I'd as soon have smashed myself, for anything I could get at. It was the way they said it. You can't believe it even when you've heard it before. "No dismissals are contemplated before the Christmas season", and that bit of pretended humanity just makes it all clear. At Christmas and on Sundays we can still take humanity into account. And in fact no dismissals are *contemplated* at all. They're just written on paper and that's something quite different. "Phased dismissals, of those parts of the labour force most recently recruited, with strict attention, wherever possible, to considerations of length of service." I couldn't believe it, just sitting in a room and listening to that. They say we're getting machines that can think. We don't need them, we've got them, we must have. No man could write "parts of the labour force". Wouldn't he look, while he was writing at it, at his own hand, at himself?'

'It was an advance, wasn't it,' Harold said, hesitantly, 'learning to look at the world like that? Learning to look at it as things you could use and separate out?'

'Do you remember copying that?' Kate said, touching his arm and smiling.

'Aye, that bit.'

'That's why I wonder if we can fight them. They've taught us too thoroughly, in their own ways. Even the thinking that's supposed to be against them is for them, on that.'

Harold turned left, into Goldsmith Street.

'It isn't a matter of thinking,' he said. 'It's just knowing. I *know* it's men being used or discarded, because I might be one of them. So we stick by each other, and then they can't touch us.'

'Is it really as solid as that, though? Here, with our actual men.'

'No, it's a struggle. But in the end it's learned.'

'As an absolute demand though?'

'Well of course it's absolute. No sackings, that's clear enough.'

'Yes, but will you all stick to it? No giving way to the usual compromises? That it'll be done fairly or with proper compensation or so on. Just the one absolute demand?'

'Of course,' Harold said. 'That's settled.'

They reached home, and Harold switched off the engine. They sat on for a minute, in the car. Harold could feel Kate's excitement, though it still surprised him. It came through as a physical excitement, and he could not connect this with the actual issue, as he felt it himself. Also, he was afraid to touch her too closely. In passing that stage, things had been easier and more settled, though not so settled that they couldn't be disturbed by some open return. The pressure was there all the time: the pressure and the recognition, that she was no longer his to touch.

'If it's that, you see, we can really fight,' Kate said, clenching her fists. 'Not just on the details, but on all of it, all out. And not just the men but their families with them. The whole city, because it's being done to us all.'

Harold looked at her again, his nervousness going. It was a very long time since they had talked like this: right back to the first fights for recognition of the union, when he had been risking his job by his organizing work, and Kate, with no security and with Peter still a baby, had agreed that he had to go on.

'Aye, the families,' he said. 'We see it like that because of back home, with the men the whole village and the women bred to it. But here, see, they've come from all over, and they can always go back, though while the money lasts they don't want to. And the city, though it lives by us, still half pretends we're not here. The work is just a traffic problem, something out on the edge.'

'But we could make this grow, Harold. It's had to grow before. We could make this the starting-point, for a quite different life.'

'Well, I hope so,' Harold said.

He opened the car door and got out. Kate could have got out on her own side but she followed him across, pushing awkwardly past the wheel. As she reached the door he saw that her skirt had ridden back up her legs, and he stared for a moment, still holding the car door back. Then he looked away, not wanting to embarrass her, though in fact she was quite unembarrassed, her legs so clear and making no attempt to hide them. The embarrassment, really, was in himself, and he knew that it protected him, from what he would otherwise have to face.

'Give me a hand, boy,' she said, reaching out to him.

'Look, you'd have got out easier the other side. Not pushing past the wheel.'

'But I want your hand.'

He reached forward and took her hand. She got her balance, stepping out, and the skirt went back into place.

Next day, in the canteen, Harold talked to Gwyn as he would be talking to hundreds of others.

'Take just you and me then. While there's work for the both of us, all right. But when they've arranged it so there's only enough for the one of us, what do we do? Their only answer's that the one of us must go.'

'I am going, boy, don't worry,' Gwyn said. 'If I wasn't sure before, I am now.'

'Yes, but hang on a minute. Yours is a special case. You've got somewhere to go. Most of the chaps haven't.'

'Except to less money, yes.'

'Well then, do we fall in with it? Did you see that bank chairman's statement? "We must rid ourselves of the costly illusion that industry exists not to make things but to provide jobs." Can you think like that, then? That's the question.'

'Well, it is to make cars.'

'And they can draw their lines in the dirt and get people inside them and that's the end of it, is it? Until they don't need so many and can just throw the scrap ones away.'

'Look, I know that's wrong, mun. But it is still to make cars.'

'There's the connections, Gwyn, you got to learn to think of. Their whole way of business is to keep the connections out of sight. Because what's industry for, in the end, but giving people what they want?'

'Look, there may be too many cars,' Gwyn said reluctantly. 'That's the real trouble, I reckon. And if it is then some of us will have to go off.'

'Look, you don't want to go saying that. It's easy enough for you. But for the rest of us, there can't be too many.'

'You said the connections, that's all I was thinking. It's got out of all proportion, the only way I can see it. If you put cars and roads the priority, there'll not be much else done. And there are things more important, you'd be the first to say.'

'All right,' Harold said. 'That may be true. And if the priorities was planned, fair enough. But it isn't for us to carry that on our own. All these buggers in the papers is always reorganizing the country, right and left, but do they stop to think what we may be feeling, that it's our bloody jobs at risk? Let them deal with that, then we'll listen.'

'I agree on that, mun. I have from the beginning.'

'Here and now, that's all, there's only the one thing to say.

What work there is we'll share between us. We'd rather all go short than some have nothing.'

'Well, that's fair.'

'Aye, but is it, Gwyn, when it comes to really going short? Yes, we've had good money, but we've spent good money too. Most of us is committed on what we've been earning, not on what we'd earn then. And unless we understand what we're doing, we'll just forget the idea, when the pinch comes.'

'I shan't forget it. I was bred too hard.'

'Well, any of us, mun. Any of us is bound to feel like that, sooner or later. And if we don't our wives and families will.'

'Kate won't. Nor Myra.'

'Aye, well them.'

'And the others too, Harold. They don't all understand it, nor do we altogether. But the lads feel with each other, you know that. And the women, almost all of them, feel first for their husbands. So it's there, the basis of it.'

Harold looked at him. 'I wish I could be as sure,' he said.

Over the next days, Harold and Kate, and the committee of stewards, worked out the details of the campaign of protest. Its biggest event was to be a Christmas march, and it was to this, at first, that Kate gave her whole time. It was meant to be all the men from the works, with their families, right through the heart of the city. Let everybody see this labour force, these redundancies, these percentages of adjustment. See the men, women and children, coming down your own street. Not the working class, or the car workers, but these actual people, that you had to stand on the pavement and watch going by.

They had got a committee together, to work out the arrangements. The most active men were on it, but also, Kate had made sure, several women. She had wanted to get one woman from every street, and then this woman would organize her own street committee. But as it turned out she could get two or three women from one street, and then from other streets nobody. And the two or three from the one street she couldn't possibly turn away, though the committee was already an awkward size. In the short time left, the only way was to organize with the people they'd got. They'd make the general arrangements and then set everybody on to canvassing the streets that were still dead.

The early decisions were much the most difficult. There was first a long difference of opinion on the date of the march. Some wanted Christmas morning, ending up at the cathedral and going into the service. 'It'll test these Christians,' Dick Manning said, 'just asking them to remember what Christmas is about. We can have placards just asking that question, and carry them right to the doors.'

But many were against this. It was wrong to bring religion into it at all, especially somebody like Dick who didn't even pretend to be a Christian. And it would cause bad feeling, among those that were, which church they should go to. In any case, think of trying to move people Christmas morning. Getting them out on the road would be next to impossible. And it was wrong from the beginning, trying to interfere with people's Christmas. 'Interfering with their dinners, more like,' Dick said. 'Well, don't you want your dinner, love?' Myra asked. It was the first time she had spoken.

The majority proposed Christmas Eve, after work. It would be easier to get the men together, and the women could join them, outside the gates. Down in the city centre the streets would be packed with shoppers, and the march would make the biggest possible effect.

'And finish the traffic off for good,' Dick said.

'Well, why not?' Kate asked. 'It's no harm to make people realize.'

'Turning them against us, though,' Len Weekes said, doubtfully.

'That's just it, Len,' Kate said. 'We've been so frightened by this public they keep throwing at us, we're afraid to move. Like they tell the peace marchers to go and walk round Stonehenge. That would just suit them, wouldn't it? Let all this protesting go on where nobody can see it, then they can go on pretending nothing at all is happening.'

'I wonder if the police would wear it, though,' Harold said.

'We can ask,' Kate said. 'I'll ask.'

It was always the easiest way to make a decision: to attach some uncertain condition to it, so that it sounded provisional. Kate had a series of interviews with the police. She was the obvious person. No one else, in their whole group, could speak so effectively to people outside, especially people in any kind of authority. She could meet every polite dissuasion, every hint of the power behind the politeness, with the same mixture of determination and reason. For a long time it seemed that she would not succeed. The effect of the march on the crowded

194

Christmas Eve streets didn't really bear thinking about. But in the end, by agreeing to put the start back forty-five minutes, to avoid the worst crowds, she got police permission, with the usual conditions. All that now mattered was to get their own people out.

Though she worked with great energy and confidence, Kate had her private doubts about getting a really big march. It was taken for granted, in the memories of the older generation, that on the right issue you could do it. But everyone recognized that the atmosphere now was quite different. Hundreds of families had moved away from the world in which politics had been a demonstration in the streets. If it counted at all, now, it was in committee rooms, in newspapers, on the wireless and the television.

Kate lay awake two nights before the march, unable to sleep though her body was aching with the rush of the day. She was remembering, vividly and bitterly, the evening of the last general election. She had been knocking up on the new estate under High Wood. It was a ten-minute walk each way, over poor roads, to the polling station, though there was a bus every half-hour from the corner. The knocking up itself was easy. Almost everyone was willing to vote and there was no question on which side. But they would not go down on the bus, and only a very few, even of the physically active, would walk. She had been promised two cars, by the committee room, but only one had turned up, and when she phoned the committee room the man in charge of the cars was out on the road, driving himself to the limit but abandoning the planning he was supposed to be seeing to.

The single car went off, crowded, at fifteen-minute intervals. But with nearly two hundred people waiting, and with only little over an hour left, it was obviously not enough. She went round again, putting everything she knew into trying to persuade the two hundred to walk or to get on one of the two buses still to run. Very few went.

'Surely the car will be back in a minute.'

'But there are nearly two hundred of you, and one car.'

Nothing more was said, but 'well, that's your problem' was the obvious unspoken answer.

At last, with the rain starting, her temper broke. 'Are you all stupid?' she shouted. 'It's for five years you're going to be ruled, one way or the other, by what's decided today. And with five years of that lot in front of you, can't you spare half an hour to go down and have your say? Even if it is raining.'

She knew that her words were wild, or would seem wild. Certainly they had little effect, though a few of the men were influenced and persuaded their wives to walk to the bus. She ran up and down the street, in the thickening rain, trying to get more out, rushing to the car as soon as it came in sight at the corner by the telephone box. But at five to nine she gave up, knowing herself defeated. Her hair was drenched, and was blowing around her face. She must look like a mad person, running up and down the street shouting, while the rain whipped down, slanting across the street in the rising wind. She wanted to stand, as she was, in the street and shout to the hundred and fifty whose votes had been wasted: 'Damn you, you bloody fools. Now you deserve what you'll get.'

But she stayed silent and bitter. In the reaction she began to cry, and the streaming tears mixed with the rain running down her face. Then the car came back for her, after the last journey, and she went home and changed and then went down to the count with Harold. They sat up with Dick and Arthur and the others, drinking, through the declaration that the constituency was lost and the country was lost. It had been like an end of everything.

Remembering that night, alone now in bed in the back room over the garden, Kate began crying again. She did not really know why. The little groups, waiting, in the shelter of their doors. The car coming into sight by the telephone box. The feel of the rain on her face. Harold. Arthur. She found, in her confusion, that she was apologizing to Harold, who was asleep in their own room only a few yards away. Lying looking at the window and down to the lights of the works, she said, again and again: 'You don't know what it does to you, to stop believing in people. If I went wrong, Harold, I went wrong from that night.'

But then her reason took over, and she was glad she was alone and that nobody could hear her. Even after a night like that, we recover. It's no use getting frightened. People can still live as they want to. Defeat can be just a beginning, and we can still be happy.

Then she cried again, more bitterly, despising her own weakness. But she could not be certain, through her pain and tiredness, what this weakness really was.

Nobody would have recognized Kate as she was that night, confused and frightened, her hair tangled and her heavy cheeks dark with crying, in the competent and inspiring woman who began work again in the morning. She was out canvassing the streets again, persuading the women to come on the march. There were endless problems, but the most common was the minding of children. She was trying to arrange that in each street some of the older women, who could not march, would take care of the youngest children. She found that she could only ever arrange this if she was working in a street with a woman who lived there. Even then, it was far from easy, but without the women who had agreed to help in their own streets it would have been impossible.

But it will be a sort of test, she said to herself that night. How many come out will decide my future. Then, having said this, she laughed at herself. She was not usually superstitious. This has to be a rational world, or we can do nothing.

One thing at least she was sure of. She would not see Arthur again, until after the march. He had rung several times, but she had put him off. While she was making this kind of effort, she didn't want to risk the effects of his scepticism. Though, to be fair, he wasn't sceptical about everything. It was just this was not his world. If she could only give him a real answer, in people. All this talk about workers' materialism and the end of any absolute demand. All right, if there are no ethics left in politics, explain this. Here are people marching for a principle, that they'll share the available work, that they'd rather go short themselves than see others with nothing. Isn't that clear and absolute, whatever else happens?

She hammered the pillow with her fists. She was again crying. Can't you at least try to recognize it? Feel your connections with it? Can't you reach this movement of feeling, beyond yourself, and the power of others to change you? The real power, don't you see, when you're bound up with others, involved with them? When at last you can know people and trust them?

She woke early, after a few hours' aching sleep. She took in Harold's tea, and sat watching him shave. He was going early to work, for every minute of this critical day must be used.

A minimum level of success was now certain, from the very hard work already put in. But Harold knew how carefully and coldly the numbers on the march would be counted, by the management and by the newspapers. 'How many battalions has the Pope got?' wasn't just Stalin's question. Nowadays it was everybody's question. Not the issues, brother; just the size of the armies.

Most of the men were with him all right. There was no real

doubt about that. But it was still a lot easier to organize a strike than a march. To get people to stop doing something wasn't all that difficult. At least it went with their feelings. But try getting them to do anything positive, anything out of routine. It was enough, these days, to break you. The most bloody marvellous negative civilization ever devised by man. The ways of saying no and finding reasons for doing nothing had been worked up to a real mass production job, so powerful and so efficient you just had to stand back sometimes and admire it.

Still, this was no time to stand back. Get moving, get hold of people, don't take no for an answer. And fight down, to start with, the no in yourself. Stick, stick hard, by the few really active ones. You'll all keep each other going. If you've got to expose yourself, do it in company. And you have got to: no argument about that. The rest sort of cowering through it all, all busily covering themselves. Right then, let's show ourselves: the trouble-makers, the agitators, the hotheads, the daft ones. Come on, brothers, let's stick our necks out. Because it's better, in the end, than being buried alive.

Harold was a successful organizer because he always looked and sounded so reasonable and controlled. What he said and did, in public, seemed the most obvious common sense. You had only to look at him to be sure he would do nothing wild; he was a practical man. Yet behind the competence and the deliberate limitation, there was a drive so strange, so distant, so far-reaching, that if it had ever appeared in anything like its original form it would have seemed as impersonal, as surprising, as absolute as history. The unremarkable figure, absorbed so thoroughly in the details of a single and local event, threw an immense shadow, even far back in his own mind.

He knew this, most clearly, while he was sitting in the bedroom with Kate, before the long effort of the day. He felt the shadow, and he also felt suddenly alone. For a brief moment, while Kate sat near him, he looked across at her with a sudden knowledge of separation. He had fought to hold back what he knew, but this instinctive recognition was at last too strong to repress. He knew deeply now, looking at her, the substantial weight of everything that was between them. But he made the effort again, and got ready for what still must be done.

The light went early, in the short December day. There was no rain, but the skies were heavy and dark. The lights in the factory yard, and in the street, were separate misted globes, pale blue and

198

orange above the hard lines of the fences and pavements. Outside the main gate, the voice from the loudspeaker van boomed continuously, its words barely audible. The leading banner, bright in its glinting silks, was held up to face every man who came out. The escorting police, in their capes, were lined out along the street, on the far side. The march leaders, from the different shops, stood holding up their identifying signs, and there was an endless shouting of directions as the men tried to form up. The groups of women, some with their children, stood on the near side, by the gates.

There seemed endless people, to any eye in the middle of the crowd, but still there was a way through, kept open by the police, and many cars, bikes and scooters were going steadily through it, carrying hundreds away home. The men standing with Dick Manning near the loudspeaker van were shouting continually at this stream of traffic, calling to most of the men by name. A few were getting off their bikes and wheeling them over to the wall, persuaded at this last minute to join in. The odd cheer would go up, as a particular man would come over, and the excitement swayed this way and that, minute by minute, as the decisions were taken.

Harold pushed through the crowd to the loudspeaker van, and the booming voice stopped and was replaced by music: a thumping and echoing military band. Against the music, the shouting of directions and the last-minute appeals went on. But already, along the street, the line of march was forming, and the banners and placards were being raised along it. Harold saw Kate, some distance away, leading a group of women into the forming line. Slowly, and with little apparent direction, the march was assembling. In its main lines it was moved beyond any kind of detailed leadership, but still the other traffic, of those who were not marching, continued to stream through.

Harold spoke to the driver of the van, and, hanging with Dick on its running-board, directed it out into the street and along with the home-going traffic to the head of the march. The leading banner came through behind them, its elaborate design and colours catching the light. The thing to do now was move, before the wait got impatient. He spoke to the police inspector who was in charge at the head of the column, and then gave the signal for the van to move off. Behind the echoing music, the banner went forward, and back along the line the column edged itself into a slow procession. The police walked at regular intervals on the outside, keeping the files.

At the corner by the crossroads, Peter was waiting. Beth and Myra had gone down earlier, and were waiting between the gates and the corner. Many of the families were strung out there, to avoid the crush at the gates. Then somebody would shout from the slowly moving line, and they would push in and join him. All the way through its first few hundred yards, the column was growing like this. Peter had seen his father pass, in the little group under the banner. In a way every face seemed familiar, but also, he could see, there was a transformation: perhaps only the effect of the music and the banners. The little group of men at the front seemed changed, in some way. Their faces were set and absorbed, beyond their ordinary habits. Most of the people behind were self-conscious in a different way, aware of the unfamiliarity, the possible silliness, of what they were suddenly involved in. Yet they kept coming, in their hundreds: tidily dressed, walking with a curious separateness, in a strange combination of embarrassment and remote self-respect.

The sharpness of the placards which many of them were carrying seemed to belong to a different world. Peter stood reading the placards, as if they were pages in a book. *Full Employment Not Unemployment. Car Workers Want Work, Not Sympathy. All For One and One For All. No Redundancy Here. Push Profits Out of the Driving Seat. The Production Line, Not the Bread Line. No Love On The Dole For Us.*

It was an effort to look down from the placards to the restrained and silent figures of the marchers. *After Christmas, What? Where Will You Put Your Brotherly Love, After Christmas? After Christmas, We've Still Got To Live.* The swinging arms, in the march. The reminder, in the stiff arms, in the squared shoulders, of the habits of military service. *All For One And One For All* again. *The Production Line Not The Bread Line. Work Not Sympathy. No Love On The Dole For Us.*

There was a quite separate insistence, a suddenly different order of feeling, as the long column imposed itself. Peter could not imagine himself stepping from the pavement and joining in, though he had come down meaning to do so. He had not seen his mother yet, but there, suddenly, was Gwyn, carrying one of the larger banners, which had curved in the wind and could not be easily read. Myra and Beth were close behind him, with plastic hoods knotted over their hair. Beth saw Peter, and looked away. He hesitated, and then stepped quickly in beside Myra. Suddenly he was moving in the line, behind the banner he had still not read. A group just in front were singing, but the words were difficult to make out. He listened intently, needing some fixed point. It was the tune of 'Roll out the Barrel', and the only line he could catch clearly was 'Look at the workers, short-time and sackings are here'. There was a ragged clumsiness in the words and in the singing. He looked at Beth, and she smiled nervously. He stepped quickly across, to walk beside her. They did not speak. Myra, meanwhile, had joined in the singing.

Down the hill the column spread out, towards the centre of the city. They were stepping more quickly now, though with sudden halts as the traffic thickened ahead of them. From the buses and cars going back up the hill, people were looking out at the long line of march, curiously and often with a puzzled sadness. Yet the spirits of the marchers were rising, and many more now were singing. The tune was still 'Roll out the Barrel', but very few were following the clumsy words of the political adaptation; the majority were making do with the original words.

'Why do we have no songs of our own?' Peter said to Beth. 'What?'

'I mean nobody could seriously sing the few political songs we've got. It's either the starvelings or the shrouded dead, and so they were and I respect them, but they're not us.'

Beth laughed as the chorus came back, suddenly loud:

> *'Now's the time to roll the barrel*
> *For the gang's all here.'*

'Yes,' Peter said. 'That's as far as we've got.'

'What's wrong with it, for goodness sake?'

'Nothing, I suppose. It's just an idea.'

Beth laughed again, and joined in the easy and cheerful singing. Peter looked ahead, at Gwyn carrying the banner. Every negative feeling, every reservation he had learned in the long business of growing up and growing away, was brought out again, sharply, in this crisis of the march. Yet in another way, as the march went on, he was becoming more settled. This kind of exposure was more feared in prospect than in fact. It quickly established, in its own rhythms, its own new kind of normality. And the great comfort, finally, was being with people he knew.

The head of the march had now crossed the river, over the long bridge, and was coming into the area of the colleges. The slowly moving van was still playing its hoarse military music, and the little group under the leading banner was more conscious of its position. People were turning round, on the crowded pavements, and watching the march approach. Above them, from one of the high towers, the three quarters were being rung, in a slow and very beautiful rhythm. The sudden quality of the stonework, catching the lights from the street, gave a new setting and a new feeling. Harold looked up at a floodlit tower, and at the statues beyond it, watching impassively over the crowded street. Many of the men immediately behind him were shouting now: *Work, Justice, Work, Justice, Work, Justice*: a long, hard, insistent rhythm. The shop windows gleamed across the pavements: hanging tinsel, silver bells, fairy lights, puffs of cotton wool stuck to the glass as snow. *Work, Justice, Work, Justice*, Harold was shouting now with the others. There was a rising power in the repeated shout. The late crowds on the pavements had turned towards it, and were still and attentive. As the march poured in, the traffic was almost halted. The police were busy ahead, and at the crossroads the march was split into sections, to allow parts of the traffic through. A huge lighted Christmas tree stood outside the church on the corner. From one of the towers in the distance there was a peal of bells. The shout of *Work, Justice, Work, Justice* continued, in its stamping rhythm. Harold watched the large banner curving as they turned right at the crossroads.

The march was very strung out now, and broken up by the traffic. By the time Peter and Beth and Myra reached the crossroads, Gwyn's banner was at the head of a clear section of the march. They were held up, as a line of traffic was let through. Standing watching the crowded pavements, Peter suddenly saw Robert and May Lane. He tried to attract Robert's attention, but there was too much noise, with the traffic and the shouting. As they moved off again, he edged across to pass near Robert, and called 'Come on, join us.' Robert smiled, taking his pipe from his mouth. 'Yes, come on,' Peter shouted, being borne past in the march. Robert hesitated, but May turned and spoke to him and they hurried along the edge of the march and stepped in beside Peter and Beth.

'I hardly expected this,' Robert said.

Peter smiled. Robert was walking easily and naturally, cradling his pipe on his chest. It was as if he were not part of the march, but simply happened to be going the same way.

'Yet you came to watch, didn't you?'

'Certainly. It's very impressive.'

May was walking with Beth. Peter was struck again by May's resemblance to his mother. He looked at her carefully, realizing how little he knew of her. He was surprised that she should have taken the initiative in joining the march. But it was evident that it meant a great deal to her. Unlike Robert, who stayed relaxed and separate, she seemed to have committed herself to it completely. When it comes to a choice like this, he thought, there's always this kind of surprise.

They were on the last lap now. The march was dispersing under the trees in the wide street ahead. For the first time there was clapping and cheering from the pavements, as the early sections lined up under their banners and welcomed the others in. The sense of excitement and achievement spread quickly. When it was their turn to disperse Peter and Beth lined up to cheer those behind them. They had lost sight of Myra. Robert was talking to Gwyn, who had put down the banner and was rubbing his arms. May was standing at the very front of the crowd, fiercely clapping as the others came in. It took a long time for them all to arrive, and everyone was speculating on the total numbers. 'At least two thousand,' somebody said, and the figure seemed to establish itself. Peter found himself reckoning from this figure. If correct, it would be about a ten per cent turnout. Presumably this was success. Yet suddenly the calculation seemed mean, in the continuing excitement. Above the clapping and cheering, the stamping shout of *Work, Justice, Work, Justice*, which had not really been planned, seemed to crown the demonstration. Peter saw suddenly, in one of the last groups, his mother. She looked tiny, in her belted white raincoat with the long black hair to her shoulders.

'It was your Mam did this, you know, Beth said.

'Yes, she's worked hard.'

But there was no excitement or sense of achievement in the way Kate was walking. She looked pale and cold, and her expression was set and abstracted. She seemed not to hear the cheering and clapping, which was now at its climax. They tried to catch her attention, but she was looking straight ahead and slightly down, her hands pushed into the pockets of her raincoat. There was a very loud final cheer, as the last banner came in, and then suddenly everybody was moving at once, and there was the pressure of a crowd on all sides. Peter saw Harold standing on the board of the van, waving to someone, but he could not get near him. He looked where his mother had been, but the tiny figure

203

was quite lost in the press of the crowd. He took Beth's hand, and they tried to move in that direction, but it was soon impossible, and they turned away and got to the pavement. He looked round, but could see nobody they knew. Moving slowly along the crowded pavement, he felt the beginnings of emotional exhaustion. This had started, really, when he had seen his mother coming in. But also he was nervous of Beth, and she of him.

There was still excitement all around them. It was only when the marchers began to merge into the crowded streets of the centre that the sense of occasion ended. By the time Beth and Peter had got to the crossroads, the city looked normal again, in its undirected press of people and traffic.

Kate, meanwhile, had gone back with Arthur. She didn't know if she had intended this, though for weeks, thinking about the march, she had looked forward to confronting him with it. Then in the excitement through the centre of the city she had forgotten this, until she saw Arthur standing, watching the march come in, near the dispersal point. He was smiling and clapping, and when he saw Kate he waved. She didn't wave back, but in the crowd at the end she found him standing beside her.

'You need a drink after that, Kate. It was terrific.'

'I wondered what you'd say.'

'Well, my heart and soul aren't entirely decrepit,' he said, taking her arm. 'The romantic ideas are all ready waiting to be touched.'

'What romantic ideas?' she asked, impatient of his arm in the press of people.

'All we learned when we were young about the workers,' he said, guiding her towards the edge of the crowd.

'I thought you'd make out it was of no importance,' she said, looking up at him, as they began to get clear.

'Why should I? There are still a few issues.'

'Well, it was a good turn-out, wasn't it?'

'Yes. For these days.'

'Look, Arthur, if you're going to start quoting percentages . . .'

'Not at all, Kate. I say it's good if one man, let alone several hundred, walks along a street for a political reason. I don't want to believe that we're finished.'

'But you do believe it.'

'Let's say that occasionally there are moments of hope. Or at least of intermission,' he added, laughing at his own tone.

'Intermission. Like Christmas.'

'Better than Christmas, Kate. Nobody else has laid it on.'

'I ought really to be getting back,' Kate said, as they turned into the familiar street.

'You've time for a drink.'

'I don't know. All right, for a few minutes.'

She looked back at the crowd, nervously. Almost everyone she knew was somewhere in that rush of people, but already there was a kind of anonymity: everyone she actually saw was a stranger. Having made the decision, she quickened her pace as she went with him.

She was determined not to stay long. Under the surface contact, she felt remote and confused, and could not bear to be touched. Arthur waited on her, with a drink and food, and talked easily and pleasantly, accepting her silence. She was very tired, and, once settled by the fire, didn't want to move. But soon after eight, with an effort, she said she must go. Arthur did not argue, but offered to drive her back. She refused, saying the buses would be all right again now. As he helped her on with her coat, he asked when he would see her again, and she said she would ring him. Then she went downstairs alone, and out into the street. It was much colder now, and she turned up her broad white collar, shaking her hair out over it. As she pushed her hands into her pockets, she heard her name called.

She looked round quickly, and at once recognized the car. It was parked only a few yards from Arthur's door. Harold had wound down the window to call to her, but she saw him draw back now, behind the wheel, waiting for her. She stood quite still, and turned down her collar again. She heard him start the engine, and then he drew slowly forward, to come level with her. She opened the door and got in, and he drove off at once.

Harold said nothing. Kate sat quite still, with her hands in her lap, knowing that she ought to speak now, that while she kept silent she was losing her last chance of any easy explanation. Yet she couldn't begin. The connections were simply not there. Harold's sudden appearance, on a night like this when she was in any case numb and withdrawn, made no conscious impression, though in her body she was afraid. Anything she said might be disastrously wrong. Yet her silence, also, was its own kind of admission.

Harold drove carefully and quietly. Everything seemed so normal that she kept thinking nothing had happened. But she knew each time, as the thought came clear, that this was the point of decision which she had often foreseen, but which tonight seemed unreal and irrelevant. There was nothing tonight to explain.

She looked out of the window as they turned into Goldsmith Street, and saw the misted lights of the Christmas trees on both sides of the hill. Harold changed gear, braking, and turned in past the low wall. She got out at once and went through to the side door. She unlocked it and turned on the light. As she heard Harold following her, she went on through the house, turning on every light. She stayed in the sitting-room at the front, where the lights of the tree came on with the main switch. She bent down and switched on the fire, and took off her coat. Harold, with his overcoat loose and unbuttoned, stood in the doorway watching her.

'I suppose Peter's next door,' Kate said.

'Yes, I saw him round there. I went round looking for you.'

'I'd better get our supper then.'

He did not answer, but stood blocking the door. His forehead and the thin hair which ran back from it were damp, under the light. He took off his glasses, and rubbed the deep red mark on the bridge of his nose. She looked down and away, seeing her white raincoat loose on the nearest chair.

'Why tonight then?' he asked suddenly, in a low, flat voice.

'Why what tonight?'

'Why did you go to him tonight?'

'To who?'

'I've given you your chance, Kate.'

'What chance?'

'So you'll lie it right through, will you?'

'Lie what, Harold?'

'Yes, I should have known,' he said, after a pause. Still wearing his overcoat, he went across to his usual chair and sat down. She moved a little away, and picked up her coat and put it over the chair by his bureau. As she turned back she saw that he was still holding his glasses loosely over the side of his chair. He was looking towards her but he would not be able to see her clearly.

'Shall I get the supper then?' she asked, moving a little towards the door. She had a sudden idea of getting to the kitchen and then running outside, through the dark garden, to Myra and the others. Yet this seemed absurd, while he sat so still, hardly able to see her.

'I never imagined you'd lie it right through, Kate.'

'But what do you want me to say?'

'Just if you won't tell the truth I don't know you.'

He put on his glasses again but at once looked away from her.

'All right,' Kate said. 'But I thought we'd made our agreement.'

'What agreement?'

'That night after the meeting. I said then I was finished.'

'I know you did, and I accepted it.'

'Well then?'

'I didn't believe it, Kate, when I was first told.'

'Told what?'

'That you were going to Dean.'

She looked away.

'What kind friend told you that?'

'It don't matter now. I wouldn't believe it about you.'

'But now you believe it?'

'I've seen it. You don't have to tell me.'

'Seen what, for heaven's sake?'

'I've seen the adultery, Kate. I've seen it feeding you.'

'You've seen nothing of the kind.'

'I'm not a peeping Tom, if that's what you mean.'

'Well what then?'

He leaned forward in his chair, his fists knotted over his knees. His trousers, she noticed, were damp from the rain.

'I've seen a lie feeding you, Kate. I've seen you growing and flourishing in this. I didn't want to recognize it, but in the end it broke me.'

'Is what you call a lie the first thing then?'

'Not what I call a lie. It's all of a piece.'

'What exactly are you accusing me of, Harold?'

'That's still a lie, isn't it? You know quite well what you've done, and so do I know it. Are you asking just to find out how much I know?'

Kate did not answer. She turned back to her raincoat and took out her cigarettes. She lit one and then walked across to Harold, holding out the packet. He shook his head.

'Because if you are, Kate, you're just wasting your time. I knew when it first happened, and it was you told me. You're worried about evidence but everything you do is evidence.'

'I thought you said you didn't believe it.'

'I didn't believe it but I knew it.'

'Who's lying now?' Kate asked, in a sudden burst of anger.

'Lying?'

'Lying. Contradicting yourself. Having it both ways.'

'And you can prove that on me, can you?' Harold said, getting up.

'Well, you did contradict yourself,' Kate said, watching him.

'You've caught me out, have you?' he said, staring at her.

'Don't look at me like that, Harold. Don't look through me like that.'

She stared at his face. It was as if something was breaking in the dry, blank features. The blood had rushed to the forehead, and his lips were wet and moving.

'Harold, I'm sorry, I'm sorry,' she said quickly.

'Sorry for what?'

'For hurting you. I never wanted to hurt you. I never meant to hurt you.'

He stared at her, lifting his hands. She put out her cigarette, but stayed facing him.

'You must believe that, Harold. You've got to believe it.'

'Using your mind,' he said slowly. 'Using your mind to break and insult me.'

'I don't know what you mean, Harold.'

'It's been that all through. From the beginning. This is only the finish of what you've always done.'

'But that isn't true, you know it's not true.'

'Using your mind to break somebody, that's worse than adultery. And it led to it. Your own mind led to it.'

Kate put her hands to her face. The touch of her cheeks was like ice.

'I don't understand you, Harold. I don't know what you're saying.'

'No, you don't, Kate. You're too corrupt to know.'

'Corrupt? Corrupt?'

'Yes, corrupt all through. The adultery is only the last of it.'

'You can't say that about me,' Kate cried. She knew now that her nerve was breaking. It was as if she was falling, through the long empty dark, and would fall for ever, until there was nothing left of her.

'It's time this was said, Kate. I've waited too long. You've seen me and the rest of us through your own corrupt mind. In the end you had to do this, go and make your body filthy, with a man of the same sort.'

Kate looked at her husband. Now that the break had come, his voice was strong and hard. She backed away, as if from a stranger.

There was no recognition between them. All the connections had broken.

'You must be mad, Harold. You don't know what you're saying.'

He jumped forward suddenly, and raised his fists.

'Don't I, Kate? Don't I? Or do you expect me to take part in one of your discussions? You bring your filth home and you flaunt it at us. It lets you run us better. Only I'm a man still at the end of it. We're people here. We marched down there today as people, yet all you could do was sneak off at the end to this Dean, who's as corrupt as you are. Sneak off so that you could giggle in bed with him. You're filth, can't you see, Kate? Filth all through, all the way, every last bit of you.'

Kate had her hands to her face and was crying. Harold stood very close to her, his hands lifted and ready. Her voice was barely distinguishable through her crying.

'You don't know, Harold, you haven't the least idea, what my actual feelings were.'

'Don't I?' he said, and his hands jerked up and gripped her long hair. He forced her head back, pulling down on the hair, and she put up her hands to resist him. His glasses were knocked from his face, and fell against the metal front of the fire. 'Don't I?' he said again, his accent much sharper, and his hands tightened on her hair, forcing her whole body back.

There was a sound at the door, and he turned. Peter was standing in the doorway, quite still. Unconsciously, Harold slackened the pull of his hands. Kate brought her head forward, and saw Peter standing watching them. He said nothing, and his face was quite blank, as if all feeling had been cancelled in it.

'Peter,' Kate said.

Peter looked at her, and then back at his father. Then he turned slowly and walked away. A few seconds later they heard the front door slam, and his footsteps moved away on the gravel and into the street.

Part Three

Chapter Thirteen

PETER drove steadily, under the orange lamps of the bypass. The warmth of the car, with the edge of oil in its breath, and the low clear hum of the engine, contained his consciousness for a while, and brought him back to stillness. When we have set the machine in motion, it takes over for a while and seems to direct us.

But the end of the bypass was soon reached, and he was enclosed by darkness again, behind the isolated headlights. He shifted his position, drumming his hands lightly on the wheel. The road ahead was empty, and he did not know where he was going. The first impulse, the answering satisfaction of the engine, was passed. Still driving steadily on, he faced the real uncertainty.

There could be no going back, on any conditions. Waiting this long had only made the break more painful. Whatever, now, they might say or do, it was ended. That long pretence of normality, the long attempt to keep going, over. Everything they had tried to cover up was now clear and in the open, at last.

But he could live in neither world: neither the anxious accommodation nor the open collapse. There was nowhere to go but into his own life: as hard and as separate as that sounded. The images of settlement—the temporary warmth of the house, the brief shouting unity of the march—had broken, as he knew they would break. And you don't stop to argue, when that has happened. Simply, inevitably, you get out. The door closing, and the steps on the gravel.

He had turned first, instinctively, to go in to Beth. But he wasn't able to face her, knowing and recognizing what he now did. It was there, between them, inevitably, as it had been unconsciously for so long. And even that house, that alternative, was going, and she would not be able to break free of it. Perhaps Gwyn was right to be going, but it seemed just another defeat. Who could have the nerve, now, to go on with the projections of a victory? At any time, in this place, it is inconceivable. It is best to admit this and go.

But go where, exactly? Where, here and now? The steps on the pavement, under the line of the street lamps. Counting the paving-stones for security, to keep away disaster. He was walking the way he had walked with Gwyn, up to High Wood. Leaving the streetlamps behind, setting out across the darkness of the field, brought a new feeling. His eyes adjusted to the dispersed light, as on the earlier walk, and this was a grace, a blessing, after that precisely lighted scene.

There was a cry of wind in the hedge. Far below, in the city, the bells of the churches were ringing for Christmas. It only brought back the lie, this reminder of the city. There, behind him, was the idea of the university, the centre of intelligence and of free inquiry. But it had broken down at the only point where it mattered: in his own need to use his intelligence to inquire. 'And what, precisely, would that be?' The sneer was made monstrous by the age and virtue of the buildings. The evasion was sealed in the weathered gateways and alleys. He saw the black edge of a gown disappearing, with its usual flair, into some inaccessible and confident room. It was always a stylish accommodation, shutting out the meagre streets, the bare hard lines of the works.

Only there wasn't reality on one side of the river, and unreality on the other. He saw again the whole process in Goldsmith Street: the deliberate unreality, worked at so hard, so desperately, to cover our actual condition. Not whistling in the dark, but in the artificial light. It was all there, once he was forced to look: the accommodated despair, the deliberately unspoken frustration, that we play with the lights to hide.

He went in among the trees. It was very different from the last time, when he had been with Gwyn. He fell, heavily, over a strand of wire, and the pain shot through his arm. Within the pain, within its actual fibres, the scene returned. Her pale, prominent cheeks, shadowed under the bowl of light. *Nothing for it but go and make your body filthy.* The hands with the veins starting out on them, the fingers holding and tearing the thick black hair. He pushed out of the wood and ran desperately back to the house, forcing his body until every breath was painful. *I never wanted to hurt you. I never meant to hurt you. Using your mind to break somebody, that's worse than adultery.*

The curtains were still undrawn. He could see the bowl of light and its whitening ellipse on the ceiling. There was a movement, and Gwyn was standing there, his back to the fire. He was looking down and talking. Peter could see his face quite clearly. *Gwyn was never interested, but he's all right, you can count on him.* The lean, tired, unassuming face. From their generation, meeting them in their generation. Able to speak, in a known voice; to speak and to intervene. But at this distance, beyond the lighted glass, no words, no connections. From here, from myself, I cannot step into that circle, cannot intervene in that relation. She would be sitting there, drawn up close, her face turned away. And his hands drawn back, limp, resting loosely in his lap. The hands that had torn at the hair, forcing the head back and down. The darkness in the hands, forced suddenly into the light.

Peter looked away from the room to the car. He knew, as he looked, that he wanted to take it. Even the idea of taking it came through with the force of desire. Cautiously now, his earlier fears forgotten, he went down the side-passage, where the light shone out over the gravel. He opened the door and went through into the kitchen. The keys of the car were on the nail by the door, and he took them down. He tossed them quickly in his hand. Then he closed the door quietly, and went back up the side-passage. He did not look back at the lighted room.

He got quickly into the car, pulling the door only partly shut to avoid any noise. Harold often worried about his car being stolen. On an ordinary night he would often walk across to the window and make sure it was there. They used to laugh at him for it.

Releasing the brake, putting the gear in reverse, Peter looked round to estimate the angle of turn to the street. He saw that he was trembling, as he bent to the ignition switch. Then it was all quite sudden: the engine starting into life, the quick acceleration, the bumping reverse into the street. It was all straight from then: the quick forward gear, the switch for the sidelights, then driving fast, faster, down the hill. Along Between Towns Road, past the familiar corner, and then through to the orange lights of the bypass. Only now, beyond the bypass, the long empty road ahead.

At Trawsfynydd, at Evans's garage, the circular sign by the pumps was set at 'Closed'. Cramped by the strain of driving, his mouth and eyes dry in the exhausted air, Peter leaned back and waited for several minutes. He had slept in the car overnight, and could hardly remember the beginning of the journey. The dry fatigue, the headache of a limited concentration, seemed final. He felt himself drifting into sleep again, and sat up and looked round.

The white cottage had a workshop of galvanized iron built on to its western end. In front of it were the two pumps and the circular sign and the dead-grey concrete stand. There was a wind in the birches beyond the workshop, as he looked up the valley. Winter, silence, the empty valley. He pushed at the handle and got out.

The mountains came closer, as he stood looking around. There, just above him, was the long dark ridge of Brynllwyd, and away to the east the dark, broken peak of the Holy Mountain. Narrowing to the west, the steep sides of the valley moved in a series of spurs. There was snow lying in the clefts of the tumbling watercourses and in patches in the scatter of rocks.

The air was very clear and cold, along the valley. Beyond the high chimney of the cottage, from which a thin blue smoke was rising, the black shape of the rock called the Kestrel was prominent. Behind the cottage itself, the rough field with the caravans in it climbed to the long dingle and to the mountain path, where the bracken lay thickly in a depth of dry gold.

Peter knew this country from summer, when the hills were olive-green and there was the soft movement of cloud-shadows. He felt now only the darkness of the ring of heights around him. He kicked the numbness from his legs, and walked across, past the pumps, to the gate of the cottage. He went in at the path, where the cloches protected a few plants of parsley and Christmas rose. He stopped at the low back door, inside its long benched porch.

He knocked at the door, but nobody came. Calling quietly, he opened the door and went into the warmth of the cottage, with its sharp smell of woodsmoke. There were voices in the living-room at the end of the passage. As he got nearer, he realized that they must be on the wireless or the television.

He went into the crowded room, and looked across at the chair by the fire. Wyndham Evans was asleep, with his head lying back and his mouth open. His boots were under the chair, and his feet, in the thick brown socks, were inside the shining steel fender where a half-burned log had fallen and was still smouldering and smoking. Peter hesitated, and then went across and put the log back on the fire. Wyndham Evans did not move, though the breathing quickened a little. Looking at his face, Peter went back across the room and turned off the television. At once, Wyndham woke.

'Who's that, then?' he asked, and then, as Peter turned: 'Good gracious, boy, what are you doing here?'

'I'm sorry I woke you.'

'Where are the others then?'

Wyndham sat up as he spoke and looked around. It was as if he was expecting one person after another to come out of the shadows of the room.

'I'm on my own, I'm afraid.'

'How's that then? Are they all all right?'

'Yes. They're all right.'

Wyndham felt under his chair for his boots, and began pulling them on. Peter looked past him into the fire, where the log had sprung up into a high fellow flame.

'You got the car?' Wyndham asked, rubbing his thick white moustache, that was stained yellow under his nostrils. The sharp blue eyes were very clear and keen, and did not leave Peter's face. The other changes were easy for Peter to accept, but he had not, since that night with Gwyn, been looked at so steadily and directly.

'Yes, it's outside.'

'Whose car, then? Harold's.'

'Yes. Ours.'

Wyndham got up. He went across to the window and looked out past the pumps at the car.

'If I'd just seen that, boy, I'd have supposed petrol. Only I don't usually get the chance. They've hooted before I've got my boots on.'

'Even when it says closed?'

'No, they don't take no notice of that. They just want what they came for.'

'Yes, well I do need petrol, but there's no hurry.'

'You going on somewhere?'

'I don't know. I suppose so.'

Wyndham looked at him again, and then walked towards the passage.

'I'll make a drop of tea,' he said, and went out, closing the door. Peter stood, surprised, and then hurried to listen at the door. He could hear nothing, and he turned away. He was being slowly forced back into himself, into the known context and the exchange of recognitions. The movement was unwilling, for he had no energy to begin again.

Some minutes later, Wyndham came back, carrying a tray of tea. He poured Peter's cup, and invited him to sit down. Then he sat in his own chair and bent forward to make up the fire. The flames went high in the chimneyback, where the soot was hanging like black flowers, blowing in the fierce yellow draught.

'Your tea all right, then, boy?'

'Yes, thank you. I didn't know how much I needed it.'

Peter went on looking at the black flowers of the soot. Wyndham waited, and then asked sharply:

'What's wrong, boy?'

'Wrong?'

'No, don't hold me off, Peter. I want to know what's wrong.'

'Why should anything be wrong?'

'Look, I said don't hold me off.'

'I'm sorry. I can't really talk. It's too private, really.'

'Aye, and this is a private house, but you came in here. Now tell me.'

Peter put down his cup. He had never before seen Wyndham like this. In all the years of the holidays he had been polite and kindly, if always a bit distant. But he was being spoken to now as a man on his own.

'Are Myra and Beth all right?'

'Yes, so far as I know.'

'Only how far is that? Aren't you marrying Beth?'

'I don't know.'

'Gwyn?'

'Yes, he's all right.'

'And your own Mam and Dad?'

Peter looked across into the keen eyes. The face was very thin, but though the age was evident there was no sign of tiredness.

'Tell me what's happened, Peter.'

'No, I can't tell you anything. It isn't my business to tell you.'

'But you've left home. Cleared out, is that it?'

'Yes.'

'Do they know, then?'

'Yes, they must know.'

'Look, answer me, boy. You're not a kid any more. Do they know you've come here?'

'No.'

'Do they know you've got the car?'

Peter looked back at him directly, but would not answer.

'I shall ring them up, now,' Wyndham said, and went across towards the door.

'No,' Peter shouted. He jumped up and stood with his back to the door. He was so very much bigger than this frail old man that he was amazed how easily he had submitted so far.

218

'Mind, Peter.'

'No, I don't want you to ring them.'

'I said mind.'

'No, you mustn't ring them. Not yet, anyway.'

Wyndham looked up into the face. His eyes were still clear and steady. There was no fear in them, and no sign of courage. He merely waited, looking up. Peter pushed his hands behind him, and held the knob of the door.

'The rights and wrongs of it, Peter, are nothing whatever to do with me. But if you're here, with the car, I shall tell them.'

'Aren't you taking rather a risk?'

'What risk?'

Peter hesitated. His grip on the knob relaxed. He moved forward a little, though still blocking the way to the door.

'Now mind,' Wyndham said, and went past him.

'But you don't understand.'

'Nor do I want to, boy. Now mind.'

'Then why interfere? When you admit you don't understand.'

'Interfere? I shan't interfere.'

Peter turned away, and went back across the room. Through the window he could see the pumps and the car. Beyond them rose the dark steep side of the mountain, under the pale winter sky.

'I thought by coming here I could get away from the pressures. I thought I could get time to think it out for myself.'

'But you came where you were known,' Wyndham said, still waiting by the door.

'I came where they came from,' Peter said. 'I wanted to see how it had all happened.'

'I don't see how that could help you.'

'No, of course. You're quite right. It doesn't help.'

Wyndham took out his pipe, and lit it, taking his time. When he spoke again, his voice was noticeably kinder.

'It isn't I don't want you to stay, Peter. I'd be glad for you to stay. Only if they know you're here.'

'Who will you talk to, though? If you mean to ring them.'

'I shall ask for Gwyn. I can talk better to Gwyn.'

'All right,' Peter said. He turned and sat in the other chair by the fire. 'And I'd be glad to stay, if you're sure I can. For a day or two, till it's a bit straighter. I can see there's no point just running away.'

'It isn't just running away,' Wyndham said.

Peter heard the door close, but his sense of the conflict had gone. He lay back in the chair for some time, then got up and stood by the window, looking out at the road.

To the head of the valley the road is twisted and narrow, under steep red banks and high hedges of hazel and thorn. Then the mountain road is suddenly clear and open: a narrow grey strip over the close wind-bitten turf, climbing into the distance, under the dark spurs.

Peter looked out, from the road, to the high scarp and rockfall of the border mountain, with its scatter of grey lichened boulders. To the east the grassland darkened into marsh before climbing again to the distant ridge of Hatteral, scarred with great patches of burned heather and whin.

Peter had stopped the car to open one of the mountain gates. A herd of wild ponies, grazing below him, galloped swiftly away towards the higher ground. He stood watching them go, feeling the rush of movement.

In the cold sunlight, the mountain wind searched out every inch of his skin. He leaned for a moment against it, keeping his eyes closed. Then he went back to the car, and drove on a few yards. When he was closing the gate again, he felt more keenly the loneliness and the silence. Far back in the valley, he could see three scattered white farms, each with its drift of blue smoke. Over eight miles, there was no other sign of human living. The fields that followed the contours were empty, though some had been recently ploughed. There was no sound of any kind, except for the wind in the diamond-wire fence, which had been put in to replace the stone wall near the gate.

He got back into the car, and drove on over the mountain. He was hardly thinking at all. The ordinary pressures seemed unimaginably distant. On this empty road, which seemed a mere accident of the mountain, there was hardly any possibility of meeting or traffic, and the silence and emptiness had passed through into his mind. It was not a feeling of freedom. It was a cancelling, an annihilation, though he could still feel the sharpness of the wind on his skin.

The road climbed towards a huddle of stunted thorns, that had grown and twisted into a hurrying from the wind. Below them, the road narrowed and curved round a long grey outcrop, on which the lichens clung in surprising colours: yellows, golds, ash-greys, reds. Below the road, the land fell sharply away to the

220

west, while to the east it climbed through scrub and whin to the spur. The golden dead bracken lay in fields in front of him, and beyond, in the blue distance, was the wide valley of the Wye, with a cluster of houses at each bridge and ford.

He was driving slowly. It would be easy, now, to just swing the wheel and go down over the edge of the unfenced road to the dark north-facing gully where the snow was still lying. He felt, at once, both the impulse and the fear. He was held, sharply, in the tension between them, but it was not the tension of indifference: each opposing force was intense and active, and seemed alive in his hands.

No other thought could enter, now. Even the conscious effort to recall the conditions of his life, to go back to the familiar world of Goldsmith Street and the university, brought nothing but distant still photographs, lying unsorted on a table, at varying angles and with the white edges showing, overlapping but without connection. As figures entered each separate scene, there was a loss of focus, and the whole scene dissolved.

He looked again at the unfenced edge of the road, where the bracken was lying. Only fear held him back from it. He could feel, as if it was happening, the jolting lurch as he went over, and the car spinning down to the rocks where the snow was lying. Interwoven with the fear, and repeatedly penetrating it, was the quick simple movement of his hands, the quick slight turn of the serrated wheel, that would turn on its own, in the pull from the road, if he relaxed for a moment the light pressure of his fingers. He could feel the decision wholly localized now, in the light touch of his hands. There were no points of reference outside. There was only the empty mountain, the bare rocks, the dead bracken. Even the broad blue valley below him seemed empty. The clusters of houses, the occasional smoke, seemed like features of the winding river.

He braked suddenly. A few yards ahead of him, in the road, was a cattle grid: a series of bars laid at intervals, in a kind of bridge, which the hooves could not cross. He had reacted instantly, as if the bars were a danger. The car stopped at the very edge of the grid, and he got out and walked slowly across it. He pressed his weight down on the bars, feeling them turn under him. At the edge he stopped and pushed the toe of his shoe down through a gap. The grid was very easy to cross, and the fence that ran away up the mountain—none was needed in the fall on the other side—was very thin and light.

He turned to go back to the car, and then quickly put up his hands to his face. The rush of feeling, of shame and of love, was of no kind that he knew. It was harsh and tearing and inarticulate, as if some unknown, neglected region had broken suddenly into revolt. He did not know what was happening to him. He could feel only the trembling, and the tears on his hands. He stood on the grid, in the piercingly cold wind. When at last he dropped his hands again, he felt bitterly cold. It was as if there was a mist over his eyes, and every shape beyond him was blurred. One of the bars in the grid turned a little, under his weight, and he looked down through the grid to the bare culvert.

He walked slowly back to the car. He wondered if he should reverse and go back over the mountain road, but it was easier to go on. He crossed the grid carefully, the bars sounding under the wheels.

Ahead of him now there were trees close to the road, on the lower side, but the pitch was steeper, in the long descent to the valley. Several miles down, there was a signpost to Glynmawr. The road was barely wide enough for the car, running through high hedgebanks under the northern slopes of Hatteral. He turned along it, and drove carefully, rarely able to see more than a few yards ahead, as it turned through its high banks. At long intervals there were openings to the occasional farms. He saw the low white farmhouses, the ricks and timber-stacks, the bare poultry-yards, the long black cattle barns. Then at last the valley of Glynmawr lay open, below the peak of the Holy Mountain. He turned for the main road, and drove up through the scattered village, past the railway station, which was closed to passengers though the signalbox was still open, and a signalman stood at the window, leaning on the single black bar. He reached the turn for Trawsfynydd again, and glanced quickly at his face in the driving mirror. He could see only the strip of the eyes, and had at once to look back at the road. He passed under the railway bridge, looking quickly back at one of the new green diesel trains that was coming out of the cutting by the station. The valley narrowed, under the Kestrel, and soon there was the roughly painted notice by the field gate: *Petrol, two hundred yards*.

He pulled in at the garage, by the ugly galvanized workshop. Gwyn's car was backed in there. Mag. He parked his car, his father's car, and got out slowly. He walked up the path, past the cloches, to the porch.

Myra was in the kitchen. She had seen him through the

window, coming along the path. She called to him, and he stopped by the open door.

'Come on in, boy. You look cold.'

'Yes.'

'You been on the mountain road, have you?'

'Yes.'

'I've never been up there. It never used to be there, only a track. They say it's lovely now in the summer.'

'Yes, it would be.'

His voice was flat and quiet. He held himself stiffly, his arms at his sides. Myra looked at him, anxiously.

'Only Gwyn wanted me to go and I never have. They say it's dangerous, the far side.'

'Yes, it's not fenced.'

'Anyhow you're back, and dinner's nearly ready, look. I brought most of it down all ready.'

'You've only just come?'

'Not long. We left after breakfast.'

'I thought Uncle would be at work. And you,' Peter said.

Myra did not look at him. She was bending to the oven.

'Well we had to come down, in any case, soon.'

'I see.'

'So when Wyndham rung up.'

As Myra spoke she turned and looked directly into his face, forcing his attention.

'I'm sorry,' he said.

'No, never mind that, Peter. We didn't mind coming. Only, of course, they're upset, at home.'

'Who's upset?'

'Well, your Mam and Dad.'

'Upset with me?'

'Well, it was a shock to them, Peter. You taking your Dad's car.'

'Is it the car they're upset about?'

'No. Though that hurt him. But not just the car.'

Peter moved into the kitchen. He took off his jacket and hung it behind the door.

'Beth didn't come with you then?'

'No, why should she?'

'I don't know. I just thought.'

'Hasn't she had enough of it from you, then? What more do you want?'

'I didn't mean it like that.'

'Who knows what you mean and don't mean? No girl in her senses would have taken what she's taken from you.'

'I'm sorry. I've said I'm sorry.'

'It don't matter that you're sorry. This time it's too late to be sorry.'

Peter moved away again, towards the open door to the passage. He stopped by the door, looking along to the living-room where he had found old Wyndham.

'I must still say it, though.'

'Say it, yes, Peter. It can always be said. You get on to saying and then it don't matter what you do.'

'What is it, then, that I've done?'

'You talk like a kid, Peter. You still are a kid. The way you've harmed Beth is all that. This running away is only the finish.'

'How did that harm her? It was nothing to do with her.'

'Just she was waiting for you to grow up and be a man. For years she's been waiting.'

'And this?'

'Like a spiteful kid.'

'Was it? It wasn't spiting her.'

'It was spiting all of us. And your Dad more than anyone. What had he done?'

Peter looked away. In the anger of defending himself, the pressure had lifted a little, but now it returned. He tried to speak more reasonably.

'It wasn't him. You know quite well it wasn't him.'

'Yes, I know what your Mam did. I've known for some time. But then, when it gets to him, and it breaks him, you join in, join in with her.'

He stared at Myra, astonished.

'Do you really think that?'

'I know that. I know what he said when he realized. From her, really, he didn't expect anything better. We all know what she's been. But you could have stayed. You could have helped.'

'How could I? By accepting it?'

'It's none of your business, Peter, to accept it or not accept it. You should have stayed to do what you could.'

'And if I couldn't bear to? Can't you imagine what it means? Seeing that, in your mother.'

'She's still your mother, Peter.'

'Yes, and can't Beth see that?'

'See what?'

It was Gwyn's voice, suddenly. He had come along the passage from the porch, and was standing outside the door, behind Peter. Myra moved quickly and made some signal to him, Peter could not see what. There was a noticeable silence, and then Gwyn came forward, standing close to Peter.

'I saw you arrive, Peter. I was up the field.'

'Yes, I got back.'

'Over the mountain you went, was it?'

'Yes.'

Gwyn laughed. He was wearing a big jersey and wellingtons with his overalls, and looked relaxed and happy.

'I was just thinking. I wouldn't take old Mag over there. Not as she is now. Not that far side, anyway.'

'You told me it was easy,' Myra interrupted.

'Aye, well, it is,' Gwyn said lightly, walking across and putting his arm over her shoulders. 'So long as you take just that bit of care.'

Myra laughed, looking up at him. Then she looked across at Peter, and smiled.

'Come on, the both of you, dinner's ready. Peter, you go and call Gran in.'

He wondered whether to go. The unexpected anger of Myra's criticism, followed with no more warning by her familiar acceptance, was beyond his range. He could not feel his way into this sudden movement, the open row and the open making-up. He knew that in his own life he could risk neither, except at times with Rose, where it was easy because in the end it didn't matter, either way. But Myra had spoken as a mother might speak, yet as his own mother had never risked. It was risk, all the time, to which his mind came back. The absolute risk as against the conditioned routine. Yet he had learned, painfully, that even in the routine there was no security.

He found Wyndham, and they went in to dinner. Most of the talk during the meal was about the garage. Wyndham had been offered a modernization grant, by one of the big petrol companies.

'It's money for nothing,' he said, 'just for keeping to their brand. And I should have a white coat with their name across the back like a boxer, and run out and say sir and stand to attention cleaning the windscreens.'

'You don't want none of that,' Gwyn said.

'Aye, but I do, mun,' Wyndham said, laughing, 'I want their money.'

Yet Kate, alone, had taken just that risk, Peter was thinking. She broke out of the usual routine, just as she had always said must be done in politics. And it's easier to talk about than to do, for it can look very different at the far end. Step out just that bit and all their easy-going is finished. If she stayed where she was she'd be broken now. And only the one other place to go. The world of Rose and Dean, where no shock had been registered since birth. Where you laughed at the very idea that anybody could ever be shocked. Or so they made out. You'd have to go inside it to see. Perhaps in fact they were shocked but had learned they must never say so; never show it by so much as an eyelid. And what happened then? What would be said, felt, done, in that mannered world? What was it like, living, when the complications of open anger, accusation, exclusion had been all overcome? Settle down to a meal, a drink, a reconciliation, like this? Back there, in Goldsmith Street?

'You're very quiet, Peter,' Wyndham said. The others had been laughing at one of his stories, about an American tourist who had asked for gas. *What's that you're driving then, I asked him. A balloon?*

'I'm sorry.'

'They keep on with this studying too long, in my opinion,' Wyndham said to the others.

'Peter's done very well,' Gwyn said.

'Only they don't seem like young men,' Wyndham said. 'They have it all out first in their minds, and then there's nothing left they can do. They know all about it before they've done it.'

'We don't understand it altogether,' Gwyn said anxiously, trying to shift the subject away.

'You're probably right, all the same,' Peter said.

'That's it, see, Gwyn,' Wyndham smiled and nodded. 'That's just how it is. They've been up the mountain and down it again. They know how it looks from wherever they might be. Everybody's probably right, they're the first to admit. Only where are they, themselves? They never look as if anything is happening, where they are. It's always the last time or the next time, that they know all about.'

'I'll clear these things,' Myra said, getting up.

The others got up from the table, leaving Myra to clear. Gwyn said he felt like a walk, and asked if Peter would like to go with
226

him. Peter agreed at once. He wanted to get out of the house, where he felt trapped again.

They walked up the field at the back, with Wyndham's collie. Gwyn threw sticks for the collie, over and over, against the excited barking. They passed the caravans, which looked very clean and smooth in the rough grass. They stopped beyond them and looked back down the field.

'Two years from now, Peter, this'll all be cultivated. Plough this spring, plant the trees in the autumn, the first lot.'

'With the boxer's white coat on your back?'

'Never mind, we'll see to all that.'

Gwyn bent and threw the stick again, high out over the barking collie. They walked up the slope to the stile of the mountain path. The sun was bright, though with hardly any warmth. As they went higher, they could feel the wind more keenly, and they quickened their pace. In twenty minutes they were up on the first spur, facing the Kestrel. They stopped, getting back their breath.

Beyond them, to the west, the mountains had moved into new shapes. They followed the dark moulding of the long curving ridges and the new peaks beyond them. Within the general move-ment lay the tracing detail of paths and sheepwalls and the steep dark watercourses.

The wind tore at them, as they stood looking out. Gwyn was very quiet, and had got impatient with the collie's insistent barking. He was looking down east to Glynmawr, past the tree-line of the river, and the white farms, to the scattered patches of houses and gardens, within the broad green valley that curved under the Holy Mountain.

'You met Aunt Myra here.'

'Yes,' Gwyn said, startled. 'She was born in Glynmawr.'

'You were in the police, weren't you?'

'Aye, I did eight months here, before I chucked it.'

'You didn't like it?'

'It was better than at home.'

Across the close river bridges, a diesel train ran north through the valley. It was very small below them, and there was no plume of smoke stretching back behind it, as he always remem-bered seeing. He followed the line back south, to the red houses of Gwenton, and the dark ridge beyond, with the old iron-works.

'We've never been back to Brynllwyd. Why?'

'Neither your Dad nor me got on with him, after our Mam died. We went down to his funeral, but just on our own.'

'Dad's never said much about it. Brynllwyd and the ironworks are just the bad old times.'

'And they were,' Gwyn said, sharply.

'Worse than Goldsmith Street?'

'There's no comparison, Peter. Don't make any mistake about that.'

'Yet you're coming back here, all the same.'

'Aye, to this.'

Peter looked again at the dark movement of the mountains. Slowly he made out the line of the Black Rock pitch, between Gwenton and Brynllwyd. He thought of Brinley Owen, six generations back, walking through the valleys and up to the new ironworks; of Harold, in the 'thirties, going down Black Rock the day after he married, and away across England to the car works; of Gwyn here in Glynmawr, meeting Myra. And Beth had been actually born here, in the cottage down at the garage.

But the actual landscape was bare and empty. It was as if all that past had been cut away. As if there had been nothing, really, before Goldsmith Street. That at least was how it felt there, in the works and in the streets. It was a place where the past was by general agreement negligible, where the fact that the university was old was enough to damn it: an old place, medieval. The break had been made with all that, all the bad old times. He looked back at Gwyn, standing beside him. The face was very set and quiet, remembering. Peter risked the question he had been waiting to ask.

'Did you know Beth's father?'

'Jack Evans? Yes. Of course.'

'Was Aunt Myra married then, when you came here?'

'No, Peter, she wasn't.'

Gwyn turned and walked a few steps, then stopped and picked up a stick for the dog.

'I'm sorry,' Peter said. 'I shouldn't have asked that.'

'It's all right, Peter. You ought to know. Only it's brought so much of it back, these last few days. I've wanted to talk to you, for a long time. Only I haven't known how to begin.'

'I didn't help much. Going away like that.'

'No, but you did right, boy. It's like I did, at seventeen. I got out, really, because there was no home left. I could imagine you feeling the same.'

'It wasn't the same situation.'

'No. This was your Mam.'

Peter moved, as if to speak, but then tightened his lips. Gwyn turned the stick in his hands, and pulled off the peeling bark.

'It's hard to talk about, Peter. She was always that bit of a stranger. Harold married her, really, for that, because he wanted to get away. And it might have been different, I don't know. A lot of it, anyway, has been good. But for years, you must have seen it, she's been moving away.'

'Why that though?' Peter asked, watching Gwyn throwing the stick.

'She went where she could get what she wanted. With a different sort of man.'

'Was it only that?'

'I think so, Peter. She more or less said so, that night after you'd gone. The other wasn't all that important, to either of them.'

Peter took the stick and threw it, far out, for the dog.

'But that's what makes it so bad, don't you see? That it was a sort of extension of the politics, and that's damnable.'

'I don't know,' Gwyn said. 'I don't think you could have stood it, or your Dad, whichever it was.'

'But I could have tried to understand. If she had loved him.'

'Love isn't often on its own.'

'But at least where it's felt.'

'We don't know, Peter. We don't know what they felt. The attraction must have been there, in that way. We don't know any of that, about others.'

The collie came back with the stick, and dropped it in front of Gwyn, barking for it to be thrown again. There were pitted teeth-marks along it, and Gwyn ran his thumb over them. Then the arm drew back, and the stick was curving away into the bracken.

'I see it as a default,' Peter said. 'I've seen it so often. Not the passion they talk about, that must break through everything. I could accept that. But this sort of balance of convenience. An emptiness really, and the emptiness making the need. The physical thing is just a way of disguising it, pretending something can happen.'

'Not only that,' Gwyn said.

'What then?'

'It may just be that, Peter. I know what you mean. But to anybody outside is it ever much more? Just dirty or just fun: that's what they say from outside.'

'But is it ever any more?'

Gwyn drew in his breath, and swung round, angrily.

'It's always more, Peter. It's more, even, than we ever mean it to be.'

'I don't believe that. I'm sorry.'

'All right, say that some can mean it. Enough to live it through, all the way.'

'But who, then?'

'I can't tell you who. You just have to watch, how people live.'

'Everything depending on that?'

'Yes, Peter. It isn't the one or the other.'

'I don't understand.'

'I've not got the words, Peter. But the life and the sex aren't separate, that's what I'm trying to say. What you do in the one you do in the other.'

'I wish I could really believe that.'

'There's so many ways, Peter. That's where I stop, every time. Just in the few of us there's so many ways, and I don't really know. It's just I feel the connection.'

'You may be right. I want to think so.'

'Yes, because you've got to face it, Peter.'

'I've got to?'

'Not just about your Mam. About yourself.'

Peter turned away. Gwyn walked on, across a strip of burned heather, to the edge of the steep slope. He stopped, with the dog at his heels, at a low, broken, drystone wall. Peter stayed for some moments, and then went across to him. Gwyn was looking at a mountain ash which seemed to be growing in the wall itself, in the broken stones. He was following the stem down, to where it disappeared among the stones that had fallen. Peter bent beside him, as he pulled away the loose stones. The first few moved easily, but the others below them were tightly wedged. Gwyn stood up suddenly, straightening his back and rubbing his hands down over the legs of his overalls.

'You asked me just now about Beth's father?'

'Yes.'

'I was lodging, then, with Myra's Mam and Dad. She was going out with Jack Evans. He used to come to the house for her, and I took it for granted. Anyway, Myra and I, at first, were shy of each other, we kept away.'

Gwyn paused. He was silent for so long that Peter thought he would say no more. When he at last spoke again, the voice was

230

low and hurried, as if he was putting these things into words, even to himself, for the first time.

'Whatever they say, Peter, the new feeling starts. The feeling starts and whether you mean it to or not it forces its way to the open. I just knew, suddenly, that I could take her away from him. That I had to take her.'

The lean face, ordinarily so set and gentle, was distorted now with pain. The very clear blue eyes stared nakedly.

'She would have come, Peter. I knew that. Only in fact, see, she was pregnant. I had to fight to get her to tell me, and it was terrible to see her. You know the life there is in her, to look at. Only now, in front of me, it was tearing her to pieces. She'd got to hate what she was and what she'd done. Yet she knew still she was tied by it, though I tried to tell her she wasn't. And in that house down there, just an ordinary decent house, the whole thing went through. They had to go to Jack's father, old Wyndham, to get Jack to marry her. Everybody knew, everybody said, it was the right thing to do. I chucked up, chucked the police, and went back to Brynllwyd.'

'How long was she married to him, in the end?'

'Not much more than a year. He was all right, he was good to her, and she had Beth. Then he was killed on Black Rock, on his motorbike. I wrote to her after the funeral, and she didn't answer. I tried again, and then I came down here. She'd hardly look at me. It was all finished.'

'But not finished,' Peter said. He was looking back down at the garage, and at the caravans, like toys, in the field behind it.

'In the end she accepted me. But the Myra I'd seen in that one moment, Peter . . .'

He broke off, and made his way slowly back to the path. When Peter had joined him, they walked down for some way in silence. Then Gwyn said, awkwardly:

'If only you and Beth can see how it is, that's all. You can't take notice of us because our skin's not like yours, it's old skin. Only it's felt the same. Me, Harold, Myra, your Mam.'

'You don't think I ever doubted that?'

'Yes, you expected different from us. We ought to be better than we are.'

'I don't know,' Peter said. 'I don't know what I expected.'

Gwyn was silent again for some time. The wind was very cold in their faces, for they were still well above the ordinary tree line.

'Only it's Beth I've been talking about,' Gwyn said, harshly, with a queer twisting movement of his lips. 'It's Beth it matters about.'

Peter stopped and faced him, reaching out to his arm.

'Yes, but Beth and I can't marry this guilt for ever. Don't you see that? Not for ever.'

'Only now,' Gwyn said, 'it's not your Mam, it's yourself.'

Peter turned away. The wind was cutting at his face. Gwyn touched his hand for a moment, and then moved right away. They walked back to the garage in silence, uneasy and unfinished with each other.

Chapter Fourteen

THEY travelled back that evening, in the two cars: at first along the narrow, steep-banked Welsh roads, then down to the wide green valley of the Severn, and up over the steep scarp to the long horizontal curves of the Cotswolds.

Peter kept a regular distance between Gwyn and Myra. Within a few miles he was following the shape of the car, and its lights, rather than any actual person. The flashing of an indicator; the reciprocal dipping of headlights; the set direction signs and crossings; the ordered sequence of the traffic lights: he acted and reacted on each of these, as if in a wholly impersonal world. His enclosed concentration, behind the wheel, included these limited signals, that seemed not so much from others as from a total world outside him. Held up for a time where the road was being worked on, across a busy market square, he saw Gwyn and Myra clearly again, and realized the pattern he had been following. As they moved away again, he lost them, and was again following the car. There was an obvious strangeness in the fact of traffic. The approaching headlights, the amber indicator, the high bulk of a lorry: these were the facts with which consciousness had to deal. Dipping his own headlights, as a line of cars passed, he remembered a definition of consciousness, in the report of an experiment: its elements were flashing lights, reactions, learned signals, learned patterns. It seemed a special case, but it was becoming reality. He remembered his own strangeness, but also his sense of renewal and discovery, when he had gone with Gwyn into High Wood, and the common light had grown through the darkness. But now, passing houses along the road, the occasional glimpse of a lighted room—a woman getting up to draw the curtains, a child alone at a piano—came through in the separate field: momentarily flashed on a screen, within the shape of the lighted window. As in the traffic, most people were known in these isolated images, with a quick decision on relevance to oneself, in the rapidly changing series.

Peter wondered how deeply he had been formed by this world. That he could now be conscious of it suggested some failure of adjustment, which seemed to isolate him. Yet he knew he was in

233

fact not alone; the adjustment was nowhere perfect. The general movement seemed clear and confident, through a conventional world. But the individual movements, individually seen, were almost always uncertain, unfinished. The general voice was confident, moving from point to point, but the personal voices, when they could be plainly heard, were uncertain, inarticulate, struggling still with original experience. The acknowledgement of another reality was continually made, at the edges of the ordinary network. And yet, collectively, this network was the reality; here, and here only, was a society confirmed. Beyond the traffic was the works and its network, itself operating within the same kind of experience. An extraordinary priority had been given to it, in the economy and the society. This was normally understood as the priority of the machine, but it was no longer only this. What was central now was the fact of traffic: its kind of movement, its kind of signal, its inherent versions of what people were like and the ways to react to them. Everyone knew, in a private way, how much was left out, by these familiar definitions, yet still, in common practice, they seemed daily more absolute and more relevant. This was the network by which the society lived, and through which it moved and communicated. The rest, ineradicably, was private.

They reached the bypass, under the high orange lights. But since it was late, and the traffic thinning out, Gwyn turned for the short cut through the centre of the city, which by day, in effect, was impassable. Watching the line of the road, Peter remembered, as if from a separate existence, the long mountain road, running up under the scree and the spurs. At the end of the road, out of place, was the white cottage, the garage, and the field behind, with the caravans under the wood. Only there was no way out, by that kind of break. Gwyn was going to the garage, however often he mentioned the field. He was simply moving, in fact, to an outlying point on the same network.

The last buses were running through the city. People were waiting in short queues at the stops, though a few couples had moved back into the darkness of doorways. At the centre, where the lights of the shop windows were still fully on, groups of girls were walking past the boys standing and watching at the corners. Peter stopped behind Gwyn at the traffic lights. He could see Myra looking out at the groups of girls, and he wondered what she was thinking. Then the lights changed, and the cars were moving again, out towards the darker streets, over the long bridge.

They turned at last into Goldsmith Street, up the familiar hill. He felt the long strain of driving through his body, in these last moments. What would now happen he didn't know. He had agreed with Gwyn to spend at least one night in his house. He saw Gwyn drawing up at the pavement, by his own entry. As he drew in behind him, the pressure of habit seemed the easiest future, but he was determined not to come home.

'Just leave her there, Peter. I'll put her away later.'

'Shouldn't I?'

There were no lights in the front of the house next door. He looked back at Gwyn.

'I'll do it,' Gwyn said. 'You go on in.'

Peter hesitated. Myra was leaning into the car, getting a case from the back seat. She turned and smiled.

'Yes, love, you go on.'

Peter nodded and walked in past the tree, and down the side entry. He left the light on in the kitchen and walked through to the living-room. Beth was sitting near the door to the conservatory. She had been reading, but as he came in she put the book down and looked across at him. His eyes followed the book, which he recognized, with surprise, as one of the texts he had been using for his thesis: a study of migrant families on a new Midlands industrial estate. When he looked up again, she was still watching him. She was wearing a pretty lime-green dress, with a white scarf pulled through a bright silver ring at her neck.

'Well?' he asked.

She got up, her attention elsewhere.

'I don't know what to say, Beth.'

'Don't you?'

She stood at some distance from him, waiting.

'Why are you reading that?'

'I thought it would be interesting.'

'But it isn't?'

'Yes, it's all right.'

'Once I change the context, I see it all quite differently. Migrant families; it's like birds.'

'Yes,' Beth said, 'you study populations.'

'You learned that bit, did you?'

'I read it.'

She bent and picked up the book, and put it away on a side table. Then she walked past him towards the door, and he reached out and held her arm.

'Leave me alone, Peter. Please.'

He drew back his hand, quickly. He was surprised at her sudden distance from him.

'I'm sorry, Beth. Everything I say seems to be wrong.'

'Yes.'

'I wish I knew why.'

'Because you *are* wrong, Peter. I'm sorry.'

She moved quickly and went out. Gwyn and Myra had come into the kitchen, and Peter heard her talking to them. He waited a few moments, and then followed her out. She had a meal ready, in the stove, and was beginning to serve it, while Gwyn and Myra took off their coats.

'Here's yours, Peter,' she said, handing him a warm plate. The kitchen table was laid, and he put the plate down in his usual place. He did not sit down, but waited for the others.

'Go on, start,' Beth said. 'It'll only get cold.'

He hesitated, but as Gwyn came back, and Beth put his plate in his place, he sat and began to eat. Myra and Beth joined them, some minutes later. Beth was asking about the journey and about Wyndham. It was mostly Myra who answered. As soon as they had finished eating, they washed up. Peter waited and helped to dry. Gwyn went round to lock up. When the table had been laid for breakfast, Myra said she and Gwyn would go on to bed.

'You'll show Peter his room,' she said to Beth.

'All right.'

Gwyn had already gone upstairs, and Myra followed him.

'I'm going on now,' Beth said.

'All right.'

'There are some things in your room.'

'Are there?'

Beth put out the light and walked to the stairs. Peter followed her up. Gwyn and Myra had gone into their own room, and closed the door. Beth led the way along the passage, and opened the door of the spare bedroom, at the back of the house.

'All right, then?' she said, turning and looking at him.

'No,' he said, with an effort to smile.

She looked away. Her face was unusually set and guarded; the resemblance to Myra was clearer than he had ever seen it.

'I wish we could talk, Beth.'

'Yes.'

'I'm being treated like a delinquent. I don't enjoy it.'

'Do you think that you're meant to?'

'A course of punishment, then?'

'No. That's nothing to do with us.'

'What then?'

'Nothing special, Peter. Why should there be?'

'Things have happened.'

'Yes.'

He walked into the room, and across to the window. He looked out, bending close to the glass. Beth stayed, without looking at him, by the open door.

'Just say something, Beth,' he pleaded, turning back. 'Say something.'

She was holding the outside handle of the door. He looked at the line of her hand and wrist. She did not speak.

'You said I was wrong. Will you tell me why?'

'What's the use of telling?'

'Look, I'm guilty already. I could be broken quite quickly. Why don't you begin?'

'That's the difficulty, Peter, and you can't see it.'

'See what?'

'That there's more to this than what you may be feeling.'

'Do you think I don't know that?'

'You can recognize it, perhaps. You can recognize anything.'

'I went away,' Peter said, sitting on the edge of the bed. 'I went away because I had to, because I couldn't stay in that house.'

'Why couldn't you stay?'

'Because the lie had come out, and that was the finish.'

'What lie?'

'Their lie. My mother's lie.'

'Which lie?'

'My mother and Dean,' Peter said, looking up at her, now really surprised.

'Only that?' Beth said.

Peter sat up, more confidently.

'Do you know that man, Beth? Have you ever seen him?'

'I've been reading his book.'

'That's enough in itself.'

'No, I don't think so. I found it quite interesting.'

'I don't understand. Are you trying to defend them?'

'No, I don't have to defend them.'

'But then you're not involved in it. Remember I am.'

'Yes, you're involved in it, Peter.'

'In its effects, I mean.'

'You've done much the same, Peter. Has that occurred to you?' He jerked to his feet. He looked angrily across at her, and she stared steadily back.

'I realize I was wrong about Rose,' she said quietly. 'That you wouldn't get anywhere.'

He tried to speak, but the words would not come. His whole body had tightened against him.

'And your plans to go to America. It was all very nicely worked out.'

He turned and moved away to the window.

'How do you know all this?'

'Is that the first thing to say, Peter?'

'I don't know. I don't know what to say. In fact it broke down. You probably know that too.'

'What broke down?'

'The affair with Rose. And the American idea.'

'Rose doesn't think so.'

'Do you mean you've been seeing her?'

'No.'

'Who then?'

'And the American idea is still open. You've left it open.'

'Robert?'

Beth didn't answer. He turned and looked at her. She let go of the handle of the door, and he watched the tiredness pass through her body. She leaned against the wall, letting the door close. She had gone very pale, and he moved quickly towards her.

'What is it, Beth? Tell me.'

'No, Peter, no. Keep away.'

He stopped by the end of the bed. The house was suddenly quiet.

'You keep asking,' she said, 'who told me, who passed the information, as if that were important. This is what I mean. You don't understand this at all.'

'I can see that I've hurt you. I knew that at the time.'

'Yes,' Beth said, nodding and opening her eyes.

'But at least I've learned something. That it didn't make sense. That I have to start yet again.'

'Which was why you went?'

'No, not directly. But it all came together.'

'Yes, it all came together.'

'What do you mean by that?'

'You and Dean,' Beth said.

Peter moved slowly, and sat again on the bed.

'You can't really mean that?'

'I do mean it, Peter. You were sleeping with Rose.'

'Once, yes.'

Beth looked across at him.

'That night I came in?'

'Yes, that night. Just before you came in.'

'You should have told me then. I was already prepared.'

'It wasn't easy to tell you.'

'Easy, Peter? Can you really say that?'

'I was already ashamed, Beth. But I was also frightened, just of being ashamed. It would have seemed like betraying her. Or betraying myself.'

Beth straightened her shoulders, and pushed away from the wall.

'You mean you had loved her,' she said.

'All the words have gone. I don't know.'

'You mustn't be frightened,' Beth said. 'You can tell me the truth.'

'When I saw her,' he said slowly, 'when I saw her ready to love me, it was like being born. The release and the strangeness, but in the end the delight, so intense a delight. So intense a joy, even while I was frightened. It's no use saying it. It's quite gone now. But what has the world ever done, but lie about that? Sneer and lie, though in fact it is so.'

Beth waited, still watching him. He uncovered his face, and looked strangely up at her.

'She wasn't involved,' he said, closing his eyes. 'I can remember that now. At the end she laughed, because she was the stronger. My skin was burning, but she was quite cool. Yes, I enjoyed her, but as a treat, a present. I was back like a child on her body. She was quite beyond me, and it was as if nothing had happened, though to me it had happened.'

Beth turned, and rubbed her eyes. She seemed almost too tired to stand, but she stayed close to him.

At last she moved away to the door. He stood up, watching her.

'I thought of moving out. In the morning. Getting a room in the town.'

'Yes, Peter. All right.'

'You're not against it?'

'No, not now.'

'Gwyn and Myra are going?'

'Yes.'

'You're not going with them?'

'No, I'm not going.'

'And next door?'

'You mean your mother and father?'

'Yes. Of course.'

Beth smiled, through her tiredness. Then she spoke as if to herself.

'You thought you were running from what your mother had done. That made it easy. But you were running from yourself, as you have for so long. On the run from yourself.'

She seemed utterly tired now, as he had seen her once as a child, going to sleep at the table, and her bright hair falling forward, and the lips parted, and the blood pressing into the face.

'Don't go, Beth,' he said, and hurried across to her.

'Yes, I must go. There'll be time.'

He touched her hand and she turned away. He closed the door behind her and went back and sat on the bed. But he was suddenly cold, and he got up, rubbing his arms, and walked to the window. He bowed his head to the glass, looking out over the gardens. There was a light from next door, shining down over the grass to the picket fence at the end. He imagined his mother sitting there, reading, with the pillows behind her. The prominent dark eyes, in the pale face, and the black hair to her shoulders. He continued to stand by the window, listening, and looking down over the fence to the lines of lights at the works.

He spent the next morning looking at several rooms. It was not so much that he had any special requirements as that he had no requirements, with which to make any choice. At last he settled for one, because it seemed easier, in that particular interview, than refusing.

In fact the room was quite pleasant. It had been originally a servant's bedroom, at the top of one of the redbrick, sprawling, late Victorian houses that had been built when the dons began to marry. The house was now divided and occupied to the last corner. The family which owned it used what had once been the tradesman's door and the back ground-floor rooms. In what had been the drawing-room a Hungarian couple lived, using the former front cloakroom as their kitchen. Two families lived on the first floor, and the top floor was divided into single apartments.

Peter unpacked the case which Myra had fetched for him, with a few of his things. Then he stood at the window looking out over the big garden, with its crowded trees and shrubs and sandpits. Later he went out for lunch to one of the little back-street Pakistani restaurants, and then walked to Robert's house. Seeing Robert, he knew, was the next real stage.

As he arrived at the house, Robert and May and Frances were setting out for a walk. May at once asked Peter to go with them. Robert was in his usual rather opulent good spirits, talking and striding in a single action. Peter trailed along, talking to May and Frances, but soon they fell into couples, and Peter walked in front with Robert. They turned out of the comfortable street into the long grey terraces running down to the canal. Dustbins were out for collection, on the pavement in front of each house, for there were no side entrances. Very little sun got into these close streets, but there was a good deal of adventitious colour, in the brightly painted front doors. Along the line of the roofs there was a thicket of television aerials.

'Do you like the look of this, Peter?'

'No. What would you call it? Residential?'

'Well, it's a residential district.'

'By comparison with Goldsmith Street it's squalid, but that isn't residential.'

'Quite, because of the works,' Robert said. 'That makes it a working-class district.'

'Residential being where people who are not working-class reside?'

'That's how it seems to be,' Robert said, laughing. 'After all, nobody has yet got around to thinking of the whole population as residents.'

'I can see that,' Peter said. He stepped off the pavement to avoid a woman wheeling a pram, which could only just be got through the gap between the house walls and the line of dustbins.

'Only I have a thing about suburbs,' Robert said, catching him up. 'I think the campaign against suburbs is reactionary.'

Peter listened, but didn't answer. He wished he had enough spare energy to talk about general questions in this alert, striding way. Yet also he did not wish it. It was in this that everything seemed to have gone so disastrously wrong. Robert went on talking, and Peter listened with a distant approval, though his attention was elsewhere.

They came out to the line of the canal, with its litter of back-end coal yards, builder's yards and dumps of material. The wooden bridge ahead of them, with its dark reflection in the deep green

241

water, seemed to belong to another world, with the muddy towpath and the high hedges and the poplars.

They crossed the bridge, and went on up the potholed road, past a newly built warehouse, to the iron bridge over the railway. There was a huge rubbish dump just before the second bridge, with hundreds of rotting cardboard boxes, old tyres, disintegrating mattresses, and half-burned paper. Beyond this, along the line of the canal, was the huddle of towers of the university.

'Nearly all the places where people have been close to each other, Peter, have also been filthy, insanitary and squalid. I think any break from that, into anything, is good.'

'But the filth still has to be put somewhere. All this, the backends, is the price of the suburbs.'

'No, Peter. That too is reactionary. It's just incomplete organization. And the answer is to complete it.'

He looked down the long railway line, to the distant station.

'We've both lived in highly organized places, haven't we, Robert?'

'Well?'

'It doesn't really matter.'

They stood on the railway bridge, looking out at the meadows, at the neglected pasture, with its tangled and yellowing grass, beyond the winter-flooded ditches and the newly pollarded willows. A large area of allotments, each with its dilapidated hut or old greenhouse, stretched away beyond the willows to the high line of poplars.

'I came to tell you that I've moved out,' Peter said, suddenly.

'In what way?'

'From Goldsmith Street.'

Robert felt for his pipe, and spent some time lighting it. May and Frances, walking more slowly, came up with them as he hesitated.

'That's probably right,' Robert said at last, as they drew ahead again.

'Is it? You can't know all the reasons.'

'I think I know more than you suppose.'

'What?'

'I know, for example, about your mother. I'm sorry.'

Peter looked away, across the flooded ditch.

'I didn't expect it to have got that far,' he said.

'You underestimate people. Rose is a friend of Dean's. She told May.'

'And am I expected to stay in this bloody place? Stay and take it while that sort of talk goes on? While everybody knows it and whispers about it?'

'Yes, you won't miss that by leaving Goldsmith Street.'

'Then I'd better clear out altogether. What's the point anyway? You know as well as I do that the research means nothing.'

'No, I don't know that. I think that what you're doing is useful.'

'To your world, yes. To me, no.'

Robert smiled, wryly, and re-lit his pipe.

'Leaving that aside though, Peter, the point is that everybody talks about everybody, and of course is talked about. At your age I was always interested in what people might be saying about me. But then one day I chucked it. I knew I couldn't keep track of that many tongues, so I just let it go. What does it matter to me, really, what other people are saying about me?'

'But it's not about me. It's about her.'

'It was about yourself that you were complaining.'

'All right. I'm sorry. But what did I get except the stock answer? About how you'd solved your problems.'

'It's been like looking in a mirror, Peter. A mirror miraculously preserved, to keep the image of twenty years back. Every feature of shame, guilt, confusion, panic.'

'Which you've outgrown, is that it?'

'Not really. But I've built up my controls, and I've built up certain actual relationships, in which I live.'

'I wonder about that, Robert. You've solved so many bloody problems you're too good to be true. All this bland stuff you give out, where does it come from, really? I suspect you just grew an old skin, at about my age as you put it. And now all we see is that facsimile of maturity, that must cost you something to keep up.'

'Yes, in part it has been like that,' Robert said, evenly.

'You see. You won't even fight on that. If you tried fighting the skin might crack.'

Robert moved a little ahead, and stood holding open the gate to the meadow. Peter went through, but Robert waited for May and Frances. The long flat meadow stretched ahead of them, down to the great curve of the river. In the distance there was flooding, and the swans had settled there. Above the river the sky was grey and unbroken.

'We haven't seen you since the march,' May said.

'No, I've been away.'

'I hadn't marched like that since I was a student. And Robert, I think, had never marched in his life before.'

'Except in the army,' Robert said, quickly.

'Oddly, I was thinking about that,' he went on. They were walking slowly down the broad path towards the river and the swans. 'I was thinking about the advance on Brussels, ninety-two miles in one day. The liberation of Brussels, that in fact became legendary. At times I can almost believe the legend myself, except that the actual experience is still available, quite close to the surface. Ninety-two miles sounds a lot in war, but there was very little opposition. And ninety-two miles, in an actual day's motorized travel, is slow, tedious, quite unexciting. As in fact the advance was.'

'Well?' May asked.

'We get deceived by pace. We get bored because of the legends, because it's the legends we're taught. But then the actual pace of anything, of history, of a life, is so different we're quite unprepared. The idea keeps racing ahead of the experience, and in the tension between them we smash.'

'Yes,' Peter said, 'it feels like that. Except that if we agree to slow down, to the pace of the experience, we're dead anyway, as things now are.'

'Yes, Robert, you've never understood this,' Frances said eagerly.

Robert stopped and re-lit his pipe.

'This is the familiar accusation of the young,' he said, smiling, 'against their parents and teachers. But I was thinking, really, about Peter's parents. I think for them it's been very hard, waiting, in a society they've experienced as continual struggle. As we get older, we either acquiesce, or we reach breaking point.'

Peter turned on him fiercely.

'What actually breaks then, Robert? Why don't you say it?'

'Our idea of ourselves,' Robert said. 'Our integrity even.'

'But their integrity hasn't broken,' May said firmly. 'They organized that march.'

'Yes, and after it?' Robert asked, again lighting his pipe.

'After it there is the same struggle. All the harder if they're left on their own.'

'You don't understand what he's implying,' Peter said, hopelessly.

'Yes, Peter,' May answered, looking into his face. 'I do understand. I've had to learn to understand.'

244

He felt a jolt through his body, as the words came. He saw the familiar strain in her lined face quite differently, in just that instant. There was an extraordinary concentration and intensity of energy, which almost transformed her but which she continued to just hold back, for some reason outside herself. She reminded him again of his mother, as he had known her many years back, when he was beginning to go beyond her at school.

They walked on, without speaking, until they reached the river. The swans crowded the floodwater, and there were a few geese and seagulls among them. Frances and Robert went to the edge of the water, throwing pieces of bread at odd angles so that the birds had to swim for them. Robert crouched and picked some grass which he scattered on the water. The swans took it eagerly, darting their necks forward and supping the grass and the water together. One swan came out on to the grass, and the beauty of its movement in the water was suddenly changed to a graceless, unbalanced waddle. Robert wrenched at more grass, and scattered it again.

Peter stood with May, watching. The grass was floating on the water, as if the hand still held it.

'Beth came to see me, Peter.'

'Beth? But you don't know her.'

'It was the morning after you'd gone. She thought Robert might know where you were.'

'She hasn't said that to me.'

'No? Perhaps she doesn't want you to know how worried they were. She said then not to tell you she'd been asking about you.'

'But why?'

May looked at him. Her face was lined and tired, and the skin was very pale and dry.

'It's a thing some people learn, Peter. Not to show how much they've been hurt, or how much they need someone. It can so easily be used against them.'

'Why are you telling me now?'

'Because I think you're in danger, Peter. In danger of losing what's finally important to you. You've been brought to the point of rejection, but you must not reject. Because what you'd call rejection, what you all call rejection, would be just hypocrisy. You'd take what you'd been given, in love and trust, and simply spite it by going away. And you've no right to do that, if you want to be yourself.'

Peter moved uneasily. Robert had gone on round the flood-water, with Frances a few paces behind him. He was clapping his hands to try to get the seagulls to rise.

'When Beth came to me,' May said, 'she had been badly hurt, yet she still came, trying to find you, because she loves you in a way that accepts being hurt. That sort of love is quite common, yet you won't see it, you go on refusing it. It's easy to go wrong, but then only love can save us. The terrible thing is that you've been taught to reject that.'

'Have I? By whom?'

'By your world.'

Robert was picking his way back along the soft edges of the floodwater. Peter looked at him: at the settled face, the thick hair, the clear health and maturity.of the body. The contrast between the legend and the experience could operate both ways. Peter had always thought of May as someone defined by Robert, existing primarily in relation to him. What he knew now was quite different: that the Robert he respected was really May's creation; that he drew all that was valuable in his life quite directly from her.

But then to realize this, with this kind of certainty, as he saw them together, was in itself overwhelming. It seemed convincing, as May had put it. For she had obviously been talking about herself and Robert as clearly as about him and Beth. Yet what was it, really, to draw life, to take life, from another person? She was keeping Robert going, in what had become his best self, but at a terrible price. He could see, now, the bitter roots of her strain. *She loves you in a way that accepts being hurt.* But was the price only to her? Was it not, also, to Robert? Without his wife he would be merely the acquiescent, complacent, rather silly man who still sometimes appeared. And why should she live as she had, breaking herself, simply to create a better man? What sort of man, finally, would it be, who could accept such a gift?

'Do you feel like going on?' Robert called cheerfully.

'Yes, if you like.'

'I'll get back, I think,' May said. 'Do you want to come, Frances?'

'Yes. Might as well.'

Peter smiled at Frances, as she turned away with her mother. He remembered her standing, very young and very exposed, in the picket-line at the meeting. There again, in this shy girl, was a feeling he could not ordinarily touch. He felt very clearly how little he understood, but also how little he had ever tried to understand. Perhaps he had been learning too much on his own, though he had been trained to learn on his own. All he could see, now, after the talk with May, was the real depth of his habitual distrust of people, at the point where it was turning into a radical distrust of himself.

He walked on with Robert, along the muddy path by the river. They talked very little. Peter could still not really see Robert, in this new way. For it was as if, though alone, his wife was still with him; as if she, really, were his whole direction and energy. 'That devil's killing her,' Rose had said, but it didn't seem like this, up close. The strain came from her commitment, to keeping a centre in both their lives. Robert was really more a part of her than a man on his own.

Peter turned and looked back. He could just see the two distant figures, at the far side of the meadow. They were so far away that they were barely distinguishable from each other. A diesel train passed on the line, making its high bugle call as it slowed for the station.

'My wife was talking to you?' Robert said, suddenly.

'Yes.'

Robert stopped, and knocked out his pipe, and put it away in his pocket.

'You won't understand this, Peter. It's been going on for too long. But when my mother was dying I went badly to pieces, and only my wife saved me. It was unexpected, and I can still hardly believe it. Because what I did then was against her, directly. Against her and against my marriage.'

They had reached a white paling bridge, over one of the muddy tributaries of the river. Robert leaned on the rail, looking down at the slow brown water. •

'When my mother was dying, I left my wife. Not to be with my mother, whose illness frightened me. Though the fact that she was dying made my excuse or reason. I remember the feeling quite clearly: a sudden life-panic that was also an insistent desire.'

The floodwater was lapping against the bridge. Peter stared down at the slow eddy around the black, rotting posts.

'I wanted the darkness: that's all I really remember. And while I stayed with my wife, the light was so fixed and so certain. I'm ashamed of this now, but I still remember it. I came back from seeing my mother. I was cold and frightened, still seeing her pain. And I went to a girl I'd been teaching, she'd just got her degree.

You may even have known her: Helen Edwards, she's in Africa now. She took me in without argument, or it wouldn't have been possible. A difficult affair would have been broken at once, by my usual conscience.'

He paused, spreading his hands on the rail.

'It was the break that mattered: I can see that now. I needed to get away from the man I had become: the man known and lived through. Helen made no demands, there were no conditions. I was able, really, to stay separate, even while we were living together. It was an affair, really, of two single persons, two people who stay single and who live together. And I felt very sure of myself, very released and alive. It can happen quite suddenly: with a different person the world feels quite different: without complications, without anxieties.'

He straightened his body, still resting his hands on the rail.

'What happened next is more difficult to talk about. The more settled it became, the more normal and permanent, the less I wanted it. I hadn't moved out for another marriage. Perhaps Helen expected a marriage. May certainly did. However bitter, it was still within her own understanding, of what people want. But the drive, in fact, was still into getting away. I can say this to you. Everything else was cancelled, but the desire remained: this bitter, isolated, frightened desire. And yet to know it directly, to know the feel of it, was to be alive in new ways. But then it wasn't a person I wanted, whatever the satisfactions of affection or habit. To be myself, quite directly, there must be no other.'

He looked down at the water, and then closed his eyes.

'I left Helen, as I had left my wife. My mother died, and I went to her funeral. The ache of crying, the fatigue in the arms, seemed the entry to darkness. I discovered a world in which others are present, yet there are no persons. I entered it, willingly, because I was already part of it.'

He took his hands from the rail, and opened his eyes.

'It's a world very easy to know. A world with its own institutions, its own citizens. Money, as in other things, is a marvellous creator. It can make its own world, its own kinds of life. The differences between people don't matter there, and where there are no differences, there are no others. There is only, quite directly, this entry for oneself.'

He ran his hands back, over the thick greying hair.

'When we want the darkness, we can very easily buy it. The trade is there all the time, in that shadow world, that is yet so

248

ironically solid and normal. The lifeline can be lost in it, and no one will notice or care. It's not even the lifeline, it's just a particular spasm. The same act, the same feel, as in the world you have left, but now without identity, without continuity, only a quickly available and satisfying present.'

'Why do you say this to me, Robert?'

'Because I've lived it through. I might have stayed in that world, but I didn't. And if you understand what I'm saying, you'll understand, also, that my wife saved me.'

'She wanted you back, after that?'

'Not by reasoning, Peter. She knows what I did, but she will never know why. I've tried to explain, but it's beyond her experience; beyond, perhaps, any woman's experience.'

'Yet she took you back.'

'I had never left her, as my continuing self. And she held to that, to the reality of that. Without compromise and without evasion, she stayed in her own world, that her own life defined: a world concerned with the reality of others, and I was still in it, though I had also run from it.'

'A love that accepts being hurt.'

'Not accepts, but meets.'

'That has been betrayed, but accepts the betrayal, is prepared to sacrifice.'

'Not sacrifice, Peter. She wanted me back.'

Peter turned away, and looked out over the fields, where the diesel had passed. Smoke was rising, from all the houses, and was hanging low, in the damp air.

'I'm sorry, Robert. I can't quarrel with you. But can't you see, even now, what you've done?'

'Yes, I came back. I learned, slowly, a quite different life. I came back to myself, when I came back to my wife.'

'But that's terrible, don't you see? Don't you ever look at her? Call it this world or that, whatever you like. What you actually did was collapse, as yourself, and then you crept back. You let her sacrifice herself, let her strain to prop up a man you could never be on your own.'

'What can any of us be, on his own?'

'But you've taken her life, as a supplement, a condition, of your own.'

'I don't see it like that,' Robert replied calmly. 'You're still so tied, Peter, to the world's calculation. The primitive calculation of an alienated world. And that, precisely, is the shadow. The way we see people, the way we reckon relationships, on some simple plus and minus. What do you think, in the end, my whole work has been about?'

'Theory's easy.'

'Theory is not easy. You talk like a fool, who's never worked at it.'

'Perhaps I haven't. Perhaps I've just shuffled the counters.'

'Not altogether. Not yet. But it will come to that, unless you understand yourself.'

Peter turned away in despair.

'Why push it back on to me all the time? You've still taken her life.'

'No, Peter, she's given her life.'

'What difference is that?'

'It's the whole difference. It's breaking the dimension. You can then either run back to the shadow, or learn a different reality.'

Peter smiled and walked off the bridge, hunching his shoulders.

'Yes. When it's over, I suppose, it can be that general, and that vague. You've got your whole system, your whole diagram ready. But it doesn't help, Robert. It can't help. I'm faced with actual people. Can't you really see?'

'Yes,' Robert said, taking out his pipe and following him. 'In that way you're on your own.'

'Without help from you, you mean?'

'I shall do what I can.'

They walked on together, under a new kind of constraint. They followed the great bend of the river, and turned back, slowly, towards the centre of the city. As they made their way through the maze of streets, they began talking again, about Peter's work. At this formal level, the discussion was easy, but they were both affected by what they had previously said. They passed the gate of Robert's college, and a porter lifted his hat to them. Robert was walking happily now, his hands in his pockets.

'You've got used to this place,' Peter said. 'But I never have or hope to. To you, coming from a distance, it was just a place of learning. To me, still, it's another world, an alternative world. The learning is just incidental.'

'It often feels like that, from inside it, Peter. Especially as we don't see enough of each other's work. I mean, when dons meet it's usually a social occasion, and that can seem the whole point. I have to read books to discover how much real work is being done here, major work that requires a quite absolute respect. Day to day it can feel different, even trivial.'

'Yes, Peter said, 'but you wouldn't judge the car works, or Goldsmith Street, just by the cars it produces. You'd judge it, you'd have to, by its characteristic kind of life.'

'In theory, yes. But I can rage against the feel of the university and yet still respect the work that it's doing.'

'Because you've sold out to it, surely. You daren't make the connection.'

Robert stopped abruptly, pulling his hands from his pockets.

'Have I sold out to it, Peter? Is that really what you think?'

'The questions you learn not to ask,' Peter said, angrily. 'The questions I was taught not to ask.'

Robert relaxed at once.

'Yes, but in your own case, Peter, there were technical difficulties, as in any new subject. In general this can't be true. The place exists to ask questions and to try to answer them.'

'In theory, as you said.'

'And in practice. Look at the actual work being done.'

'Look at the car works.'

'That's entirely different. You're letting your own history ride you.'

'No, Robert. This is not two cities but one.'

'When in fact they don't mix?'

'That's exactly what's being learned. Not to extend, not to expose yourself. Just learn the terms of your own institution and conform to it.'

'What conformity is there, in fact?'

'Ask anyone seeing it from outside, Robert. They get the feel.'

'Yes, as prejudice.'

'Ask your own students, then. Ask them the reality of it.'

'Well, you're telling me,' Robert said, smiling.

'Yes, to meet just that kind of genial tolerance, that last turn of the screw. You're here, you're established, you don't have to argue. So you can be so bloody polite you kill people''

Robert turned to him, widening his eyes.

'But I thought I was arguing, Peter. I thought we always had.'

'Yes, to clarify my mind, not yours. That's the relationship, isn't it?'

'Formally, I suppose it is. But it hasn't been formal.'

'It hasn't been anything, really. You've been a polite machine, dealing with the paper I feed you.'

'I'm genuinely sorry if you feel that, Peter. I can say that I've tried to do more.'

'I'm in no real position to criticize,' Peter said, turning away. 'I'll go, if you like.'

'No, Peter, I don't want you to go.'

Peter hesitated, and then spoke with a rush of feeling, clenching his fists.

'Look, Robert, what I'm asking from you I can't get from anyone. I'm asking for the connection, between work and living. I'm asking you to live in my work, and of course you can't. You have to detach yourself, or we'd overwhelm you.'

'Yes, but I want to see this. I want to learn it.'

'No. You're scared, Robert. You're scared of really meeting anyone. You're scared, really, of being anyone. It might not fit the institution.'

'And you?' Robert asked, more sharply.

'Yes. Of course.'

'Then at least you can respect the difficulty, Peter.'

'Of course I respect it. I could even respect a defeat. What I can't respect is a surrender. Yet in a way it's nobody's fault. You were the first generation. And we can respect your work, your patience, your strength even. But did you have to become like them? Did you have to change your whole voice, your whole body, every bit of yourself?'

'I don't think this is true,' Robert said, precisely. 'In part, yes. In externals.'

'No, it's much more than that. I know because I can feel it happening to myself. And when I look at you I know in a way you're the enemy, Robert. The respected enemy.'

'But I don't feel it like that at all,' Robert said, smiling.

'Of course you don't, because you've lost any way of feeling it. I've only to look at you to know it. I think as yourself you've caved in, and your wife is just propping you up.'

Robert was silent for some time. They walked slowly down the broad street, under the trees. It was getting colder again, and dust was blowing across the road.

'But you see what you're doing,' Robert said, at last. 'You're taking me as a parent, and rejecting me. Always, Peter, you're looking, unconsciously, for another family, and you must ask yourself why. I don't mind being baited, but you must see what you're doing. This is simple displacement. And while you're caught in that, you'll never understand your real situation.'

252

'This is my real situation. What I'm trying to say to you is a kind of truth. The connections are deeper than we ever suspected: between work and living, between families, between cities. You surrendered by breaking the connections, or by letting them atrophy. We shall try not to do that, in this generation. We shall hold to the connections and ride our history.'

'The original phrase was your history riding you.'

'It's the same thing, Robert. If we have the strength.'

'Then I don't understand you at all.'

'That's what I've been saying.'

Robert looked away, and refilled his pipe. Peter had the sense of being expected to go: the polite and unspoken dismissal, as at the end of a tutorial.

'I'd better get a bus, I suppose,' Robert said.

'Will you? I'm going to walk.'

'I think I'll take the bus. I'm expecting a phone call.'

'Yes. Of course.'

They stood uneasily, for some moments.

'Incidentally,' Peter said, 'I'm writing to Kissler to decline.'

Robert turned to look at him, with surprise and irritation.

'Are you? Is that wise? I should have thought now, particularly.'

'Yes now, particularly. I have work to do here.'

'You've almost finished your work here.'

'My work with you, yes.'

'But then?'

Peter waited. There was a bus coming, and it would be better to break off.

'Can I come and see you officially, Robert? In about a month?'

'Officially or whatever, you can come any time.'

Chapter Fifteen

UNIVERSITY term had restarted, and the city was crowded again. At the end of the first week, Robert was surprised to get a note from Arthur Dean, whom he knew only slightly. He was invited to dinner in college, on the following Wednesday.

'Should I go?' he asked May. 'I can very easily say that I'm booked.'

'Yes,' May said. 'To see him you should go.'

'I don't know. From what I heard of him I don't like him.'

'I was thinking of Peter.'

Robert dropped his hands to his side.

'I don't know,' he said. 'I'm beginning to get tired of him.'

She did not answer, but he could feel her disapproval.

'The point is I get so much of that adolescent ranting, though I suppose it's an occupational risk. You can do nothing with them, when they go as wrong as that.'

'The Pharisee pointed that out,' May said.

Robert turned back and laughed.

'Yes, perhaps, but there was only one he left lying. We get scores, year after year. And they won't be helped, that's the beginning and end of it. He told me with some force and clarity precisely what was wrong with *me*. I was even the enemy, the respected enemy.'

'You're still responsible.'

'For his work. Nothing more.'

'And can you separate that?'

'Not altogether, but still. Look, it's Dean who's asked me. The connection, there, is with his mother. And what can I do? I can't charge Dean with adultery.'

'You could charge him with anything else. You could say what you thought.'

'And do you really think that would help? After all, she's a woman of forty. It's not exactly a seduction. So what do I say? You deceived this woman?'

'You must help Peter. You must help him to understand it. You can only understand it if you know about Dean.'

'All right, I'll try.' Robert said, smiling.

'Which was your original decision.'

'Was it?'

'I think so. Whenever you go into this elaborate act, it's just the enemy talking.'

'What is this enemy business? Have you caught it from him?'

'I don't know. You used to say, at the beginning, you were in enemy country.'

'But now I've disguised so perfectly I've become the enemy. That's what Peter was saying.'

'I don't know, Robert. But on this business I'm certain. For once we joined in. Not the playing at politics, but an actual life, that's still quite unfinished. Not a Sunday attitude, about industrial workers, but a particular place, where men are losing their jobs. And then, since the issue was actual, it was much more than politics. It's the Owens, and Dean, and Peter and Beth, and still also men losing their jobs. If we can't deal with this then we can't deal with anything. This is where we are tested, not at all on attitudes, which we've been trained to manage, but in ourselves, quite directly: who you and I actually are.'

'Yes, of course, except that it's terribly complicated.'

'Because it's complicated. Anything else we could deal with, as in enemy country.'

'Enemy there being what?'

'That these are separate issues: redundancy, adultery, a boy leaving home. That they're fantastically complicated, so that wisdom blurs in the face; the wisdom of recognition, that ends in an expression: an expression to be set and preserved, in a photograph, in a poem, in a theory.'

'We don't give the answers, we just ask the questions,' Robert said, smiling.

'Certainly. But we joined in, that day. It seemed very simple, just stepping from the pavement. But in that moment, suddenly, we were giving an answer for once. Or rather we were asking a quite different question, that won't end in a resigned wisdom, but will have to end, whatever the cost, in an answer. And this isn't a question that needs a phrase for an answer. It's a question, now, needs our lives for an answer.'

'By seeing Dean?'

'That with the other things.'

'Keeping in touch with Owen?'

'Yes, the son and the father.'

'In fact, interfering,' Robert said wryly.

'Yes,' May said, 'that's the last word, holding the fat in place.'

Robert nodded, watching her stub out her cigarette.

'You should read a book called *Social Method*,' she said. 'By a man called Lane.'

'I think I have.'

May smiled, and then suddenly turned away, pain crossing her face.

'What is it?' Robert asked, going quickly across to her.

'It's all right. I'll be all right.'

'Is it some actual pain?'

'Yes, the same pain.'

'It all happened together: finishing the book, my going away, your illness.'

'It wasn't to do with the book.'

'I know.'

'And the rest is unfinished. We shall just have to see. The one thing we got out of it was the book.'

'It seems little enough.'

'No, Robert. It is really enough. It's enough for me, if we can really hold to it.'

She turned away again. He followed her quickly, and put his arm round her waist, holding her to him.

'I'll be all right, Robert. I'll lie down a bit.'

'Do you want anything?'

'Yes.'

'Tell me.'

'I've already told you.'

'I meant medicine. Or a drink or something.'

'I've got medicine upstairs. I'll go on up.'

'I'll come with you.'

'You don't have to, Robert.'

'I want to come with you.'

She smiled and looked up at him. He kept his arm round her waist, and walked awkwardly up the narrow stairs, still trying to support her. But she was walking freely again, and he felt her life coming back to him. He lay with her in the bedroom until the light went, in the early winter evening.

He replied to Arthur that night, accepting the invitation. When he went in on the Wednesday, he had thought carefully about the whole matter, and had cleared at least his own mind. In the years since the crisis that had begun with Helen, he had not, he

256

realized, brought this kind of thinking to anything personal and immediate. His work, ordinarily, involved so much of his mind that it seemed a whole life, but now, suddenly, there was a sense of waking, and he could feel an active energy moving out into new areas.

Arthur's rooms were pleasant, looking out over the long garden to a high, slender tower. Arthur was quiet and genial, in the familiar manner of receiving a guest, and they drank sherry before putting on their gowns and walking through the dark passages to the common room.

Robert did not know several of the other men dining, and the ease of introduction sustained the pattern of reassurance. After many years, Robert still found a college warm and relaxing. It was as if the putting on of gowns, the slight ceremonies, brought everyone to a level of conscious politeness and social effort which temporarily cancelled personality, and indeed brought relief from it.

They went in to dinner, with the same slow formality, in a order of seniority broken only by guests. They stood while the long Latin grace was read, and Robert looked down the long medieval hall, watching the shadows against the bare white walls. As the grace was ending, he noticed that many of those dining used the familiarity of its phrasing and the slightly reverent bowing of heads to read the little menu cards that were set at each place. And why not, he thought, in the pulling-up of chairs and unfolding of napkins. For what we are about to receive. Just as well, perhaps, to be certain.

The good humour of the table was quickly infectious. Michael Swinburne, Rose's husband, was on Robert's left, and was telling the story of a recent television interview, on wildcat strikes. The relaxed, friendly, spontaneously charming personality who had been interviewing him had had three pink cards literally up his sleeve, and had taken each out, with great speed, whenever the cameras were off him. In the very brief interval before the next spontaneous question, he had feverishly practised, with lips and eyes, its precise rhythm and address.

'I mean I thought he'd gone suddenly mad,' Michael said. 'Sitting opposite me while I was talking and then going into this mirror routine. Though I should have known. I had to say, at one point, in answer to a supposedly difficult question, some malarkey about better human relations, "Well no, not altogether". Well no, not altogether, when the thing was absolute bloody nonsense, like an amateur talking about God. But it would give the impression of care and thought: the cautious academic at work on a problem. Well *no*, not *altogether*. Well *no*, *not* altogether. And the charming frown at the right stress. He threw me off so much, rehearsing his pink cards, that when he asked the difficult question I just grinned and said "No, certainly not".'

'You won't be asked again. Then where will your career be?' Arthur said, across Robert.

'Quite. I mean I'm prepared to be a slave to the box. It's just I can't quite manage the servility.'

Arthur smiled, handsomely.

'You should leave it,' he said, 'to people like me, who've had plenty of practise.'

'At servility?'

'Of course,' Arthur said. 'How else does a radical survive, in these ancient apartments?'

'Oh yes,' Michael laughed. 'You're a radical, aren't you, Arthur? One keeps forgetting.'

'My dear Michael, you wouldn't know a radical if you saw one.'

'I shouldn't know a ghost if I saw one. A phoney ghost, or a phoney radical, I could recognize at once, from the books. But a real radical? Well yes, I suppose, by the smell. A certain musty smell. For I believe there were radicals once.'

Robert looked down, concentrating on his food. The exchange had reminded him of the conversation with Peter. Yet there was nothing he could say. He had once been asked to give two broadcast talks, on 'What's happened to the Radicals?' and 'What's happened to the working-class?' 'Don't Know' and 'Still doing the work' had been the only answers he could think of, and he had refused the invitation.

The white-sleeved arms came over the gowned shoulders with ease and regularity. In the rush of talk, there was no time to look up and see where the arms came from. The self-effacement of long training, in the waiters, was as complete as possible, within the limits of flesh and blood. Unoccupied for a moment, while both Arthur and Michael were talking away from him, Robert saw the faces of two of the waiters, on the far side of the table. There was a similarity of expression which startled him: very set and tight-lipped. Watching carefully, he thought the expression might well not be resentment, but simply a training against breathing while leaning over the diner's head. He was still questioning this explanation when Arthur turned and began talking again.

The meal was excellent: game soup, plaice, woodcock. Before dessert they picked up their napkins and went out in a warm, swaying procession to another common-room, where the wine and nuts and fruit were laid. Robert found himself sitting with a geologist, Horseman, though Michael and Arthur were not far away. The candles shone on the silver dishes and on the water of the fingerbowls. In the marble fireplace, a bright log fire was burning, throwing heavy shadows across the room.

'This is very pleasant,' Robert said. He was feeling increasingly relaxed and tired, with the wine.

'Yes, it's all right,' Horseman said. 'All that's missing is our wigs.'

'Don't let that bloody scientist corrupt you,' Arthur said, across the table. He seemed always to be listening, to every conversation within range, and he obviously enjoyed making this kind of sudden intervention.

'You've got me wrong,' Horseman said. 'I'm serious about the wigs.'

'You can't be,' Robert said.

'Snuff?' Horseman offered, passing the tiny chased silver box.

'No. Thankyou.'

'I will. That's my point, you see. I believe in consistency. No half measures. If we're acting a part, let's bloody well act it properly.'

'Now there is a radical sentiment,' Michael said, laughing.

'Too true it is,' Horseman agreed, taking the snuff from the back of his large hand. 'You see, Lane,' he added, his eyes watering with the snuff, 'my father was a collier. He was kept ignorant. Only I was to be a mining engineer, perhaps even a manager. When I got to grammar school they put us with the free places in a special part of the classroom. They used to call us the free boys. The masters started it, and the other boys picked it up. So I thought, right, you buggers, let's see where we all end up.'

'Yes?' Robert asked.

Horseman looked at him again, his eyes still watering. He said nothing, but picked up his glass of claret and looked through it at the nearest candle.

'But Bill, have you ever thought,' Michael said, 'what wigs would be actually like? I mean the one thing about our mature eighteenth century which nobody thinks to mention is the smell. Just imagine those sweaty headpieces, night after night.'

'Everybody mentions the smell,' Arthur said. 'It's the one bit of history they know. Even undergraduates know it.'

'It comes in different brands in different centuries,' Horseman said morosely.

'No, but seriously, Bill,' Michael said. 'People have sat round this fire in every kind of dress and undress.'

'Don't be crude,' Arthur laughed.

'No, but I mean why pick on the eighteenth century? We're as much in our time and out of it as they ever were.'

'Only it's all over,' Horseman said to Robert, ignoring the others. 'No use keeping on about it. In that same school now they're all free boys. They wouldn't know what that bloody nonsense meant.'

'Well that's good,' Robert agreed.

'It's good, all right, if people would only leave it alone. Not always keep harping about it, keeping those days alive. The kids now don't want all this nagging about class. They want the pops and the Italian suits and they're right. It's only here, really, you still get that dreary old stuff. So it was bad? So forget it.'

'That's the one sensible opinion he has,' Arthur said. 'I can guarantee it because he got it from me.'

'I don't know,' Robert said. 'I saw the car workers marching. I think that was a class issue. Or at least an issue, in our own place and time.'

'Don't ask us to weep for car-workers,' Michael said, conclusively.

'When I go back home,' Horseman said, 'I stoke the boiler and I help my wife wash up. O.K., so I know the difference, I step from one century to another, I get a sense of proportion.'

'And a nagging about the meal, I expect,' Michael said.

'We're not the masters any more,' Horseman said, loudly, with the wine in his voice. 'We're the bloody apprentices, and it's about time. The world has changed, and there are no masters left in it. Those who think they are still masters are just walking ghosts.'

'Like old Timothy,' Arthur said, looking down the table to the elderly don, with flowing white hair and a plump childish face, who was presiding.

'Not only old Timothy,' Horseman said. 'Some of the old men know how little they know, in this new alien world. That's at least a start. The rest of us divide in two ways. A, whether we know there's a different world. B, whether we've done anything about it. Those of us who know are the apprentices. There are no masters.'

'This is the most absolute . . .' Arthur began, but as he spoke Timothy rose, and everyone rose with him. There was a slow, scattered procession back to the other common-room. Robert wanted to talk to Horseman again, but the geologist stepped out of the procession, pulling off his gown, and got his bicycle clips to go home. Arthur took charge of Robert, and after a short conversation with Michael, over coffee, suggested that they should go back to his rooms, for a drink. Michael wasn't able to come. He had to go round to the local BBC studio, for a discussion on industrial relations in the car industry, which were still, as he said, in the news. Robert and Arthur walked slowly back to Arthur's rooms.

'Whisky?' Arthur offered, when they were settled again.

'No, really. I've drunk enough tonight.'

'You won't mind if I do? I want to talk, and I find I need whisky to do it.'

'Go ahead.'

Arthur filled his glass, and sat opposite Robert. He was flushed and nervous, though his voice was still confident.

We pay a great deal, Robert thought, watching him, to keep our voices right. Pay with everything else we have or might be.

'I wanted to ask about a pupil of yours. Peter Owen.'

'Yes?'

'I've heard a good deal about him, but I've never met him. Is he any good?'

'You mean can he do his work?'

'Of course. What else could I mean?'

'I was just challenging a habit. I'm a bit tired of this confusion of virtue and ability.'

'Yes, I can see you would be. You're probably tired of the fact of ability at all. But still, is he any good?'

'He's very able. He's also quite demoralized.'

'Who isn't?' Arthur said, taking a long drink. There was a protracted silence.

'You've heard of him through his mother, I suppose?' Robert asked, sitting forward.

'No. Through Rose, actually. But I know his mother.'

261

'So we seem to have heard.'

'What have you heard?' Arthur asked, sharply.

'That you've been having what I suppose you'd call an affair with her.'

Arthur leaned back and laughed, moving his hands affectionately around his glass.

'What you suppose I'd call an affair,' he repeated, incredulously. 'Really, do you talk like that at home too?'

'I'm not at home.'

'It's a relief to know you know that, anyway. Your aura's so thick I wouldn't be surprised if you got lost in it. But I suppose wherever you are you have to keep up the act.'

'What act?'

'Lane, the new moralist. It would be quite convincing if your morality could even pretend to be new. You're the loop in time, actually. You waited until Puritanism and Victorianism were dead in England, then you simply trotted them out again, unaltered, and got a reputation for novelty.'

'But why should this concern you, either way?'

'It doesn't concern me. It concerns you. Do you think this petty-bourgeois preaching will get you anywhere, in fact?'

'Does it need to get me anywhere? I just say what I've learned.'

'Learned where, though? Have you ever risked yourself, for one minute, outside your own petty-bourgeois morality?'

'Not for one minute. For many years.'

'And then you got frightened?'

'Yes, among other things.'

'What other things?'

'I saw what happened. To others and to myself.'

Arthur laughed, and refilled his glass.

'The classic revivalist cant, in fact. Grace abounding, to the chief of sinners.'

'No, not much grace.'

'Not even that? You are in a bad way.'

'I suppose you realize all this is projection,' Robert said, leaning back.

'Is it? Well I admit one doesn't often meet a super-ego like yours. Naturally one abases oneself.'

'Is that what you want to do? Since you're quite obviously guilty.'

'I am guilty, as a matter of fact. But that doesn't mean I've come crawling to you about it.'

262

'No, of course,' Robert said. 'There are others more concerned.'

'There is one other concerned. All the rest is a fiction.'

'I remember believing that myself. I discovered otherwise.'

'Yes, well, we can do without your autobiography,' Arthur said, and got up.

Robert smiled, and said nothing. Through the silence of the room he could hear the alternating chimes of the hour.

'I was just rather worried,' Arthur said, 'about this boy leaving home.'

'When he learned about you and his mother, yes.'

'Whether it was meant to or not, it's in fact broken everything up.'

'But you must have known it would come to this.'

'I didn't know what it could come to. I don't spend my life calculating.'

'Did you intend to marry her?'

'Yes, as a matter of fact, I did. I suppose in your eyes that makes it all right. Or at least makes it better.'

'And now?'

Arthur hesitated. He walked across to the window and stood looking out into the darkness of the garden.

'I've written asking her to marry me,' he said. He was speaking so quietly that Robert had to strain to hear him. 'She hasn't replied. Not only hasn't replied, but puts down the phone when she hears my voice, misses every meeting I might be at. The complete boycott.'

'Then why not accept it? You've no rights in the matter.'

'Because it was more than I thought it would be,' Arthur said, and sat down.

'What did you think it would be?'

'Oh, for Christ's sake be your age,' Arthur said angrily, emptying his glass.

'A lower-class woman, whom you thought you could take to bed on the side.'

'Not a lower-class woman. God, how class-bound can you democrats be?'

'That didn't enter it at all? Even from her side?'

'No, of course it didn't. She's an exceptionally able and an exceptionally likeable person. She's a victim of the class system, if anything, not an example of it.'

'A victim you could use.'

'No, not use. It was open and equal, all the way.'

'You said a victim.'

'Well, of course. Have you ever seen Goldsmith Street? Can you think what it was like for a woman of that intelligence, that kind of energy, to be shut up there? Do you wonder she came out of it?'

'But came to you.'

'Well?'

'To someone who wouldn't involve her, who wouldn't really force the break.'

'Why should she think that?'

'Just that whatever you say, Dean, you're not a sexual offender at all. You're a sexual defaulter, and that can be attractive.'

'You must provide me with a Victorian dictionary,' Arthur said, smiling.

'I mean only this,' Robert said. 'Women often make mistakes, but hardly ever that kind of mistake. When they want to be changed by love, they go to a man who is capable of changing them. When they're working out something else, they go to one of the many defaulters, who can give them what they want on their own terms.'

'What did she want then, in your version?'

'I don't know. I can only guess. But my guess is adventure, a political and intellectual adventure. You were very precisely cast.'

'Yet still the victim I could use?'

'Yes, even then. Because, of course, you saw her situation. You used her adventure for your own purposes.'

'I feel I should have a moustache to twirl at this point,' Arthur said, lying back in his chair. 'All this stuff about purposes and sexual offenders puts me right back in the stalls.'

'But you chose to talk to me about it. You knew, when you were choosing, exactly what I should say.'

'Yes, you're predictable all right. What you're saying, though, is still a bit odd. If I'd been what you call a sexual offender, it would have been better?'

'It would have been clearer.'

'But offender? Why offender?'

'Yes, I agree, that's Victorian. I think I learned this too hard and too late. But the lover, the active lover: that's where life is, but also that's where others can be outraged and even broken, if the situation is wrong. That can be life or tragedy. This of yours is neither.'

'Yet it's common enough.'

'I think it's very common. The interlocking of fantasies is common.'

'The intercourse of fantasies, aren't you saying?'

'Yes, naturally. The intercourse in its place. And indeed in its place, in that place, it is just as we say. It doesn't really matter much. It's pleasant but nothing to get frantic about. If not here, then there.'

'What you won't admit,' Arthur said, 'is that this is how we know sex to be, once the old conditioning is off. When it's not busy propagation, or worse than death, it relaxes to that. And of course spreads terror to all the old women of both sexes. A few still try to whip it all up, as personal relationships or the dark gods. But it's no good. Ask any boy in the street.'

'He knows, does he?'

'Well, ask the happily married couples, in Goldsmith Street or wherever. More energy goes in their gardens than in their beds.'

'Their gardens are also where they live.'

'Or the women in the supermarket, the women queueing at the schools for their children. Ask them what's important.'

'Their families are important.'

'Ask the whores, then. They've seen how men are, with the family conditioning off. Ask any honest man on his own. You'll get your answer.'

'What answer?'

'If not here, then there. What else do you think the answer is?'

'This is what you said to Mrs Owen, I suppose?'

Arthur looked away. His face was drawn and serious, and he seemed at the limits of his strength. The resilience of his familiar manner jerked up, automatically, but he could not go through with it. When he spoke again, he kept his fingers lightly over his mouth.

'No, it's not what I said. You want this too easy. Simply I think while we tell lies about sex we stay paralysed. The lies keep catching us out.'

'But you haven't been caught out?'

'This is why I asked you, about the son. That's where the guilt is, in Kate. That her son has rejected her. And the other, less serious guilt, about her husband. Not as a man but as an old social loyalty, to the people she grew up with.'

'And you want to destroy this guilt?'

265

'Of course I want to destroy it. It's breaking her, and she doesn't deserve that. She deserves to live on her own terms for once.'

'Live with you?'

'Certainly. That's what she would freely choose. Not just me either, but the life she could have with me. Here, not there, and the difference is real, whatever you may pretend.'

'You'll find the son against that.'

'Yes,' Arthur said, his smile coming back. 'So I gather. Because there, from what Rose tells me, is the real defaulter. Rose has wanted him for years and he hasn't had the energy to take her.'

'But she's married, after all. To Swinburne.'

'That isn't the end of the world.'

'And you speak very easily about taking people.'

'It happens very easily. But this boy is just nothing. Neither Rose nor anyone else. Nothing.'

'Yes, I think it's been like that.'

Arthur smiled, his point gained.

'Well it's not going to be,' he said. 'I'm going to fight this. I don't see why people should be made into nothing, by a set of false and boring and antique ideas.'

Robert was about to answer, but then stopped. He looked at his watch, and got up.

'Must you go?'

'Yes.'

'Well, I didn't expect to convince you. Or to get any real help.'

'You should have insisted on Swinburne coming. Perhaps that would have helped you.'

'Michael's a fool, but Rose is all right,' Arthur said, getting up. 'You wouldn't begin to understand her.'

'I've heard that phrase before. I still have the right to look.'

'Look wise?'

'And act, where necessary,' Robert said, picking up his coat and gown. 'Thankyou for dinner.'

'Will it be necessary to act?' Arthur asked, following him across to the door.

'Yes, I think so.'

'All right. So we know where we are. I'll just see you to the gate.'

On the following afternoon, in Goldsmith Street, a lorry loaded with scrap passed noisily down the hill, following a diversion caused by a series of roadworks. As it rattled over a manhole cover, Kate started and looked up from her book. The lunch she had carried in was on the stool in front of her, hardly touched. There seemed no time for anything, though equally nothing got done.

She had to try to avoid reliving the crisis with Harold. Yet her thoughts went back to it, and to the times with Arthur, whenever she was momentarily disturbed. For she couldn't accept the verdict that everyone else was taking for granted. This isn't some commonplace adultery, she continued to insist. Even the word makes nonsense. But then no adultery ever is commonplace, she corrected herself. There never has been a guilty party, has there?

It was worst at night, lying hopeless of sleep in the lonely bedroom over the garden. Because if not adultery, then what? For you never loved him, Kate. It was without conditions, wasn't it, including the condition of love? And it was true that the word had never been mentioned. Though would a word have altered it? We have all to learn to make an adult definition of need. As we actually talk, this is always enough. Or if not enough, then significant. For it had really been liberating, in its own way, a way that the others had no words for. She could get on the bus and go down now to Arthur, for the same reasons and with the same feelings, whatever the others might say. That is, in her mind she could go, but no longer otherwise, for she had learned painfully, that she was no longer free. Their words meant nothing, but still they entered and held her. She was not like that. She could not go.

She looked down again at her book. It reminded her of the effort she was making. She had always thought of herself as an educated woman. Then, in the middle of the row, she had suddenly seen herself differently. Like so many people she knew, with whom she could talk very easily about politics and society, she in fact read very few books, though she endlessly read reviews, and a great many newspapers and magazines. The only books she could read easily were those which were like magazines, where she could feel that the author was on her side, was in fact involved with her and talking to her. That, always, had been reassuring.

The remoteness, the intransigence, the indifference even, of other kinds of book offered nothing comparable. Such books were as alien as her own thoughts, in the long silences which she had taken for granted as the intervals of living. These books spoke, if at all, to that kind of attention, which was also a kind of let-be. The ordinary manner of address to others; the quick and available knowledge; the quick and available interest and habit of interest: all these were gone. In their place was what she had once experienced as cold and distant: a restless scanning; an endless parenthesis which could only occasionally transform itself into substance; an extraordinary and unvalued persistence of detail, in its own terms. It was the feel of a life which she had been taught was not real life, but only some deficiency in herself. The newspapers and magazines had seemed to meet this deficiency, quickly, and overcome it. But the books she was now reading hardly even existed until some answering pattern, some definition within herself, had been reluctantly awakened. Yet when this happened, she felt quite exposed and naked. She was unprepared for this other touching, this feel of another life. To be moved like that was to be moved as yourself. It was not setting yourself aside or redirecting yourself, and yet it was not simply taking what you wanted. It was taking and responding to another life being given, in its own fibres.

Kate remembered her shyness, and yet her genuine openness, as a girl. She had learned to overcome both, in what had seemed the business of growing up. And the pressures, there, had been real. But, now, really, it was back to that condition again. Back to it in her deepest feelings, though with the reality of a used body and a used mind, that she must live with and answer for.

She had cancelled all the newspapers and magazines she had once so eagerly looked forward to. Only Harold's newspaper was still taken. He wanted it, and she did not look at it. The routine of the day was comparatively easy to get through, and at night they separated. He was always tired, with the endless round of meetings, but beyond that he was being genuinely kind, in a familiar patience that was part of his whole adjustment. Either Gwyn or Myra came in often and sat with them, or invited them round.

It was all very sensible and kind. Yet, in fact, she recognized, with a sudden insight and contempt, the crisis was being treated as a sort of bereavement, a prolonged mourning. Nobody was forcing the issue, or trying to revive the memory. If everyone kept very still, and behaved as if nothing had happened, nothing would have happened. While she herself did nothing, made no new move, this adjustment would last and would eventually be called a life.

Yet in fact, as she now was, there was really nothing she could do, no move she could make, in the old ways. The books, with their strange silences, were her only adjustment. On her own and Harold's library tickets she could get six books out at a time, and almost her only trips to town, now, were for shopping and the library. She forced herself to the books she had once instinctively avoided: the books everyone knew about but did not read. She found no help in them, of the old kind: only the restless scanning, the relentless parenthesis of fact, the pattern of feeling that in being separate from her could suddenly move her to a new kind of attention: the steady, unemphasized growth of another life and another world.

There was again a sound in the street, but she did not look up. She was disturbed only when the front doorbell rang, and then she looked up quickly, knowing she could not be seen from the window. She sat quite still, for she had decided not to answer it. If it were Myra, or anyone else with the right to come, it would be the side door. Then the bell was rung again, and she moved impatiently in her chair, folding the book more closely over her arm. Suddenly she heard the front door being opened, and she jumped up at once, in alarm. A voice called, and she fought against recognizing it. Then she went across to the door.

Arthur was standing in the narrow passage. He smiled nervously.

'I'm sorry, Kate, but this seemed the only way to see you.'

Kate looked away, holding on to the handle of the door from the sitting-room.

'No, you must go,' she said. 'You can't come in here.'

'But I must talk to you, Kate.'

'No.'

'We can't possibly leave it like this.'

'It's left us, Arthur. Now please go.'

He turned and closed the front door. Kate watched him, in despair. She was afraid to move, or even to let go of the handle she was holding.

'I'm sorry, Kate,' he said, coming towards her. 'But this is in your interest, honestly. You're just surrendering to this place, letting it swallow you again. And you've no right to do that. You're needed outside.'

'Is that your language, Arthur?' she asked, looking nervously up at him. In her own breakdown of confidence, she felt his authority as almost overwhelming.

'Perhaps I was wrong from the beginning, to let you see only the cynicism,' he said, moving near her but making no attempt to touch her. 'But you can understand this, Kate. You've known the same pressures. What seems cynicism is a way of keeping alive, in a world that continually disappoints and outrages us. It was on that we met. It was that we had in common. But we made the mistake of letting it turn in on ourselves, to hurt even more.'

'No, Arthur. That's just sentimental.'

'You think I'm sentimental?'

'Yes, about yourself.'

'You prefer the cynical gestures, even though you know they are only defensive?'

'There isn't that much difference, Arthur. Not really. Disillusion is no excuse for behaving badly.'

'So we must live on whatever terms they offer us? Whatever they've decided is good or bad?'

Kate let go of the door handle. She put her hands back over her hair, momentarily closing her eyes.

'Yes, that sounded convincing, Arthur. That was why I came.'

'But what's different? What's really changed? You know quite well how a commitment builds up, becoming all the time more explicit. You had the courage to begin it, and you can't turn back now.'

Kate sighed, dropping her hands to her waist and letting the fingers go loose.

'This is all just talk though, Arthur. It might deceive a young middle-class girl. But not me.'

'Nobody's trying to deceive you, Kate. You're trying to deceive yourself.'

'A working girl wouldn't know what the words meant. She'd be lucky. She'd just look at the man.'

Arthur frowned, and looked away.

'I don't share this cult of the beautiful poor, Kate. I'm sorry.'

'Not the beautiful poor. Simply the habit of having to live with what you do. The man you are looking at is the man who will be your child's father.'

Arthur was silent for some time. When he looked back into Kate's face, he saw that she was on the edge of crying.

'What is it, Kate? Tell me.'

She looked angrily up at him, fighting to control her voice.

'I'm the age to be a grandmother, Arthur, not to be looking for a husband.'

'But this is ridiculous. You could still have children, if you wanted.'

'Yes, if I wanted.'

Arthur hesitated. He did not know what to say, but his voice was ready, impersonally.

'There's been no worse slavery than this, Kate. At the age when most middle-class women are settling down to enjoy life, most working-class women are expected to write themselves off. All this stupid nineteenth-century persistence, that between thirty and forty you're finished, and must just reach for the shawl.'

Kate was very pale as she watched him.

'I'm forty-one, Arthur.'

'Yes, and in fact you're young.'

'Whether I am or not, I'm already married. I have a grown-up son.'

Arthur lifted his hand.

'I know, Kate. I know all the difficulties. But people have to get back their nerve, to go on and live as they want. What's the whole tragedy of England but this meek acceptance of what the others have lined up for us?'

'No, Arthur. I lined this up for myself.'

'Yes, in a different situation. That's how it's always worked on us. When the situation changes, we haven't the nerve to change with it.'

Kate turned away. She seemed to have mastered her feelings, and to be quite in control again.

'You make it sound like a part of politics, Arthur.'

'Well, the two are connected. We let the situation master us, everywhere.'

'We've got to know what we want, first,' Kate said, and went back into the room. Arthur followed her, hesitantly, and stood just inside the door.

'You did know, Kate,' he said, watching her.

'They make jokes about women in their forties,' Kate said, picking up her book and laying it face-down on the mantelpiece above the electric fire. 'The unsatisfied women in their forties, just letting sex run them, making fools of themselves.'

'It was more than that, Kate. It was more than sex.'

'No, Arthur, it was less.'

He looked at her quickly, and then again looked away. He moved on into the room, looking around and recovering his confidence. He glanced down at the book she had been reading, and at the other books on the table.

'You're just letting books run you, Kate. You're much too

reverent about print. What do you think they're written for, but to condition people?'

'Are they?' Kate asked. 'Was yours?'

'Mine and Robert Lane's and all the rest. But at least I said something different. I didn't say give in. I didn't chuck the old wissdom at people.'

'You made a campaign of it, Arthur. It didn't work.'

'A campaign of what?'

'Of being free.'

'Well?' he smiled. 'Should I apologize for that?'

'It doesn't work, Arthur. I knew the first time it didn't work.'

'What didn't work?'

'This fantasy of the personal break-out, through sex.'

'Fantasy?'

'Yes, don't you see? The old bourgeois fantasy. That you can do what you like. Pretend society doesn't exist. Dismiss all the consequences as the old wissdom.'

'Now who's getting politics and sex mixed up?'

Kate moved her lips, and leaned back against the mantelpiece. Her long hair brushed the convex mirror in which the room was distortedly reflected.

'I just saw the pattern, Arthur. That's all. I saw this marvellous revolt as just a fantasy.'

'But it wasn't fantasy. It was real.'

Kate looked down over her body, her hair falling forward.

'No, Arthur. What I got from you was my own energy, fed back.'

'Yet it began when you came to me.'

'It began again. The fantasy pleased me.'

'Not the fantasy.'

'What else was there?' she said, looking up at him. 'You had nothing to give me.'

Arthur stood very still, facing her.

'It's too easy to say things like that, Kate. It's easy to hurt someone who has loved you.'

'What? Did you love me, Arthur?'

'I still do, Kate. Why do you think I'm here?'

She moved impatiently, and her voice was harder.

'Because I let the fantasy down. Because you can't bear that.'

'No, because I need you, Kate. More, much more, than you ever needed me.'

Kate laughed.

'Yet it's me you're proposing to rescue,' she said.

'Rescue? It isn't like that at all.'

'To get me out of Goldsmith Street and into a flat in the centre. To give me books and politics and parties and wine.'

'You say that as if you wanted them.'

'Of course I want them,' Kate said. She pushed herself suddenly forward, and walked away across the room. 'Only I'm tired of this sort of lying. This fantasy of the sleeping beauty, and any man is the prince come to wake her up. That's for the boys and girls, strictly. The woman will look at what she's waking to.'

'Now who's cynical?' Arthur asked, steadily.

'I've just looked at it, Arthur, that's all. Most of the men I know are caught up in this. All the poor little princes, touting their magic kisses around.'

'You mean you've hardened, Kate, that's all.'

She joined her hands across her breasts, looking back at him.

'I was hard when I came to you, Arthur. I had my eyes wide open. I was taking my chance, wasn't I?'

'No, I don't accept that. It was never like that.'

'It's what everyone believes. Try shifting them on that.'

'What everyone believes is no argument for anything.'

Kate laughed. She looked round, quickly, at the street, and let her hands drop to her side. When she spoke again all the tiredness had gone from her voice, and her whole body was excited.

'Well, I've got my chance then, haven't I? I can move in, can't I?'

'If you mean will I marry you, Kate, I've already offered. I would have offered at the beginning.'

'But you didn't, did you?'

'Would it have made any difference?'

'It would be a different world. I know that.'

'That isn't what I was saying.'

'A world well worth getting into bed for. And cheap at the price. Especially to any married woman, who's got used to it.'

He drew back. Her intensity frightened him. She seemed to be losing control. Her eyes were bright and staring, and there was a hysterical edge to her voice.

'Kate, you really mustn't talk like this.'

'Mustn't I? It's your line, Arthur, isn't it? How many others have you got into bed like that?'

'Look, anything can be cheapened. It's my own fault, as I said.'

'No, it's not your fault, Arthur,' she said, laughing. 'You flatter yourself. What do you suppose any woman thinks, when a man starts up one of the usual lines? She lets the boy play, if she likes him enough. But when it comes to the decision, the talk can stop.'

'I'm not offering you talk, Kate.'

'Aren't you?'

'And there haven't been any others.'

'Since your wife, you mean?' she said, sharply.

'Yes, since my wife.'

'And why did she go? Had you talked somebody else into bed?'

He turned away angrily. All the habitual lightness had gone, and he looked a quite different man.

'I've had enough of this, Kate, do you hear? You were never talked into bed. You came of your own free will. It was all equal and open from the beginning.'

'Yes, and it would be equal and open the next time, I daresay.'

'What do you mean?'

'Equal and open with your wife. Equal and open with me. Equal and open when the next one comes along.'

'But this is absurd, Kate.'

'Yes, Arthur, that's what I'm saying.'

He turned away, and sat in the nearest chair. He lit a cigarette, without offering one to her, and stared down through its smoke at his shoes stretched on the black rug. Kate was moving restlessly around the room, and once she went to the window and stood for some time, looking out at the street. He stayed silent, until he had finished his cigarette. Then he got up and moved to the door.

'I'd better go, Kate, I suppose.'

She turned and looked at him. Against the light of the window he could see only her tiny figure and the long sweep of the hair, but as she came forward he saw her heavy cheeks and the extreme pallor of her skin. She was looking at him, intently and curiously.

'Though you'll admit,' he said suddenly, 'you're a different woman from when I came.'

'Am I?'

'It's happened as it happened before, Kate. Of course we argue, even quarrel. But the thing is we need to talk to each other, and the talking releases us. When I came you looked as if you hadn't opened your mouth for a fortnight.'

She smiled faintly.

'I hadn't, really. They're all in mourning for me.'

'Then why submit to it? Why not just walk out on it?'

She was still looking at him. Her dark eyes were so set that the whole face, pale and with the unusually heavy cheeks, seemed for a moment a mere mask.

'I'll just get my coat,' she said, slipping past him. 'I'll walk down the hill with you.'

He waited for her, lighting another cigarette. He looked round the room, trying to get back his bearings. It seemed very cold and formal, like an unused waiting-room. He saw the view from the bay-window of the line of bay-windows across the street, and the occasional lights coming on in them. Then Kate came back, fastening the belt of the familiar white raincoat. She did not look at him, but went on to the front door. He followed her, and they stood for a moment looking along the street. Then she went ahead, and turned down the hill.

'I left the car at the bottom.'

'Yes, well I'll walk that far.'

'You won't come on?'

'No.'

'But I'll see you again?'

'I expect so. At the meetings.'

'Back to what it was, in fact?'

'Back to the very beginning,' Kate said.

Chapter Sixteen

THE memory of the march had now faded. That hour in the streets, in the intensity of protest, had been overlaid with the detail of quite different kinds of living. The rhythmic shout along the street, *Work, Justice*, was remembered, but only as an incident, in the more complicated rhythm of statements and negotiations. The men had gone back after Christmas, under more than ordinary pressures. Restarting after a holiday was always difficult: getting used again to the noise, the paint-smell, the filtered light of the shop, starting up again from cold after the few easy, untimed days. Tempers were short, and there was little time for talking. Each man's adjustment, back to the speed of the shop, seemed to take all his energy. Yet it was on this day, according to previous announcements, that the redundancies were to start. The lists were waited for, through the cold tension of the day.

Harold stood numbly and coldly, watching the next body for inspection being moved up to him. He knew that he ought to be thinking about the next step, once the lists were posted. But the days since the march had driven the dispute from his mind. Walking round the car body, staring into the details of its paint-work, he could still think only of Kate and Peter, and of what seemed their rejection of him. All the words had gone, and he was left with the pain of the fact. For years, he had known, things had been far from right, in the home and family on which he depended. Yet today, forced back into the familiar routine, he would have given anything to recover the state of a year, even a few months, earlier. He and Kate had been drifting apart, and Peter, growing up, had become like a stranger, but still, within some normality, he had felt his connections with them, known some underlying assurance. That, now, had been broken, and could not be recovered. Kate had withdrawn, into both guilt and resentment, and Peter had left, to live in another house. In the cold noise of the shop, he took the full weight of his exposure and loneliness. There was no available life, now, against which the work could be measured.

He sat with Gwyn in the canteen for dinner, and saw Myra briefly. They were doing their best, to keep some normal continuity, but they were not close enough, against this kind of hurt. He went back to his place after dinner, and watched the next body moved up. Best settle for this, and a wage, letting the years drag out. At least, on this job, he would work without strain till he had to retire; only the standing got difficult, towards the end of the day, and the worry about his eyes, which had always been weak, and which watered often, under the glare of the inspection lights, staring into the details of the paint.

He took the slip from the windscreen, and started checking the nearside panels. As he unfolded the slip, to mark his check, a note fell out. The redundancy announcement had been posted; the word had been passed along. Harold crumpled the note in his pocket, and looked around. It was difficult to get away now. There had been endless rows when he had left work, even for a few minutes, to do his job as a steward. It had got as far, in the summer, as the Labour Relations Manager, Wall, who had given him a final warning.

'What you do in your own time, Owen, is your own business. But in the Company's time, let's get this quite clear, you're paid for the Company's work, as a checker, and not in any other capacity you may choose to assume.'

'It assumes me,' Harold had answered. He had been having this kind of argument for twenty-five years, with Wall and his predecessors, back to the days when even membership of a union was against company rules. He had learned a quiet stubbornness, followed by going quietly his own way, and he had managed to survive.

'And I'm the Minister of War to the Queen of Sheba,' Wall had said. 'After all, why not? We can call ourselves anything.'

'I was elected convener,' Harold said, with an edge of apology.

'All right. I know that. But I'm telling you again: not in the Company's time.'

'No, of course not,' Harold said. 'I understand.'

He had gone straight from that interview to take up a difficulty on the new assembly line. It was easy enough to manage, if you carried something. When he was caught again, he would be caught again; that would be on the next agenda.

For months it had been like this, and he would not usually have hesitated. But now, crumpling the note in his pocket, he realized suddenly that he would not go. The risk, quite suddenly, had assumed a different proportion in his mind. Against his ordinary habit, he pushed the problem away, and went on inspecting the body. There would be time to see the announcement when the afternoon shift ended.

He worked on steadily through the afternoon, but with a headache that got slowly worse, until in the last hour he could hardly keep his eyes open, under the glare of the lights. His eyes kept watering, and he had to take off his glasses and wipe them every few minutes. But the worse this was, the more stubborn he got in his inspection of the quality of the paintwork. He marked several jobs, for redoing, that he might ordinarily have just passed. And he took more time, on every inspection, until his line was badly delayed. He took no notice of the attempts to hurry him. The headache now was a pulsing noise in his head, more real than the noise coming through from assembly and from the overhead runways. When the hooter at last went, he finished the job he was on, before going for his coat.

As he walked across to the yard, he saw a crowd around the main notice-board. He joined it, and tried to look over the heads to the notice, but the attempt was hopeless. Somebody near him shouted 'Read it out,' and Harold saw Dick Manning, turning by the notice.

'All right then. Keep it quiet,' Dick shouted.

The excited talk faded, slowly, and Dick read out the notice:

Having undertaken a comprehensive review of the whole situation at this time, the question of possible temporary reductions of the labour force, made necessary by the general marketing situation, is being further discussed, through the appropriate machinery. While no guarantees can be given, at this time, it is considered unlikely that any actual redundancies will come to implementation within the next ten days. This opportunity is taken of reminding all workpeople that unless the general marketing situation shows some early and substantial improvement, maintenance of the present labour force remains, until further notice, impracticable.

There was a brief silence, when Dick had finished reading, and then several of the men near the front began cheering. Len Weekes was standing near Harold, and asked him:

'What is it, then?'

'Ten days' postponement.'

Several men turned to him, and there was a shout of 'Let Harold see it.' A lane opened, between the standing men, and Harold walked slowly through, to where Dick was standing.

'It's victory, boys,' Dick shouted.

'In a way, yes,' Harold said, turning and raising his voice.

278

'Without the march, there wouldn't have been this postponement. Only don't relax, don't think it's all over. In ten days' time we'll be facing the same situation, and the effects of the march will be just far enough back.'

'Maybe,' Dick shouted, not to Harold but to all the men listening. 'Only if we've beaten them once, we can beat them again.'

'Not beaten,' Harold shouted. 'Postponed.'

Dick turned to him and laughed.

'Ah go on,' he said, much more quietly. 'You're a bloody old Jeremiah, Harold. You ought to be dancing on their guts.'

Harold blinked up at him, his eyes watering badly again. His headache was still violent, and his voice seemed to come from some separate part of himself.

'And do you think I wouldn't,' he said, 'if I was that much stronger?'

Dick laughed, and put his arm over his shoulder.

'Go on, you don't know your own strength.'

'We'll have the meeting, as we arranged.'

The stewards met, when the homegoing crowd had dispersed. Harold found, a bit to his own surprise, that in the meeting his authority still held. He still felt guilty that all afternoon he had done nothing, but the prestige of the march, and of this successful postponement, was still clearly given to him, and to Kate. It was finally agreed that he should write that evening to the Labour Relations Manager, Wall, requesting an interview for information.

'Because the point is,' he said, taking up something the others had missed, 'they carefully don't say what kind of further discussions. Just the appropriate machinery, and that could mean anything. And the fact that they're vague about it means that they're probably up to something.'

'London,' Dick suggested.

'Aye, quite likely. It may be easier for them, on this, to negotiate nationally.'

'With some nice responsible official trade union leaders,' Dick said. 'Nice chaps, that they can ask to a nice hotel.'

'Don't worry,' Harold said, 'I'll see all the stuff goes up, wherever they take it.'

When the meeting broke up, he walked across to his car. His headache had almost gone, and he felt more himself again. But then, as he drove up Goldsmith Street, he remembered what he was going home to. He went in, quietly, holding himself in

279

deliberate check. Kate was waiting in the kitchen, and had his supper ready. She did not offer to talk, and they ate in virtual silence. But after supper, when he went to the front room to write to Wall and to report to his union district secretary, Kate followed him in and asked if she could help. She had heard the announcement, she said, on that evening's regional news.

'I can manage,' Harold said.

'You sure?'

'Aye, it's all right.'

Kate did not believe him, but said nothing. She went back to the chair by the fire, where she had been reading all day. For the next hour, Harold sat at his bureau, writing.

The interview with Wall was finally arranged, for the Friday. It was set for quarter of an hour before the dinner break: a piece of timing that Harold would have been angry about if he had not understood it so clearly. The formal concession was made: fifteen minutes. Every opportunity had been given, it could be said, for consultation with representatives of the workpeople. Only if Harold insisted on staying longer than fifteen minutes, he could take the time out of his own dinner. It was not surprising. It was part of the usual game.

Harold played, as always, just within the rules. He took sandwiches for his dinner, for whenever the interview might finish. And he worked until twenty to twelve, which gave him just time to change his coat and walk across. He insisted on wearing his best sports jacket to this kind of interview. In the early days he had always gone up in his working clothes, but he had learned the disadvantage of this, the subjective disadvantage, going into a tidy office with the other man across the table in the usual business suit. The biggest danger, always, was accepting, in spite of yourself, their version of the relationship. It was easy to be firm, even militant, in a crowd, or at a formal meeting. At a simple interview it was much harder, against the combination of pleasant informality and the visible marks of an inferior position.

He walked through the paint shop and down along the first assembly line. When he was not concentrating on his own work, he always noticed the noise and the smell of the shop more vividly. The sour heavy edge of oil seemed to hang in the air, after the acrid fumes of the cellulose. The sound of heavy footsteps on the oil-stained concrete floor punctuated the general noise of the shop: the repetitive hum of the machines; the uneven rattle of the overhead runways; the clanking wheels of the line itself. The voices were pitched high and harsh, against this unceasing background of noise.

He went up the metal steps towards the office block, and stopped on the metal gangway, to look back over the busy floor, which now had perspective, so that the line of the whole operations could be clearly seen. Just below the high roof, the car bodies moved, with an impressive slowness. The men below looked small, in their hurrying clusters, gathered around each point.

He turned and opened the heavy dividing door, which swung back behind him by its own weight. The sudden fading of the noise came through almost as if it were a distinct sound. As he walked along the linoleum corridor, he felt the change in the air, which was at once warmer and softer: the edges of oil and of paint smoothed away. With every step he took, the atmosphere seemed to be changing. He was off the linoleum now, at the first turn, and on to parquet, in the next long corridor. He walked along it, looking out through the wide glass windows to the lawns below. There was a line of evergreens, moving in the wind, beyond the small formal pool.

He stopped at the familiar varnished door, and knocked. A typewriter stopped clicking inside, and a girl's voice called to come in. Harold pulled down the edges of his sports coat, and opened the door. The girl behind the desk, a girl of Beth's age, did not get up, but she looked across at him.

'I've an appointment with Mr Wall.'

She looked down at her desk diary.

'Mr Owens?'

'Owen.'

'I'm sorry. Yes. Mr Wall is expecting you. If you wouldn't mind taking a seat.'

Her voice was pleasant, but what Harold noticed most was its pitch: so much lower and quieter than the shouting voices on the floor. He felt that he himself had spoken too loudly.

'I'll tell Mr Wall that you're here,' she said, getting up, and opened the door into the inner office. Harold watched the swing of her skirt as she went through the door. He checked himself, looking away at the electric clock on the wall, with its silently moving second hand. It was exactly eleven forty-five. Only it was habit, really, watching her as she went through the door. The edge of the embroidered white blouse had pulled up, in one place,

281

from the waistband. A turquoise blue cardigan lay on the desk. The office was warmer than summer.

She came out and went back to her desk.

'Mr Wall won't be a minute. He's just on the phone.'

'Right.'

He watched her again as she pulled her skirt out under her as she sat at the desk. Her small breasts were firm, under the prettily embroidered blouse. She glanced up, feeling him watching her, and he looked quickly away.

'That tart in Wall's office,' Dick Manning had said, when he had come up with Harold on a previous interview. But it was not true. She was an ordinary girl, who might have been his own daughter. Jealousy, suddenly, is complicated. He had not wanted to embarrass her, staring at her breasts. She went on with her typing, and he watched the clock.

The clock was silent, in the steady sweep of its long red needle. While he waited, Harold closed his eyes for a time, to see if he could still count seconds accurately. At the third attempt, he was not far out. He shifted on his chair, and the girl looked across at him. It was ten to twelve.

'Must be a long phone call,' Harold said suddenly.

'I don't know,' she said quickly, and looked away. The buzzer went on her desk. Harold found himself thinking that it had been pretty accurately timed. She spoke into the dictaphone on her desk, and he heard the other voice coming through.

'If you will go in now.'

He got up at once, and saw her hesitate. She clearly didn't know whether she ought to get up and open the inner door for him.

'All right, love,' he said, quickening his pace, before she could decide. He opened the door, and went in. Then he turned, closing the door. He did not want to look across the office straightaway. It was not very large, but it was carpeted, and had venetian blinds on the large windows, which looked out over the smaller car park, reserved for monthly staff.

'I'm sorry to keep you waiting,' Wall said pleasantly. 'Only these things come, just at the wrong time.'

'That's all right.'

There was a brief mutual appraisal. Wall was in his early forties, dark, with a small moustache. He was deeply tanned, and seemed even in winter to be living an outdoor life. He was wearing a dark grey suit, white collar and regimental tie. He was
282

less sure of himself than he at first appeared. His hands were small, and moved nervously over the desk.

'Yes, well, do sit down, Owen,' he said, after the pause.

'Thank you.'

'Cigarette.'

'No, thank you.'

'I will if you don't mind. It's been the hell of a morning.'

'Yes.'

'It's not easy, you know, a situation like this.'

'No.'

'And I'm just Joe Soap, when a thing like this starts. When the production boys move, then we all move.'

'Yes.'

'And all the reps have been back. Sales Manager's conference. It's been pretty rough going, I can tell you.'

'Yes.'

Wall looked across at him. The brief answers were evidently not what he wanted. He hesitated, and looked quickly over his desk. Then he pressed the buzzer again. The girl came in.

'Miss Lawrence, Mr Owen's letter, do you have it?'

'It's in the file. I'll get it.'

'There's no need,' Harold said.

'If you wouldn't mind, Miss Lawrence?'

She went out, and Harold decided to wait. When she came back in with the letter, and walked round to put it in front of Wall, Harold was still sitting patiently, making no move.

'Ah yes,' Wall said, as the girl went out. 'The statement on redundancy.'

'Yes.'

'What was it exactly you wanted to know? I'd have thought the notice was clear.'

'Well, two things,' Harold said, watching him. 'First, what the plan is, when the ten days are up. Second, what's meant by *further discussed, through the appropriate machinery.*'

'Ah yes,' Wall said, and re-read Harold's letter.

'You won't get anywhere on this, you know,' he said, looking up.

'You think not?'

'Well look, Owen. The whole situation's perfectly clear. On two lines, we're still selling, mainly for export. On the others, nothing. You must have seen it yourself. The yard's full, and every field we can get. They're just lined up there, that's as far as they

283

get. And you know as well as I do they'll stay there, until Easter at the earliest.'

'Yes.'

'So look what you're asking. I mean it's obvious nonsense. If we kept the whole labour force, even on short time, we'd be just jamming more on to the lines we can't sell, and if the short time was spread reducing the lines we can.'

'Nevertheless, that's what we're asking,' Harold said.

'Well yes, of course you ask. Who wouldn't? I'd do the same if I were in your shoes. But you must see it's nonsense. No management could possibly wear it.'

'If they want their workers, on the lines they can still sell.'

Wall looked at him, and put his hand up to his face.

'I see. Yes. But that won't work, old boy. The chaps on those lines will still want their wages.'

'We all want our wages.'

'Well yes. And I wish I could help. If it was only different, if the slack was more even, we could go on to short-time, though nobody likes it, the costs go bang up straightaway. But with demand unequal, there's no chance of that.'

'It's what we're asking.'

'No room for manœuvre at all?'

'I'm not authorized.'

Wall hesitated, lighting another cigarette.

'There's no chance of it of course, but in fact from your own point of view you could, I'd have thought, make a better case. I mean keeping the selling lines running, full-time, and the others on short.'

'We'd look at it,' Harold said, waiting.

'I only used it as an example. There's not a hope in hell of it happening. If we kept open, even on short-time, there isn't room for one more car, anywhere we can store it.'

'You mean for ten days? For ten days you can manage.'

'No. Not for one day. The ten days was a concession.'

'To what?'

Wall smiled.

'You're a good negotiator, Owen. I sometimes wish you were up here, facing the real problems.'

'I asked, a concession to what?'

Wall put out his cigarette.

'As you perfectly well know, the company's policy is to have a happy and well-paid labour force. It regrets as much as you do

284

this kind of difficulty, with loyal servants of the company. Naturally, in such a difficulty, it does all it can to make things easier for them.'

'After the march. After the public comment.'

'No, no, no,' Wall said, smiling. 'That march, yes. Well, marches, nowadays: everybody's doing it. They probably thought you were ban the bomb.'

'Nobody did think so.'

'Didn't they? But it's a joke, Owen. And even if it looks all right in the street, you still have to come back to the real situation. If you could persuade the cars to march, that might be a real contribution.'

'I asked you two questions. You've answered neither.'

'Really? I thought I had.'

'The redundancy plan hasn't changed?'

'No. Not from our side. The facts are the same.'

'And the discussions?'

'Well, as we said.'

Harold laughed, playing his only card.

'You're meeting in London on Monday. With the national officers of the unions.'

'That hasn't been announced.'

'But it's been arranged.'

'Has it? You seem very well informed.'

'It's as well you should know, now, we're not being split from our unions, or our unions from us. If you try to bypass us, you'll find us there all the same, when the decision's made.'

'There's no question of bypassing. This is a perfectly normal method of negotiation.'

'All right. Only don't forget us. You still know what we'll settle for.'

'Settle for? Be your age, Owen.'

Harold smiled.

'Settle for,' he repeated.

Wall leaned back in his chair.

'But without one constructive suggestion. Without one idea on which we could really help you.'

'I've already said the idea.'

'What idea?'

'That the available work should be shared.'

'But how, Owen, how? Haven't I explained the facts?'

'How is the management's problem.'

'It's your problem too.'

'No, we don't run the place.'

'I'm glad at least you know that. But you're trying to tell us how to run it.'

'Nothing of the sort,' Harold said, standing up. 'Simply I'm telling you the conditions we'll accept.'

Wall pushed back his chair, and also stood up.

'Well, you live in a very airy-fairy world, Owen, that's all I can tell you. Conditions you'll accept? Don't you think we'd all like to lay down conditions? For a start that people all over the world should hurry up buying our cars. Conditions. There aren't conditions. There are only the facts.'

'Including the fact that men will be thrown out on the street.'

Wall closed his eyes, and nodded.

'I agree. That's bad. But you should tell it to our customers. If they were as sympathetic as we are, there'd be no problem.'

Harold turned to go. Wall seem surprised, but at once hurried across to open the door.

'You'll have missed your dinner,' he said.

'That's taken care of.'

'Well anyway, I'm glad you came up. Only don't start any false hopes now.'

'I don't live on false hopes.'

Harold went down to the yard, and found a corner out of the wind where he could eat his sandwiches. They were dry in his mouth, and he did not finish them. He went back to the afternoon shift, and at the end of it made a brief report to his committee. For the next few days, they could only wait.

He missed talking about it at home. Kate wanted to ask, but she seemed unable to get close enough to him. Only on the Sunday morning, when she took in his tea, she found him sitting up in bed, with the light on, staring across the room. He had been awake, he said, since before five. Something had woken him; he didn't know what.

'It's this redundancy business, isn't it?' she said, when she had given him his tea.

He drank from the cup, awkwardly, like an invalid. With his glasses off, unshaven, and without his teeth, he looked very much older; he could have been a man of sixty. Kate felt a sharp movement down through her body, as she looked at him. She sat on the edge of the bed, and waited.

286

He finished the tea, and she leaned forward to take the cup from him, but he avoided her hand and put the cup away on the bedside table.

'They've announced the meeting in London tomorrow,' she said.

'Aye.'

'Will they stand with you?'

'I think so. This time. They're getting worried about redundancy all over.'

'That would really be something,' Kate said, 'if the union leaders came back to the Left.'

He pushed his hand back over his eyes and forehead. He was again very tired.

'I mean if they fight sackings they'll find they're again fighting capitalism,' she continued. 'That nerve could still be alive, even after all this.'

'It is alive,' he said, reluctantly.

'Otherwise if you want to understand a Victorian employer, meet a post-war trade union leader,' Kate said. 'The same physical complacency, the same crude tones of voice, the same conviction that he's the man that makes the decisions.'

'That's bloody silly talk.'

'Is it, Harold? How many times have you been supported?'

He turned away from her. His hand went out to the cup, and he picked it up before he realized that it was empty.

'It's no use talking,' he said, putting the cup back. 'It's just all bloody talk.'

'That's what human beings do,' Kate said.

'Aye.'

He was silent for some time, looking across at the heavily curtained windows.

'I'll tell you,' he said suddenly. 'When I was talking to Wall, I could feel it happening, inside my own mind. And it's still happening.'

'Wall's a smooth bastard.'

'No. Not very. He isn't even very good. I've heard men in the university a damn sight smoother.'

'His father was a railwayman. Did you know that? He's a scholarship boy.'

'What do that matter?'

'It's the usual route. He's gone where his education's taken him. Into the Company's pocket.'

287

'I don't care about that. And he's not all that educated. He don't talk like it, anyhow.'

'How could he? If he used his skills, on that situation, he'd break it wide open. And he can't afford to do that.'

'I wonder,' Harold said. 'That's what I've been thinking. He's not very good, I already said that. But what he said was strong even when he was saying it. That's stopped me a bit.'

Kate moved further on to the bed. She sat with her back against the endboard, and drew up her knees in front of her. Her long hair fell forward, over the lapels of her dressing-gown.

'What is this marvellous case then?' she said, smiling at him. Harold looked away.

'I know what you'll say,' he began. 'But go into it, on a practical basis, they're right, really. Production's got to be stopped, for the next few months, on at least two of the lines. And the others have got to keep going. Turn it which way you like, there's only one answer. What we're asking cuts right across it.'

'Because production isn't planned,' Kate said. 'Because you're all at the mercy of the market.'

'All right. That's easy to say. But now, in these actual few months.'

'You stick out for the principle, because the principle's right.'

'And get called airy-fairy,' Harold said, moving.

'Did he really say that?'

'Never mind him. It's the situation that matters. Like they talk on the wireless: a new spirit in industry, better human relations, harmony. It's as easy as a bloody mouth-organ when the situation's easy: no need to have conferences on it. When things are going all right, and the cars selling, it's all straight bargaining, and we swear for a bit and then make an agreement.'

'Yes.'

'Only change the situation, and what are you faced with? When the cars were selling, you accepted the set-up, and bargained inside it. That's what they mean, experienced and sensible negotiators. And it's right, we usually are. But once that yard's full, once the reports come back from the dealers, demand slack, what's the set-up then? They can use against us the arguments we've been using ourselves, when the going was good. We've got nothing to say, in the terms we've been used to. And fall back on an idea, well yes, but we've got out of practice.'

'We've always said this, Harold. There's no place for sentiment.
288

A system works as itself. While you've got the system, only its ways are practical.'

'But we have got the system. Go down there and look. And it's right what they say. The only practical thing is to lay the men off.'

'Sure. That's the point. Only those ways are practical, inside their system. And the ways include throwing men on the street, when the market's difficult. You oppose the ways, you've got to, these are your own people. But if you oppose the ways you end by opposing the system, and no chance of compromise.'

'And where does that get you then?'

'It gets you to socialism. That's what our history's about.'

'Aye, it gets you to that in your mind,' Harold said, lying back. 'It gets you to that, talking down in the colleges. But what good's that to me, going down there this week? No compromise with the system: that's easy to say. But I've got to go down and compromise, I've got men under pressure, for the rest of this winter.'

'I know, Harold.'

'So what's the good of bloody talking? It's just running out on us, all that sort of talk. You go off down there and you forget what it's like. You can sit around and sneer at the daft old trade unionists: trade union consciousness, that used to be it. But do you come and tell me what I can actually do? Are they on target-practice down there, so we can take the bloody place over, have your bloody revolution? Is that what they're doing?'

'No,' Kate said.

'Or this battle of ideas? Where are they, then? When the men are laid off, for the rest of the winter, what shall we get from them all? A bloody soup-kitchen?'

'No.'

'For a principle, you say. All right, it's a good principle. But I have to go in where there's no principles, only too many bloody cars in the yard. I have to sit and be told I live in an airy-fairy world. Me, the bloody convener. Do I look like I do?'

'You're living the principle,' Kate said quietly.

'Am I? Well, that's bloody news for a change.'

'Most of us know about it, and most of us have failed. You haven't failed.'

'Haven't I, then? You wait till the end of the winter.'

'I'll wait as long as you like,' Kate said, and got off the bed. She paused, at the foot of the bed, waiting for him to speak again, but he said nothing, he had even turned his head on the pillow and closed his eyes. She waited again, and then picked up his cup and went out.

On the Monday, the meeting was held, in London. Harold waited for news, but the only news was that there would be another meeting, on Wednesday. By the end of the week, the ten days would be up, but he could still only wait. On the Thursday, at last, the message came through. The unions had accepted nothing, but the best the management could offer, after prolonged pressure, was a complicated system of selective transfer to the lines being kept open, for sixty or seventy of the long-service men in certain grades. At the same time, inevitably, most of the unskilled and semi-skilled men on the lines not in demand would have to be laid off, with some small compensation. They hoped for no more than seven or eight hundred men, for up to eight or nine weeks, until trade, it was hoped, revived again in the Spring. The private advice from the unions was that no better than this could be got; the few concessions were about the practical limit. Harold put this to the stewards' committee, without comment. By a majority the committee rejected the compromise, and re-affirmed their original demands. If these were again turned down, the unions should be asked to support an official strike. In a way, Harold was pleased by this decision. There was really nothing else that in conscience he could accept. But at the same time he had no real hope left, that they could actually win.

The reply was still being considered by the unions when, on the Friday afternoon, a new and quite unexpected element entered. There was another walk-out, at the West Longton factory, where the last dispute had been only temporarily settled. The walk-out, on an overtime issue, was led by Rathbone, who had come down as a delegate in the autumn. The West Longton management reacted at once by dismissing him. He was described in a press statement as a persistent troublemaker. A mass meeting at once decided to stay out until Rathbone was reinstated, and it was clear that the dispute would be long and bitter. The effect of the West Longton stoppage, on the rest of the system, would be what it had been in the autumn. Ironically, one of the busy lines would be hardest hit, since it was especially dependent on the West Longton instruments, which were never stocked beyond three days' normal production. By the Tuesday or Wednesday most of the men would have to be laid off, quite apart from the general redundancy still being negotiated. After hurried consultations,
290

another national meeting with the unions was arranged for Monday, no action meanwhile to be taken on either side.

Harold was well used to this kind of complication and delay. 'That's life,' was all he would say. Dick Manning, however, was sure the whole thing had been planned. Obviously the West Longton management wanted to get rid of Rathbone, but they mightn't have risked it, making a long strike certain, if the situation elsewhere, with falling demand, hadn't been so favourable.

'They're all in with each other, these buggers, don't tell me they're not,' he said, at the committee.

'You overestimate them,' Harold replied. 'You see plots where there's only muddle.'

'They're not muddled when it comes to getting rid of a militant steward. You want to watch out, Harold, it'll be us next.'

'I've been on that spot for twenty-five years.'

'Aye, but what has it taught you? We've got to fight this now, in the worst conditions. If we'd supported the Longton men in the autumn, we'd have had a much better chance. Only you opposed it, remember?'

'That was then,' Harold said. 'We're talking of now, or supposed to be.'

'So am I talking of now. Don't make the same mistake twice. We should come out straightaway, in sympathy with Longton. We've got nothing to lose, just sitting around for the chopper.'

For a time it looked as if this proposal would carry, though Harold opposed it, saying they should wait at least until Monday's meeting. But in the end there was other opposition, of a quite different kind. The representatives of the men on the lines which would have been kept on full time had been ready to stand by the others in their own works, but were now suddenly in the position that whatever they did, they too would be out, because of the Longton dispute. Their arguments weren't always clear, but their resentment was perfectly clear. They would do nothing, now, to help Longton, who had got them into this worse mess. This led to very bitter arguments in the committee, and it was always likely that they would be defeated. But a majority here or there didn't matter any longer. What did matter was that, however accidentally, the collective feeling, so strong hitherto, had been broken. The original simplicity, of the principle on redundancy, appeared to be complicated, even if it was not, by this other dispute. The chance of any agreed action seemed increasingly remote, and Harold, worried more by this than by any of the other developments, fought hard for his own programme: wait for the meeting on Monday; if unfavourable, go himself to West Longton, and get information. In a confused and angry atmosphere, the meeting ended, with this programme if not accepted at least assumed in default of any other agreement.

The general situation was now so confused that it was easier to follow it on the wireless than in the factories actually concerned. The only difficulty, listening to the news and the sudden rush of commentators, was keeping any sense of the sort of men you were, as the familiar phrases—'unofficial action', 'strikers' demands', 'mass meetings', 'troublemakers'—made their own world. But still the news came through of the meetings. The West Longton men reaffirmed their decision to stay out. The West Longton management reaffirmed their already final decision on Rathbone: that he could under no circumstances be re-employed. Production elsewhere would have come to a halt by the Wednesday.

On the Wednesday morning, Harold went down early to the works. In spite of the warnings, hundreds of men had turned up, and stood waiting outside the gates, in the steady drizzle. At the ordinary starting-time, notices were posted. Because of the dispute at West Longton, production had temporarily to cease. The angry men, reading the notices, were like strangers, suddenly. Harold stood miserably among them, with nothing to say. He had never for years felt more beaten and helpless. When he saw Len Weekes, in the crowd, he made his way across to him. There, at least, he would know what to say, or what did not need to be said. Eventually, as the crowd began to drift away home, Harold walked back with Len Weekes to his house in Between Towns Road. Len asked him in, and they stayed talking for some time: easy talk, about the weather and holidays and gardening and football. Len kept very still, always, as if any change, any movement, would be for the worse, and his conversation had the same quality, a restful talking for reassurance rather than for any exchange of information or ideas. He was both wary and good-humoured, settled and passive. This, Harold thought, was his own generation, which had been bred to defeat and had learned to live in its shadow. But still learned to live, Harold thought, watching Len. Very few things could happen to break Len, for he had his reserves: not just the money put by, for when times would be bad, but also the ironic resignation, the strength of sitting still and being ready, which could absorb most setbacks and leave him waiting for the next. Against all the odds, and underneath the actual struggle, this kind of life steadily and decisively matured.

Harold walked back to his own house. As he turned in at the gate he remembered how critical he had been of Len Weekes, back in the autumn. Was it only defeat that bred this kind of respect? Had he not, after all, been right then? Might not Len's adjustment be one of the reasons for the defeat, as well as containing the reserves to meet it when it came? For whatever reason, he could not himself settle to this. Who could count, in the end, how many mature and settled people were in fact being carried by those still struggling, frustrated and unfinished? Most calm people, like that, usually had someone in the background, taking the real tension. Even this whole society, this attractively mature and soft-voiced Britain, had got other people—Africans, Asians— to pay for the margin within which it was composed. Mature and soft-voiced: it depended where you were. Harold smiled wryly, going in to look up the trains for West Longton.

He caught a train at midday. Kate had packed his sandwiches, and he ate them at one of the four changes. From the station he rang up Meeson; he would rather talk to him than to Rathbone. Mrs Meeson answered. Her husband was down with the others, in the Labour Club. Harold went for a bus. It was all downhill to the club. The streets were much bleaker here. The whole town, in its blackened brick, and in its bare treeless streets, was harsher than anything he had known. Brynllwyd, in detail, had been as hard and lifeless, but you had only to look out from it, to the broad green valley and the mountains in the distance, to see another kind of life. In West Longton there was no view, except the stacks and warehouses, and the blackened streets.

There were several cars outside the Labour Club, filling the narrow close. A television van was parked further down, and a camera and cables were being unloaded. Harold went inside. The narrow passage was lined with Labour Party posters, in bright primary colours. There were five separate posters with the heads of smiling children, looking much as they did in any other advertisement. *For a Better Britain*, the sharp lettering repeated. In the crowded clubroom two reporters were talking to Rathbone, who was wearing a blue sweater and light fawn trousers and sitting behind a trestle table as if at a desk.

'Certainly I could tell you more, if you'd ask the right

questions,' Rathbone was saying. 'But all you're interested in is the strike. Never, by any chance, the grievance.'

'We've already got that,' one of the reporters said, closing his book.

'Where? In your bottom drawer? There's not been ten consecutive lines, setting out the facts, in all the acres you've printed.'

'What we write, brother, and what gets printed, aren't always the same thing.'

'Then you need a bloody strike yourself,' Rathbone said. 'Print your own troubles for a change.'

'That'll be the day,' the younger reporter said. They moved away. Two young men immediately took their places. They were dressed like undergraduates, and seemed not much older. Rathbone evidently knew them, and was at once less defensive.

'In about ten minutes, O.K., Ted? Now if we can just go over it again.'

Rathbone smiled as the taller of the two spoke to him. Harold, watching, got the sudden sense of Rathbone enjoying his situation. He moved away, as the conversation continued, and sat down by Meeson.

'I just wanted a quiet talk,' Harold said. 'I never thought all this lot'd be here.'

'Oh aye, they're building it up.'

'Brother Rathbone looks in his element.'

'No, no, he's had a hell of a time. Reporters at his house, questioning his wife and his neighbours. Even his kids at school have been asked what they think of the strike.'

'What's this lot then? The TV?'

'Aye, Ted's doing an interview. That'll really do some good.'

'Let's hope so anyway.'

Harold got the facts that evening, from the strike committee. It was an expected kind of dispute, over compulsory overtime. It had been argued for months, but until Christmas many of the men had been glad enough to work it, for the extra money. Now, with the tiredness of winter, and a lot of illness, the hours were too long, whatever the money. When the management appealed to a previous agreement, they had no formal answer, except that they wanted it revised. When this was refused, they had walked out. It mightn't have happened, in just this way, in another factory, but here, for the last eight years, since a change of ownership from a local firm to one of the larger organizations, there had been almost continual disputes. In a real sense, it seemed to Harold, the issue was less important than the total situation, but this didn't mean that a dispute over the particular issue was irresponsible. People lived, after all, in total situations. It was always the whole life that counted.

He walked back, after the meeting, with Rathbone and Meeson. They went first to Rathbone's, to watch the television programme in which his interview was being included. Just before the time of the programme, Mrs Rathbone brought down her two children, to see their father on the screen. The two boys were in their pyjamas, and their thick dark hair was carefully brushed, above the clear, glowing skin.

The programme was called a Special Investigation. It began, dramatically, in silence, with the camera moving over silent and deserted factories: all those, in many parts of the country, that had been brought to a halt by the West Longton dispute.

'*It looks like death, this uneasy silence. The death of industrial Britain.*'

The voice had come, quietly, as if from the eye of the camera, which continued to move over the empty roads, the locked gates, the silent machines.

'*The machines, in their thousands, idle. The men, in their thousands, idle. A great industry has been brought to a halt. These factories, on which we depend; these machines, which finally pay for our food; these men, taking home wages, bringing up their families.*'

There was a quick traverse over a crowd of men moving in through the gates of a factory, then a series of scenes of houses, gardens, children playing at a school. Music had started, with these moving images, but then stopped suddenly, as the original shots returned: the deserted factories, the machine-shops empty.

'*Why, suddenly, have the machines stopped? Why, today, are the factories idle, and the men turned away?*'

Over the last questions came the beginning of the scene with Rathbone. He was standing in the street, with the other men behind him: waiting, as he had been told, for the signal to begin talking. He was smiling nervously, and looking around. One of the boys moved across to his father, and touched him, while still looking at the screen. Rathbone himself still stared at his picture, hardly noticing the boy's touch. It was only a few seconds, this preliminary scene. But it seemed to last endlessly: the clear, firm questions, from the anonymous voice, and this man standing, nervously, looking around. He nodded, now, at the unseen signal, and began to talk.

'Well, speaking on behalf of all the lads here, I'd like to explain our point of view.'

Harold looked quickly across, from the man talking on the screen to the man leaning tensely forward, his face set and dark. It was like and yet unlike: the same man, but in so different a setting. Harold scarcely heard Rathbone's voice developing the case. The tone of the voice was what first came through. After the practised rhythms of the anonymous introduction, this voice was rough, jerky, heavily accented. The pitch was too high and too loud, as if to an open-air meeting, not to a microphone. Harold tried to force himself to listen to the arguments, but he was aware of something else: the sense of unreasonableness that was mainly coming through. At the autumn meeting, outside the gates, Rathbone had seemed a persuasive and practised speaker. Here, in this different setting, he seemed truculent, anxious, unconvincing. Meeson was nodding, as each point was made. Within the situation, he was holding firmly to the sense of the argument. But even from Harold's distance, the sense never really took hold.

'What I mean to say, there's us to consider. Not just the cars and the exports. And we've had to learn, time and again, if we don't stand up for ourselves, nobody else will. That's why we're convinced of the justice of our case.'

Rathbone stopped, and looked inquiringly into the camera, which still held the scene for some moments. Then the group in the street faded, and the camera moved again to the deserted factory. A new face filled the screen: the director of labour relations whom Rathbone had described at the autumn meeting. He was sitting at his desk, smoking a pipe and looking easily and frankly at his interviewer, who came on screen suddenly, giving a face to the introductory voice that had already been heard.

'So they got that bastard, did they?' Rathbone said, as the interview began. Harold was too used to the style now being
296

practised to be influenced by it, but still he noticed the contrast. 'Of course.' 'Certainly.' 'Yes, that's a good question.' The voice was insistently polite and reasonable, even before the answers were given.

'Haven't you got to face this, Mr Allison? Men don't strike without some sufficient cause, sufficient at least in their own minds. When your men walk out, don't you ever feel that you, as a management, may be also at fault?'

Allison drew on his pipe.

'Well yes, certainly, that is the question one asks. And one wouldn't deny, one wouldn't want to deny, that mistakes can be made, on both sides. But I'd ask you again, Mr Wells, to look simply at the facts The dispute here is on a matter covered by agreement, by a properly negotiated agreement through the constitutional machinery. That agreement may be wrong, I don't know. It may need revision. But the way to revise it is through the properly constituted machinery. We place great stress, we always have in this organization, on consultation, discussion, regular negotiation with the men's representatives. But all of it, all of it, Mr Wells, has been just swept aside. Under the influence of one man, and of one man only—make no mistake about this—all the normal machinery, by which disputes are settled, has been simply and categorically ignored. And the management is entitled, in such a case, to say perfectly clearly, without vindictiveness and with full respect for the rights of all concerned, that it cannot tolerate thousands of men being thrown out of work, with all the hardship that implies, and a severe loss of production, extremely damaging not only to the organization itself but to the export trade and the country as a whole, because of one troublemaker, one perhaps sincere but misguided man, who because of his presence has succeeded in misleading many hundreds of his loyal fellow-workmen.'

'Mr Allison, thankyou.'

Again, after the interview, the image was held. Allison re-lit his pipe, and looked steadily into the camera. Then the scene faded, and the interviewer, standing in the street with a hand microphone, looked round quizzically at the camera.

'Well, as you see, it's a difficult and complex situation, though also a dangerous situation. You've heard the views of two of the men most closely involved, and it's for you, the public, to try to see where the truth really lies. In any dispute of this kind, there are strong feelings, partisan

297

feelings, Before we end this special investigation, we thought it might be useful to get the views of somebody not directly involved, but with expert knowledge of this kind of situation. Dr Michael Swinburne, University Lecturer in Industrial Relations.'

The scene switched again, to a college window-seat. Michael was sitting, with a book on his knee, looking out through the window.

'What's your own view, Dr Swinburne, of this particular dispute?'

'Well, of course one would need to know a great deal more, not only about the particular dispute, but about its background, which is so often important. Industrial relations, in my experience, are never as black and white as the protagonists make them appear. The truth probably lies somewhere in a shifting series of greys.'

'That's very general, Dr Swinburne. Can you come down to cases at all? On this particular matter? Do you accept, for example, that the management has a right to dismiss a man whom they believe, rightly or wrongly, to be a troublemaker.'

'The right, certainly, in a legal sense. They can hire or dismiss whom they choose.'

'Do you think it's a failure of the unions, when this kind of unofficial leader gets thrown up?'

There was a pause.

'Well no, not altogether,' Michael said, leaning forward. 'It may or may not be, in the particular case.'

'But in this case?'

'It's difficult to say. I listened to Mr Rathbone with great interest. Unfortunately, as so often, what he had to say was extremely general. It was very difficult to form an opinion.'

'And Mr Allison, for the management?'

'Yes, I heard Mr Allison. What he said was probably right. But what he still has to ask himself, I think, if it is all as reasonable and well-managed as he made it appear, why, to put it quite bluntly, his whole factory is closed down.'

'Because of a troublemaker. That was what he said, surely.'

'Yes.'

'Do you believe, yourself, that this troublemaking is organized? That there is, for example, any communist influence?'

'Well, you know, that's very hard to say. We need to be wary of these simple explanations.'

'But then is there any explanation at all, Dr Swinburne?'

'*In the short run, probably not. We need much more research, and that will take time.*'

'*But is there time, Dr Swinburne? With a whole industry paralysed, by this one dispute?*'

'*That's a much wider problem, of course. But I'd just say this. When there are symptoms of sickness, there probably is sickness. The cure, of course, is quite another matter.*'

'*And on that you have no suggestions?*'

'*I'm like yourself, Mr Wells: an investigator.*'

'*Dr Swinburne, thankyou.*'

The scene faded, and the closing music came up. The last things shown were the first things: the deserted and silent factories.

'Well, there you are,' Rathbone said, getting up and switching off. 'Did it come over all right?'

'Your bit did,' Meeson said.

'What did you think of it, Owen?'

'They can make their plays,' Harold said, sitting forward. 'They got you identified anyhow.'

'Me?'

'You don't think you won, did you?'

'Not won, no. But we had our say.'

'So did Dr Swinburne. And Mr Allison and Mr Camera Wells.'

'Swinburne didn't sound too bad. That about reasons for sickness.'

Harold got up, moving to ease the strain on his back.

'What you'd better not forget,' he said, 'is that you're the sickness. That's what the play said.'

'Look, Owen, from the start, you've been against us. You were against us in the autumn, when you could have been useful.'

'Useful?' Harold said. 'That's how it all is, isn't it? We're useful to the management, useful to the country, useful to each other. That's where it all goes wrong. We start out being useful, we end up being used.'

'In a capitalist system.'

'In our system too. You just said it. Like we talk of solidarity, only we don't organize for it, we just do what suits us and then appeal to the loyalty of the others. Our own little groups: West Longton; England. And it don't work.'

'Not if we get let down, it don't.'

'Get a man selfish enough, he'll always be let down. The world won't dance to his tune. We've learned it this winter, but we've

299

learned it enough before. You acted when it suited you; we acted when it suited us; we both lose.'

'We haven't lost yet.'

'We've never won yet. All we've ever done is make the defeat more bearable. The whole lot of us.'

It was eventually agreed that Harold would report back to his own committee, for any further action. It was further agreed that, when the present dispute was settled, they would set up a joint committee, representing all factories in the organization, to co-ordinate all future policy. Harold knew this would mean trouble, and would be called troublemaking. But in these last weeks he had come to the limits of the world in which he had been accustomed to work. It was now a question of changing that world, at the only place he could touch it, or resigning himself finally to the experience of defeat: the worst kind of defeat, which showed itself, always, as a limited victory, a qualified acceptance. The reality, he had decided, was always precisely in these limits, these qualifications. It was here the change had to be made.

Kate was eager to know about his West Longton trip, and he told her all he could, as well as reporting to his committee. Rathbone's name and picture were now in every newspaper, in that sudden explosion of publicity which had begun with the television programme. Harold, remembering the house in West Longton, regretted this kind of pressure. But Kate, surprisingly, welcomed it.

'Yes, certainly, it's like the pillory or the stocks. But Rathbone's tough, this won't break him. And it's right that it's out in the open. There are only two chances, for any working man. He can be a star footballer, or the leader of a strike. Then they take an interest in him, not otherwise. He stops being available labour and becomes a man.'

'He becomes a character in a play. Hero the one and villain the other.'

'He becomes a man, a recognizable man. He has a name, he gets recognized, and that makes the difference. Anything's better than their ordinary language: the odd case, the few hundreds, the negligible percentage.'

'That's not the only alternative.'

'Perhaps it isn't. But at least it breaks this block in the mind, this mass anonymity on which the system depends.'

'That breaks at home or nowhere,' Harold said. 'That isn't the system.'

Over the next weeks, the West Longton dispute was very bitterly fought. Until the third week there was no sign of a break, though every kind of pressure was brought, and the unemployment elsewhere was heavy. The national union leaders, having tried all normal ways of getting a settlement, decided at last to make the strike official: whatever the rights and wrongs of the dispute about overtime, the dismissal of Rathbone was straight victimization. The Ministry of Labour now at once intervened, and new negotiations began. It looked, as so often, to be an impasse, but within forty-eight hours a formula was devised: Rathbone's dismissal was renamed a suspension; there would be a return to work on the following Monday; the suspension of Rathbone would then be reconsidered. For a time it looked as if the West Longton men would still reject this, but in the end they accepted, and in fact, within a fortnight, he had got his job back. The thousands involved, elsewhere, began picking up the pieces.

Harold went in to see Wall, on the day of the West Longton return. It was expected that production could restart on the Thursday.

'Everybody back?' Harold asked.

'Well no, not immediately. It's bound to take time.'

'Look, you haven't been without wages this last month,' Harold said angrily.

'I know, I know. But that's hardly been our doing.'

'Come on,' Harold said, 'let's have it.'

'Well, Owen, as I said, we'll take men back as the work becomes available.'

'It could become available everywhere.'

'You should tell that to the production boys.'

'What is it then?'

Wall outlined the arrangements. They were what Harold had expected. Two lines would restart, during the week: the two lines on which, originally, there would have been no redundancy. The other lines would be restarted, as opportunity permitted.

'So we're back where we were, at Christmas.'

'I don't understand,' Wall said, smiling.

'What we fought at Christmas, as a redundancy programme, you're now going to implement, as a re-engagement programme.'

'That's rather hard, surely. I mean, it's been a practical problem throughout. The other lines will restart as soon as it's humanly possible.'

'Can you give us a date?'

'Well no, not really. Though if I were making a private guess, I'd say not before the middle of March.'

'The date when the original redundancy would have ended, is that it?'

'You keep bringing in redundancy. That isn't the problem. We've had our whole programme disrupted by this damnfool West Longton dispute, and now we just have to do the best we can.'

'What would you originally have done, though.'

'Look, Owen, you'll get nowhere, just labouring this. I've told you the situation. There's nothing you or I can do about it. The facts are the facts.'

'We'll see,' Harold said, getting up.

As he walked back, to report to the committee, he knew, however, that it was as Wall said. It might have been possible, in January, to hold everyone against the redundancy programme. It would not be possible now, after weeks of unemployment, to persuade those offered re-engagement not to take it, simply because others would have to wait. The principle, indeed, might be the same, but the practice would be different. Everyone on the committee agreed on this, though he took care to point out what in fact had happened. Dick Manning would still have supported a common policy, though he himself would be one of the first to go back, while Harold would have to wait with the others. But the vital attention had shifted. The policy finally agreed on was simply continued pressure to get as early a restart as possible on the other lines.

Harold walked back up Goldsmith Street, going over his own situation. Like all the others, he was short of money. Since Christmas, on top of everything else, Peter's bit for his room and food hadn't been coming in. Still, with care, they would manage. They could use the money put aside for the caravans for the summer; that could be made up, later, or if not the holiday cancelled. Everything seemed to come together, from the long months of the autumn and winter. What was then only talk had now to be lived through, but this was common enough. Still, he remembered too much from this winter to want ever to live it again.

Kate came out to the kitchen, when she heard the door. She stood and looked at him. He told her the news quickly, while washing his hands at the sink. As he was drying his hands, she moved up behind him, and put her arms round his waist. He smiled, but then moved away.

'Oh, I forgot to tell you, I had a visitor,' Kate said.

'Who's that?'

'Mrs Lane. Robert Lane's wife.'

'Was it about Peter?'

'No, they've not seen him. He's been keeping away.'

'Beth sees him, doesn't she?'

'Yes, so Myra says.'

Harold sat at the kitchen table. He stared down, for some time, at the worn shiny oilcloth.

'Don't you want to know what she came about?'

He looked up at her. He had taken off his glasses again, and he blinked against the light.

'She asked me,' Kate said, 'if I'd consider a temporary job. Apparently her husband has more paper work than he can manage. There's a whole set of proofs to check, of his new book, and some checking of quotations, in the libraries.'

Harold said nothing.

'I said I'd be frightened of it, but they were both sure I could do it. And we'd be glad of the money. For a month or two. Anyway, I said I'd talk to you about it.'

Harold went to the sink, and again washed his hands.

'Is there anything wrong with it,' Kate asked.

'No. Nothing wrong with it. If we need charity, there'll always be someone to offer it.'

'Charity! It's not charity. It's a job I can do.'

'But offered now,' Harold said.

Kate put her hand to her hair.

'What's happened, boy? What's brought you back like this?'

'Back where?'

'Back alive.'

He walked through to the living-room, and picked up the paper. She followed him, and sat opposite.

'So I oughtn't to take it?'

He put down the paper.

'For yourself, if you want to. Not just for the money.'

Kate laughed, throwing back her long hair.

'Go, that's just a wangle, mun.'

'I been wangling all winter.'

'No, Harold, you haven't. You been fighting all winter.'

'And lost then.'

'Not lost altogether. There's more than one sort of winning.'

He looked across at her. She smiled, holding his look. They had been married for twenty-four years, and there was now only the table between them, but they still could not move. At last Kate pushed out her hands, and caught his hand between them. His whole body was aching, but he stayed where he was, watching her. Kate accepted the watching, and waited. They went back over years, at this same table, though nothing was said.

'You need to sleep, love,' Kate said, at last.

He released his hand, and got up and walked round the table. He stood close to her, looking into her face. The heavy cheeks were flushed, and the dark eyes were unusually bright.

'Take me back, love,' she said. 'Take me back now.'

He lifted his hands, slowly, and ran his fingers through her hair. Then he touched the back of her neck, and she laughed and moved closer to him.

'I don't have that much choice.' he said, very quietly. 'Not with you, Kate.'

'Yes, love, really, all the choice in the world.'

'All the choice where we are,' he said, and at last held her close, releasing himself and feeling his body move again. She was surprised, even now, by his passion, as he suddenly came to her.

Chapter Seventeen

PETER sat alone at his desk, looking out through the high window to the trees and the gardens. It had been important to say, to Robert, that he would ride his history. The phrase would be taken as rhetoric, but in his own mind it had a precise meaning. Simply, what he did about his work he would do about his life: not because the work was a priority, but because each decision led into all the others.

He had wanted, originally, to do certain work, which mattered directly in his own experience. That work, whatever its future, would have been a way of living: a commitment to understand and to describe, not primarily for people outside, and not as a means of getting away. But, imperceptibly, the definition had altered. He was seen, and had seen himself, as having moved out, moved on, because he deserved to, having proved his ability, and because he could be useful, in this different world. To see it otherwise was to give way to nostalgia. Nostalgia indeed was the word, the ratifying word, to mark and confirm the distance he had travelled. Call it continuity, loyalty, memory, and the distance might worry him. Call it nostalgia, and he could make a clean break.

So he had moved out because he deserved to, and because he could be useful. Had he still hesitations? Did he criticize, even radically, the new world now shaping him? The reason for this was again straightforward: no longer nostalgia, but anxiety, its counterpart. He was a victim, like so many, of a rapid educational mobility. He was anxious, irrationally anxious, because he did not altogether belong in his new world: educationally he did, but socially and personally it often seemed not. Yet of course this would go, given time. It would end when adolescence ended: that anxious period between identities. He could then move on into a society in any case changing, with thousands of others in very much his own position. Only a continuing immaturity could prevent him making the sane and necessary adjustment.

Consider him then: purged of nostalgia, freed from anxiety, doing useful work. Like who? Like who exactly? Like the people telling him.

He got up and went out. The decision he had to make needed strength, certainly, but even more it needed movement. He had never realized, till now, how perfect the trap was. The account was ruled off, and would be accepted by anybody. The usual auditors would arrive and certify it. And if it showed signs of not working, at the conventional level, there were ample reserves. Nostalgia, anxiety, confusion: if these didn't engage, at the level of argument, they would engage very quickly once he really looked into himself. He was told what to find and he found it, because it was there. All the hesitations, confusions, the actual harm done to others. He must be a fool to fail to see it. But then how comforting, finally, to see his life as this mess. He could take the confusions, the betrayals, into his own person, and surrender to them. He would no longer criticize the life that engendered them, and the system that sustained them. Having broken in himself, he would have made the system safe. And at just that point, the system was waiting, with some precise and limited ends, towards which he could work as an adjusted person. The nostalgia redeemed, the confusion resolved, the anxiety ended. The proper name now is maturity.

He was walking fast, along the towpath to the meadow. The floods had begun to go down, and the grass that had been under water was yellow and matted. A branch lay stranded, on the yellow grass. It was alder, still carrying its hard black cones.

The original work still mattered, and this was the only point of decision. Behind their talk was this one fact: that he had wanted to do particular work, and he had been stopped from doing it. But neatly, politely; nothing so vulgar as actually pushing. As he learned their language, he had found he was pushing himself. Respectable work, work that has currency. Only nothing so vulgar as working for gain. Merely appropriate working conditions, for it's self-evident, isn't it, he would need a bigger house, better meals, wider opportunities for travel and leisure, if he was writing a book than if he was making a car. Appropriate living conditions, at an appropriate level, with appropriate differentials, after full and frank and appropriate consultations among ourselves. And incidentally, had he noticed what happened to the odd few, the very odd few, who did their own work and be damned? The eccentricity, the bitterness, the corrugations of exposure. We put them right, in the end, with appropriate and standard biographies (for which, of course, we need appropriate and standard living conditions: a bigger house, better meals, wider opportunities for travel and leisure). But with a little effort, a little insight perhaps into their often obscure motives, they could have done real work, respectable work, work that has currency.

Along the line of the allotments the wire had broken, in several places. At the corner it lay looped across the path, reddened with rust, and the yellow grass had grown over it. The earth of the beds had caked and hardened, through the long winter. On one of the huts a panel had come loose, and was beating in the wind. Away on the far side a man was working, along a row of bright kale.

Whichever direction he took, he would not convince them. Whatever he did, their frame of explanation would hold: that was what it was for. The confident patterns, the prepared tones and sentences, the marks on the words that could not now be used. While he hung around, waiting or trying to convince them, he was simply entering an appeal to be approved by this system. The only thing to do was to stop it, now. Stop living, endlessly, on approval. Come back to himself, to his own world.

He settled his plans, walking back. He would tell Robert that he was chucking the thesis, to get on with the work he had originally planned. He would not ask for Robert's support; if he even looked for approval, it would all work out as before. He would live as he could, for as long as it took him. There was no other way.

He ran up to his room, excited and eager to start. He typed a first draft, of his new programme, and as he read it through he noticed, wryly, that it was indeed more mature than the programme he still remembered, which he had first put up nearly three years ago. He reached out and took the manuscript of his thesis from its place on the desk. He held it, lightly, between his hands. Why, now, should he not literally chuck it? He turned its pages. It was almost complete. Only the checking of references had still to be done, and it could be typed, bound and submitted. But if the decision was real, he would have to chuck it: burn it, walk out on it. Otherwise it would always be there, and he could hear the plausible argument: it's ready, so submit it, then go on to the other. But it wasn't the thesis, the actual work, he now needed to reject. As far as it went it was necessary, even useful. What he had to reject was the pattern: the confirmation, and all that would follow from it. He could still, quite reasonably, doubt his own strength, if things got that far.

He sat for a long time, looking down at the manuscript. Then he got up, smiling. This would be his insurance. He would finish, the job on the references, and then put it away in a drawer. At any time, in the next few years, he could take it out and use it, if he really needed to. He had nothing else behind him; he would at least have this. And if it seemed sly, this silent reservation, he just had to accept that. It was the sort of thing he couldn't tell anyone, even Beth. Anyone, if they knew, could simply use it to destroy him, and he didn't intend, in what was anyway a risk, to be destroyed that easily. He smiled again, though not liking the smile. Then he walked down to the library, and put in the first order for the books to check the references.

He was seeing Beth that evening. They had a meal and went to the cinema. Walking back, afterwards, he wanted to tell her about his decision, but he still hesitated. The one thing he had left out, from his immediate plans, was the problem of money if they in fact got married. But since this was uncertain, and anyway too important to be discussed in that context, he waited, for the time. What he was actually feeling was quite different, as they walked. For years, really, he had never been away from his work. But for the next three weeks, while he was doing what was really only office work, he would work regular hours, and stop when they stopped.

He was holding Beth's hand, lightly, as they walked up the hill. He saw her, always, to the last lamp-post before the houses, and then watched her in. She told him he was much too protective, but he only laughed. He stopped, suddenly, pulling back on her hand.

'Would you like to go dancing tomorrow?'

She looked into his face, and laughed.

'How many years is it, Peter, since we last went?'

'I don't know, I don't count them.'

'But do you really want to go now?'

'Yes, I'd like to. With you.'

'This is almost a proposal.'

'It is a proposal.'

They went together, on the following evening. It took some time, getting back together again, for they were over-anxious, relaxing too far. What nobody outside seemed to understand about this dancing, seeing only its apparent withdrawals, the separations to dance virtually alone, was that to get anything, when you had moved away, you had to be so in touch, so really in touch, that the separate movements were still made to the other, without, for the moment, any physical contact. Peter and

Beth assumed too easily, at first, that they had this touch, but then they would stop and look and want to go to each other, before laughing and trying again. When they did touch at last, having held away from each other, they were beginning, slowly, to feel the music moving, as part of themselves. Before the end of the evening they were noticeably closer, in this quite different way. The rhythm was between them, and they were able to hold it. They stayed late, and Beth had to have a taxi home. From that evening on it was as if they had moved, clearly, into a new part of their lives.

During the next weeks, they danced every evening they could. For the first time in years he was happy, and to Beth his happiness was a rediscovery of the boy she had always known, who in these last years, and especially in these last months, had seemed wholly lost. It was a quite physical recovery, easy to know in the dancing. Much of the heavy awkwardness of the body, the fierce tension of the walk, had disappeared, and he was dressing differently, in brighter colours and also, to Beth's amusement, more tidily. In this renewed excitement of life in him, she was herself, though still cautious, happier than she could yet believe. For so much of his attention was now on her, as if a screen had been taken away. He went with her to buy dresses, and kept challenging her ideas of what she could not possibly wear, with hair her colour. The girls in the dress shops laughed at his persistence, and often agreed with it, though whether because they liked him or the colour she was never sure. She knew that she was always safe with greens and blues, but she had never risked the bright yellows he now kept choosing (even he had agreed that most of the reds were impossible). When he had finally persuaded her into a lemon-yellow coat, she went in to her mother wondering what on earth she would say, and was amazed when Myra liked it.

'At least while you're happy, love, you could wear it anywhere.'

Beth still wondered, and sometimes, wearing the coat when they went out in the evenings, she tied a thin yellow scarf over her head to hide most of her hair. One of the first things Peter did, each time, was to untie the scarf, and make the hair come loose.

'I might lose you in the street, look, if I can't see that.'

'What about when I'm grey then? It's only my hair, after all.'

'Then we'll make the most of it, while I can still stand upright to see it.'

'You could make do with a wig, at that rate.'

'Aye, see a wig dancing. Come on.'

The three weeks of his work in the libraries passed. They still went dancing, and were still happy, though towards the end she noticed signs of the old tension. It was almost, she felt, as if a holiday was finishing.

One evening he showed her, laughing, an invitation he had just got. Mr Peter Owen and Lady were asked to a party to meet His Excellency Mr Joseph Akande, Trades Minister of the West African Federation.

'Now tell me why they would ask us, Beth.'

'They haven't asked us. Mr Owen and Lady.'

'Do you want to go?'

'If you do.'

'It's just the usual left-wing circuit, from the look of it. Still, we'll see.'

He wrote to accept, and they made their arrangements. The party was at six, and there wasn't much time for Beth to get home and change.

'You could change at my place,' he said.

Beth looked at him. He was reading the football scores in an evening paper he had just bought, in the street. She could hardly get his attention.

'What is it?' he asked, when he looked up again.

'Nothing. I was just wondering about changing at your place.'

He looked away.

'I shouldn't have offered, I suppose.'

'Yes, Peter, of course.'

'You could just as easily go home and get a taxi.'

'I'll do whatever you want.'

'For Christ's sake, Beth, is it that important?'

'That was what I was wondering.'

'Well, stop it. Forget it.'

They didn't discuss it again until lunch on the day of the party. Then Beth asked him to meet her at the bank, after work. She had brought her party dress down. He agreed, reluctantly. Much of the old tension had come back, suddenly.

'Look, Beth, I don't see why we're going. Yes, sure, I'd like to meet an African politician, but not at a party. And if you want to meet any of these men, you find you've got to get on to the circuit. You can't meet a revolutionary leader, from anywhere in the world, except over sherry or champagne at some party or
310

reception. They've got it well organized, this English radical bunch.'

'Is he a revolutionary leader?'

'Well he was. He's had two years in gaol.'

'Then he's probably glad of the parties.'

'It would be better if he could meet some English people for once.'

'Won't these be?'

'Of course not. Since there've been revolutions elsewhere, and lots of reputable excellencies about, it's become quite a way of life, going from party to party to meet them, and thinking it shows your solidarity with the struggling people of the world.'

'All right, if you don't want to go.'

'We'll see.'

He met her that evening, outside the bank. They got a bus, and then walked to his room.

The big house was silent. They walked to the stairs, very conscious of the sound of their footsteps, but there was nobody about. At the second landing the thin stair carpet ended, and was replaced by worn strips of a dull linoleum. A door opened, somewhere down in the well of the house. Peter went quickly ahead, swinging the case, and opened the door of his room. He switched on the light, and Beth followed him in and closed the door behind her. He put the case down, and turned to look at her.

'Do you like the room?'

'It's quite nice.'

'I'd better draw the curtains.'

'No, leave them. We're high enough up.'

He stopped at the window, and looked down across the dark gardens to the distant street lamps.

'I must hang my dress for a while,' Beth said, and opened the case. She laid the dress on the bed, smoothing it out, and then hung it over the wardrobe door. Peter was still looking out of the window. She walked across to him, and stood beside him, looking far out across the lights of the city. A car was turning, in the first street beyond the gardens, and they both watched it, as if it were an action in a different world.

'It's lovely and quiet up here,' Beth said, very quietly, hardly confirming her voice into words.

'Yes, for a time. Though I can't stay here, once the new work starts. Only I've wanted it to be quiet. Still and quiet, just for a time, so that I know what I'm doing.'

Beth didn't answer. He turned and put out his arm and held her close to him. They stood for what seemed a long time. Neither wanted to move or to speak. At last Peter moved, and kissed her lightly on the forehead. She looked up at him and he kissed her lips, very softly.

'Do you really want to go to the party?' he asked.

'Yes,' Beth said, smiling.

'Back to the lights and the talk, that terrible spinning of talk?'

'Look, we're going together,' Beth said. 'And in any case there's the rest of our lives.'

She went back across the room, and stood by his bed, undressing. He stood very straight by the window, looking out. She put on her party dress, and her other shoes, and then sat on the bed with the wardrobe mirror turned towards her, brushing her hair.

'You're standing like a sentry, Peter,' she said, suddenly.

'Well yes, what else?'

He walked across and sat beside her on the bed. She went on brushing her hair, and he watched her closely, seeing the lights spring up in the coppery brightness as the brush passed over it. Her skin was very delicate, the high colour translucent. At last she stood up, ready. She turned quickly in front of him, showing him her dress, and he smiled.

'What shall we do with the case?' he asked.

'Leave it.'

He looked at her, but she turned away, reaching for her coat.

'You mean this is really a marriage?'

'Yes,' Beth said. 'What else could it be?'

He helped her on with her coat. She leaned back in his arms and he held her close to him, holding her breasts gently with his hands.

'Between us, yes, what else could it be?' he said, touching her face with his cheek.

It was not very far to the house where the party was being held: a big red villa, two streets away from Robert's. They had held hands all the way, but at the lights and cars in front of the house they separated a little. Peter led the way to the open front door, and they went in, towards the sound of voices. He stood by the drawing-room door, holding the invitation card inside his pocket. There were about fifty people in the room and in the lighted conservatory beyond. He looked around, seeing nobody he knew. Then a maid came, a German girl, and took their coats. They moved into the crowded room, and a waiter in a short white jacket came up with a tray of drinks. They stayed very close together, trying not to look around.

The nearest people to them were a group of young African men, two or three of them in African clothes. They were talking to a tall, dark-haired girl whom Peter thought he recognized. Watching the group, uneasily, he suddenly saw the girl looking at him, and then she came across.

'You're Peter Owen, aren't you?'

'Yes.'

'You don't remember me. I'm Helen Edwards. I heard you speak once at the Labour Club.'

'That must have been a long time ago.'

'It was,' she said, and turned to look at Beth.

Peter introduced them, and was glad that Beth started to talk. The name had in fact come, just before Helen said it. She had been chairman of the Labour Club, in his first undergraduate year. But it was Robert now he remembered: the hands spread on the rail of the bridge in the meadow. 'I found her attractive, intelligent, self-contained.'

'You must come and meet the boys, Peter,' Helen said, turning to him. She led him across to the group of Africans. He looked round for Beth, but a man he didn't know had come up and was talking to her, and she stayed where she was. Helen shifted her glass to leave her right hand free, and caught Peter's wrist lightly, as she led him into the group. She introduced him to them, in a rush of names that he couldn't catch. He shook hands, bowing slightly each time. He was conscious of the others as men, but the line of contact was still held by Helen, who behaved as if she were in charge of them.

'Somebody told me you were working with Robert,' Helen said, smiling.

'Yes, I have been.'

'He's here somewhere. Yes, look.'

Robert was standing quite near them, in an unfamiliar dark suit, his back turned.

'Robert,' Helen called.

He looked round at once. As he recognized Helen, he smiled, nervously. He put down his glass and came across.

'This is unexpected, Helen.'

She smiled, took his arm, and introduced him to the group

of Africans. Peter kept his eyes fixed on Robert's face, but he noticed no strain.

'Anyway, when are you coming to Africa, Robert?' Helen was asking.

'I don't know, really.'

'Well you did promise a girl, you know,' Helen said, with a touch of mimicry.

The anonymity of the party was fading. Several names, and more faces, came back to recognition. Then in the far corner, behind the door to the conservatory, Peter saw Rose sitting with a man he recognized as Arthur Dean. Her husband Michael was not far away, talking to a very pretty fair girl who was watching him intently over the top of her glass.

'You are a teacher in this university?' one of the Africans asked.

'No,' Peter said, jerking back. 'I'm a research student.'

'In what faculty?'

'I'm a sociologist. We don't have a faculty.'

'Really? Do you know, I had heard that, but I could not believe it.'

Peter smiled. Over the African's shoulder, he was watching Rose again. She was listening very intently to Arthur, who was leaning forward in his chair and bowing his head close to her.

'Well, at least, Robert, let Peter come,' Helen said, reaching out and again touching Peter's arm. 'I mean, honestly, Peter, don't you feel you have to get out of this country? I mean everything, literally, is so staid and old and self-satisfied and stuffy, you simply can't believe it when you come back.'

'You seem to believe it,' Peter said. He looked back at the African to whom he had been talking, but whose name he still didn't know. Helen took her hand from his arm.

'You persuade him, Okoi.'

'No, I will not do that,' Okoi said, smiling.

'I would not go,' Peter said to Okoi, 'merely because my own country was wrong.'

'Yes, I understand this.'

'Well, I don't,' Helen said. 'You know perfectly well, Peter, if you stay here you'll just die by inches. I don't know how you can bear it, when in fact elsewhere there are real things happening.'

'There are real things happening here.'

'What real things? I don't see them.'

'You're not exposed to them, Helen. You went away.'

'What else is there to do, with everything so old and hopeless? It's so damnably easy to mistake your own small island for the world.'

'Yet without the island it isn't the world, after all. Some of us have to live where we are.'

'Get old where you are,' Helen said. 'Don't you agree, Okoi? It's only in the new countries, honestly, that people know what it's like to be young.'

Okoi smiled. New and young were glib words. Peter looked at the silent group. The Africans were young men, but they seemed to him old, in their stillness; old in settlement and dimension of being. He looked at Okoi's face, where he knew he hadn't enough experience to interpret the features. The expression seemed to him extraordinarily formed, contained, as if the limits of tiredness and waiting had been reached and passed, and a power of resting had grown and matured. The break to movement might come, but it would be from a known energy: a power of activity that could in fact interlock with stillness.

'I must just go and have a word with our guest of the evening,' Robert said in the pause. Okoi smiled again as he made way for Robert to pass.

'Robert's not changed much, anyway,' Helen said, after the required moment of waiting. 'I suppose that's why one comes back here, really. The familiar men and the familiar buildings. Still here, just gently weathered a bit.'

'The men get to confuse themselves with the buildings, that's the only trouble,' Peter said.

'Not Robert, surely?'

'No, not Robert.'

'But England is still the museum, Peter. Honestly, the moment you step off the boat.'

'No, I don't agree.'

'It's because you've not seen anywhere else.'

'I've seen the people here changing. I've seen myself changing. Yes, we're the children of an old civilization, and we must stay children, not really grow at all, if we're to avoid upsetting it. But it is all changing, nevertheless.'

'For the worse, perhaps.'

He was suddenly impatient, hearing the loud medley of all the separate conversations behind him.

'This isn't changing, Helen. It's what it always was. But for

315

the first time ever, perhaps, most people in England can afford to live as themselves. Only a few are doing it, but almost everyone's wanting it. On the old networks we still get stopped, but elsewhere, more and more, it breaks through. It's still only beginning, and if it's to grow the networks will have to be changed.'

'Do you think there's a chance? Once it's more than personal? Once it hits the networks?'

'It's immediately different. Not alive and exciting, as so often elsewhere, but more tense than ever. The young peace marchers, the young trying to change the society. They're a generation in mourning, and the mourning is conscious. The dark clothes, the set faces, the voices subdued almost to silence. This is what I was trying to say, about living where we are. It's a total exposure, and the rhythm of exposure is grave and settled, it must be. When we let it go, say the hell with it, we can pretend excitement. But mostly we are learning a total exposure, and then beyond it, perhaps, a total involvement.'

'And meanwhile, elsewhere, people are making a new world, not simply being exposed to an old one.'

'In the end, surely, they aren't separate worlds. There's nowhere to go away to. Wherever we are, we're present in much the same way. We're at the breaking point everywhere, and at the growing point everywhere. To move away is just shifting the burden.'

'But this isn't politics at all,' Helen said.

'It's not the old politics. It's not the white man's burden. We have to pay our debt for all that, and the price will be heavy. But what we can't do, in conscience, is start our own lives somewhere else. Using other people to live out our mistakes and frustrations. All we can honestly do is face what we are, here.'

'But that's just resignation.'

'No,' Okoi said, 'it is not resignation.'

'You tell me what it is then, Okoi,' Helen said, with a quick smile of encouragement, a teacher's smile.

'It is freedom, I think, what Peter is saying. It is the language of freedom.'

'No freedom that I've ever heard,' Helen said.

'I too, you see, am not in my own country. But I shall go back to my country.'

'Yes, Okoi, because you're needed.'

'And because I need.'

'I'll return the visit, Okoi, if I may,' Peter said.

'Yes, you will be welcome.'

'So we've persuaded you, after all, Peter,' Helen said.

'No, not persuaded,' Okoi said. 'He is a free man,'

'Not yet,' Peter said.

There was a movement behind them. Another group were being taken forward to meet the Foreign Minister, who was standing by the fire, under a large mirror. Across the crowded room, Arthur was leaning back in his chair, with his fingers loosely on his empty glass. Michael and the fair girl had gone out through the conservatory and down into the garden.

'The girl's nice,' Arthur said. 'Who is she?'

'She's called Lena,' Rose said. 'She comes from Sweden. She married old Elliott.'

'Lucky old Elliott.'

'No, not lucky old Elliott.'

'Has Michael known her long?'

'Since we came back. Though in fact it doesn't take long.'

'Miaou, Rose.'

'Yes, Arthur, miaou.'

They moved into the lighted conservatory. Okoi and Peter followed them. Rose put her hand up to her hair and then turned, deliberately, to talk to Okoi. Peter noticed how calm and unembarrassed she was, when she talked. She had only just met Okoi, but she could talk to him as if they were old friends.

'You're working with Robert, I believe,' Arthur said to Peter.

'Yes,' Peter said, without interest. He was listening to the other conversation.

'And this is your last year?'

'Yes, it is.'

'What had you thought of doing then?'

'I shall go wherever my work is.'

'But of course,' Arthur said, with a slight shrug. 'The problem then is, what's the work?'

Peter turned and faced him. The eyes were narrowed and watchful, in the easy, still genial face. Too much was at stake, between himself and this man, for any action to be simple. The pressure towards a formal politeness was as insistent as a personal habit; the habitual politeness, containing edge and malice, of the university world. This is how life is, the pressure insisted. You can't really, while you're here, talk in any other way.

There was a long pause.

'You don't really want to know,' he said, temporizing, but still with some edge.

'Would I have asked if I didn't?'

Peter felt the break in his mind, but he was still uncertain. In the narrow conservatory he felt trapped. Everything in his life commanded him to speak, but the only voice he could use was the voice he was trying to reject.

'It will at least be against you,' he said quickly. 'Against you and against your legion.'

'Really?' Arthur said. His voice was still light and casual, though his face had flushed dark. 'But actually I wouldn't have thought I was that important.'

'You're not, but you rule England, as master and servant. It's time and overtime you were fought.'

'This is very flattering, if still quite untrue.'

'Yes, say that. It's all you can say, but all you need to say. You have this manner that's the ultimate weapon, that makes the rest of us feel so wrong and ridiculous we simply throw our own strengths away. We give up our causes and our voices to become like you, and then you congratulate us, and what sounds like England tells us we're right. I tell you the opposite. I tell you you're wrong. I tell you England must be won back from you, urgently and completely, or we shall all die.'

'Well, here endeth the first lesson,' Arthur said, smiling at Rose.

'Get out of my way, do you mind?' Peter said, and pushed past.

He wanted to get out, quickly; to get right away. The dispersed talk of the room was still loud, but for the moment he could see only the darkness of the road out of the city, after the long chain of the orange lamps of the bypass. It had seemed like a liberation, that road, but it had led nowhere. There was nothing left now but to stay and fight, yet to stay seemed like giving up fighting. All the energy he had learned to release would simply flow down the usual channels, that existed to carry it away. And there was nowhere else, except in some fantasy. Identical channels had been built everywhere, so that the movement away from the point of tension was never more than a temporary relief. Then the same world closed in again, so sure and certain that at last you bowed to it, admitting that you had been inexperienced, impatient, arrogant; everything you had in fact been, but then with no alternative, no living alternative.

Beth saw him standing alone by the door. She could feel his disturbance, as if in herself. She hurried across to him, but did not

318

speak. The convention of splitting couples, at this kind of party, was relentless. Temporary couples were all that seemed to matter. Yet for a moment, until they were noticed, the ordinary reality could be recognized. They stayed close, not speaking. The people around them were obviously getting tired. The voices did not stop, the glasses were still firmly held, the contacts were still being made, but the eyes were tired, the eyes looking continually away, towards others, towards the way out.

Helen, unnoticed for a moment, was lying back in a chair just beyond them, her eyes closed. Okoi, moving back across the room, hesitated for a moment near her chair. He made no move towards her, but she opened her eyes and looked up at him and at once jerked to attention. She got up, quickly, and offered her place. It was a strange reversal of the ordinary sexual roles, and Okoi, firmly, refused to accept it, insisting that she should keep her chair. In the drive of her feelings, Helen could not accept this; it was for her to give place to him. As she stood, insisting, Peter clenched his fists. Every error was being paid for, even in the patterns of the guilt.

He saw Rose quite close to him, looking at Beth. He glanced back at Beth, and could feel her nervousness. She was suddenly very like Myra, in the colouring of her face and hair, and in the tense heaviness of her body.

'We've not met, have we?' Rose said, looking her over.

'No, not actually.'

'But I've wanted to meet you.'

Peter stood between them. He was deeply embarrassed, but he could feel all too easily the learned reactions to cover embarrassment: an easy, fast conversation; a careful modelling of normality. Rejecting these, he started to move away.

'That's right,' Rose said. 'You go on, Peter. Find somebody nice to talk to. I've been wanting to talk to Beth.'

'I want Peter to stay,' Beth said, warmly. The unexpected directness was even more like Myra.

'That sounds like orders, Peter,' Rose said, smiling. Her lips curved and rested.

'I'm not being possessive,' Beth said, angrily. 'It's just I want Peter to stay where he's known.'

'Well, that's one kind of compliment.'

'There's nothing for him to run from.'

Rose lit a cigarette, and shook out the match. Her eyes were bright and amused.

'Are you sure, Beth? Are you sure you know what he's like when he's not with you?'

'Yes, I know. I see him when he comes back.'

'You're more confident than I could be.'

'Yes, perhaps I am.'

Rose stood, watching her, taking in every detail of her dress and appearance. Then she turned, making her point.

'You see, Peter? You don't have to worry. Your future's nicely settled.'

'That's quite true.'

'While the rest of us just have to muddle along, in all the untidiness of real situations.'

'As you like it, Rose.'

'No, Peter, not as I like it. But it's at least not reversion.'

Her voice had hardened suddenly. He saw again what he had only recently noticed: how quickly her face could change from the naive expression, which her normal manner supported, to a much shrewder, experienced mask.

'What does that mean?' Beth asked.

She was leaning slightly forward, her arms tense in front of her.

'He knows,' Rose said.

'You tell me.'

'All right. All right, Beth. Just that he's had his bit of adventure and now he's running for home. Just as he always has.'

'Not much of an adventure,' Beth said, bitterly. 'No danger, anyway, with it coming that easy.'

Rose inhaled, slowly, and then smiled. Her face resumed its familiar simplicity and openness.

'All right, dear, we won't brawl. He's a nice boy, don't you think? If you treat him right.'

'That's none of your business.'

'Ah, manners,' Rose said, slightly raising her eyebrows and with the familiar edge of mimicry.

'Look,' Peter said, 'this has gone far enough. I'm not standing here like a bloody bone.'

'The bone has been won,' Rose said, smiling. 'It's now being lovingly chewed.'

'You're just stupid, Mrs Swinburne,' Beth said, staring forward. 'Not because you're immoral but because you're nothing. What he had with you he could get anywhere, and the only pity is it was still nothing. I've given him nothing either, though at least I've tried. And that's how it is, what you call reversion. We're trying

320

to begin, that's all. To begin where we are, and playing it straight. If it makes us ridiculous, then we'll be ridiculous.'

'That's a fine speech, for a registry office,' Rose said.

'Never mind the speech,' Peter said. 'That isn't what counts. And the rest we play on our own. That's what we're both telling you.'

'Well yes, clearly,' Rose said. 'I have to be told something.'

'Good night, Mrs Swinburne,' Beth said.

Peter reached for her hand, and held it. Then:

'Good night, Rose,' he said, evenly.

Rose stood for a moment, looking at them. Then she smiled, from a distance.

'Aren't you lucky, Peter?' she said with a lilt in her voice, and went away, very sure of herself, looking for Arthur.

Peter felt shattered and hopeless, in his own inadequacy. Then he looked at Beth, and saw the breaking strain in her face. It was as if his body moved, suddenly, and he forgot himself, seeing her.

'I'm sorry, love. Shall we go?'

'Where?'

'I'll take you home. I'm sorry.'

She turned and looked up at him. Her face was twisted with pain, so that he could hardly bear to see her. But he tightened his grip on her hand. There was a voice behind them, and May Lane came up beside her. Beth turned to her, impulsively, and May put her arm round her shoulders and kissed her cheek.

'Go on for a minute,' May said to Peter.

The room was beginning to empty. Peter saw Michael Swinburne leaving, with the fair girl, Lena. He was talking, confidently, about trade unions in Sweden.

Robert and Okoi came up to him.

'You must meet the Minister,' Robert said.

Peter agreed, and followed them. He was introduced to the Minister, a surprisingly young man, with handsome, rather arrogant features.

'I have been having an argument with the Minister,' Okoi said. 'I have been saying our nationalism is now too evident, and that we are not doing enough in the struggle with poverty.'

'The distinction is false,' Akande said. 'Poverty, now, is a condition of relations between states.'

'Is that really so?' Robert asked. 'I mean, when you need to develop, though of course you need capital.'

'We need capital,' Akande said. 'But this is still the class

321

struggle, only now between nations. We do not want you just to start us in productive enterprises, or to give what you call aid. In the nineteenth century these were also your solutions, with your own working class. But if you do only that, you will find your subscriptions and your charity thrown back at you in the end. What we are asking, in fact, is equality. We intend to take equality.'

'But now, with so much to do,' Robert said. 'So much actual suffering.'

'You are still living on this,' Akande replied. 'It is undiplomatic to say so, but your country is living on this actual inequality. What we are sent, collectively, in aid and development, is less than is taken back from us, by your own advantage in the terms of trade in our products. We desire aid for development, and we do not reject charity. But these are palliatives. The solution is radical. You will learn with us, as with your own working class, that the only solution, the first stage of solution, is to pay a just price.'

'Yes,' Peter said. 'Except that we haven't reached that, even here.'

'I accept that. But you have narrowed the margin. If you see us as comrades, we can find common interests. If you see us as competitors, the suffering will continue.'

'But that is what I was saying,' Okoi intervened. 'That a nationalistic emphasis prevents this.'

Akande smiled.

'Nationalism,' he said, precisely, 'is in this sense like class. To have it, and to feel it, is the only way to end it. If you fail to claim it, or give it up too soon, you will be merely cheated, by other classes and other nations.'

'I agree,' Peter said. 'This is what I've been learning.'

'Then I wish you luck, Mr Owen.'

'I wish you luck, Mr Akande. Both of you,' he added, smiling across at Okoi.

'It will be more than luck, it will be struggle, Peter,' Okoi said.

'Yes,' Peter said, and put out his hand. Okoi took the hand, and pressed it. As they stood together, Beth and May came across to them.

'Are you ready, Peter?' Beth asked.

'Yes.'

They walked in silence out to the street, where several cars were starting. The wind was colder than when they had arrived, and at first they walked quickly. The lamps were yellow, and there were long dark stretches between them. But the main road, which they had to cross, was more brightly lighted, and the lamps had hardened to white. Peter took Beth's arm, and they crossed.

'How was the Minister?' Beth asked.

'Accurate,' Peter said. 'Not particularly pleasant, but why should he be? He was talking of disease and starvation, in that hothouse.'

They were walking more slowly now, in the quieter street.

'What did Mrs Lane say to you?' Peter asked.

'She said to go on loving.'

'There are many ways of that.'

'Yes. She's a good woman.'

The wind was loud in the bare trees, and there were ragged clouds blowing fast across the moon. Light and shadow, in the moving sky, seemed quite changed, as they stopped to look up. The darker patches of cloud were suddenly highlighted by the moon, and while the dark was concentrated the light seemed to flow across the sky, like light on the sea: moving, extending, springing up within itself, around the islands of darkness. There was a rapid chasing of darkness and light, from the dark heavy swell of cloud to the sudden brilliant outlining of its leeward edge, and then to the lighter clouds blowing very fast across the tumbling disc of the moon. The disc was hidden suddenly, by a new darkness, but they could still feel the speed of its movement and could see where the light was growing again, in a long narrow channel running back over the sky, and suddenly the channel was pure light again, and there was a movement of shadows on the edge of the moving cloud.

As the road curved, and the houses grew above them, they looked down and recovered their presence, their bodies so close that they seemed to be breathing together. Peter turned Beth towards him and held her, unbuttoning her coat so that they could touch more closely. He could feel her breathing against him, and his own breathing on the softness of her breasts. She moved her hands on his back, and the breathing quickened, the rhythms crossing each other, not merging, though they held so close that it seemed each was breathing for the other.

'Are you going to stay, Beth?'

'Yes, my love, if you want me.'

He stood back to arm's length, and looked into her face.

'What is it, Peter?'

'I've been evading so long, Beth. When I thought I had ended it, I was still evading.'

'But how, my love? Tell me.'

'I'm chucking my thesis. I'm not submitting it. I mean to do what I originally planned. And that means no job and no money. Though I can earn a bit, just enough to keep going, doing some adult classes. I want to do these anyway. But still not enough to marry on. And that, it seems, is my last evasion. I could get a job, as everyone has to. If I submitted my thesis it could be a very good job. And we could marry on it.'

'Well?'

'Just that I'm saying now, after all this waiting, we must still wait.'

'We shall have my money.'

'Exactly. That would be it. After eighteen years, eighteen years education, I should still be living on somebody else.'

'We'd be living on each other. Don't you think I need you?'

'But if I took a job it would be so much easier. And I ought to be willing to do it, for you.'

'Ought you, Peter? What makes you think I'd let you?'

'Because it's only an idea that makes me do otherwise. Perhaps a stupid idea. Everyone else will say so.'

'No. I've seen what happens, when you go any other way. If I'm ever to marry you, Peter, marry you and not your shadow, it will have to be you doing the work that you want.'

'I don't know. There's something else I never thought I could tell you. In fact, I've finished my thesis, deliberately, in these last weeks. And I've put it away, as a sort of insurance.'

'Well?'

'It takes the edge off it all. It's still just calculating.'

Beth pulled away, sharply, though she continued to look at him.

'I don't understand you, Peter. I don't understand that growing up as you did you can be so stupid.'

'You mean to hide the thesis?'

'I mean to be guilty about it. To think it's anything wrong. Haven't you seen your father doing things that he hates, because he has had to survive? Haven't you seen him calculating, because you'd have starved otherwise? Always he did what was necessary, to live as he had to, to carry on with his work and still keep alive. That's the morality, the only morality. The test, finally, is what you do with your life.'

'I'd have preferred playing it straight.'

'You mean burning your boats so that you're more likely to fail. But listen, Peter. You have played it straight. You've told me the conditions and I've accepted them. And you've told me now, when it matters.'

'Beth, do you really think we could manage?'

'I've said so, haven't I?'

'It could be a long time. A couple of years.'

'It had better be longer than that, mister.'

He laughed and she swung away, still holding his hand. He followed her quickly, and they ran for some yards. At the street-lamp they stopped, and looked at each other. Then they laughed again.

The house was quiet, though there were lights still on. They closed the door quietly, and walked softly through the hall and up the stairs. When they came to the upper stairs they could hear their footsteps more clearly, and Beth moved quickly and went in front. She stopped at his door, and he came up to her.

'I love you, Beth,' he said, whispering. 'Though I've hurt you so often I don't want to hurt you again.'

'You won't, Peter, unless you leave me.'

'I won't leave you. I want to give you my life.'

'Yes, love, give it to me.'

'I've wanted to feel my own life, to feel where it grows. And it will only grow if I give it to you.'

'I want to grow with you, Peter.'

'It will feel like your life. It will feel so to me.'

He leaned and opened the door, and they went into his room. An edge of shyness, of a different consciousness, kept cutting towards them, but they had learned to be sure of each other, in the long years which had once seemed to divide them. They were able to look and to touch, to come together in new ways, with the warmth of recognition, of finding what had been known but was now more perfectly known. Peter touched and knew her whole body, and she held him close to her, knowing him again as they touched. Slowly, as they moved, came a new feeling, that seemed, in the warmth, an actual change in their bodies, a change of tissue and substance so that they felt quite newly alive, newly capable of life. They responded, wondering, to this transformation, and again it seemed a deep recognition. The known features were blurred and their separateness lost, yet in the change they were more deeply known. The touch between them was warm and moving, and yet reached beyond them, to a felt consummation, that would again flow and continue, beyond itself, into sleep and into life. Beth turned, with Peter's weight on her, and they lay close and still.

Myra was upstairs, mending curtains, when Beth got back from work the next evening. Beth went into her room, and straight across to her. She put her arms round her and kissed her, and Myra said nothing, but held her very close. After a while Beth wanted to talk, and Myra listened, while she told her their plans.

'Only I haven't done wrong.'

'I don't know about wrong,' Myra said, looking down at her hand and trying to turn her ring with her fingers.

'It isn't wrong, being lovers.'

'I used to be able to turn this,' Myra said. 'I could take it right off, when you were little. I've got fat, I suppose.'

'No, you're your proper size,' Beth said, laughing.

'Am I?'

'Yes, love. I think so.'

'And I went like you, before I had this.'

'I know, darling.'

'It seems a long way back, all that in Glynmawr.'

'Well, you've got me to show for it.'

'Have I? I married Jack.'

'Yes.'

'Only it's Gwyn and me brought you up. It's Gwyn's your father, as you are now.'

'He's your husband. It was Jack was my father.'

Myra got up, carrying the curtains back to the table by the windows.

'It wasn't only the once,' she said, as if to herself. 'And we wasn't thinking of that.'

'Why should you?'

'He was always dancing and joking. And mad, like riding that bike.'

'I'm sorry you lost him. I'm sorry I lost him.'

'Well yes,' Myra said.

She cried suddenly, a tearing cry from her throat. She lifted her fists and threw herself to the bed, her face down in the pillows and her whole body writhing as she cried. As Beth moved to her, she lifted her fists and beat them into the pillows. Beth

326

leaned over her, soothing her, but the heavy body still twisted and moved.

'There, love,' Beth whispered, stroking and kissing her hair. Myra turned, her hair down on her face. She was wet with crying.

'I wanted him then. I was glad of him then,' she said, harshly.

'Yes, love, I know.'

'I never thought I should say it. I oughtn't to say it.'

'You can say it to me.'

Myra sat up, pushing back her hair. Beth took out a handkerchief and dried the wet cheeks. Myra took the handkerchief from her, and got up, still wiping her face. She went across to a drawer in the little dressing-table, and stood for a moment, before opening it.

'This was Jack's ring, that he gave me,' she said, turning. 'Can I give it to you?'

'If you want to, love.'

'Only keep it safe, for when Peter can give it you.'

'I'll keep it safe.'

Myra closed the drawer, and looked round the room.

'I'll tell the rest,' she said quickly.

'But can't I come?'

'You can come, yes.'

They went downstairs, Myra leading the way.

'Only be nice to Gwyn,' Myra stopped and whispered. 'He's been like your father.'

'I don't have to be told to be nice to him.'

'And he's my husband. My real husband.'

'I know.'

They went through to the living-room. Gwyn and Harold were sitting at the table, reading. Harold got up as they came in.

'You'll have to get yourself a new suit, boy,' Myra said to him.

'How's that then?'

'Well you'll want to look smart at the wedding. Even if it is the registry office.'

Harold didn't smile. He was looking from Myra to Beth. Beth hesitated, and then went quickly across to him, and kissed his cheek. He stood awkwardly, his arm raised but stiff. Then he put his hand on her shoulder. She kept her head down, against his cheek.

'There, girl, I'm glad.' he said, at last.

Beth lifted her head, and looked at him. Her cheeks were wet

327

with tears, but she managed to smile. Gwyn was standing on the other side of the table, grinning.

'Look at that one then,' Myra said. 'Grinning as if he was getting married himself.'

'Well, not too old for it either,' Gwyn said.

'Aye, only what about me then?'

'You be my maid of honour,' Gwyn said, drawing himself up. 'Keep me off the beer after.'

'I'd be on the beer myself,' Myra said. 'And a drink now wouldn't hurt us. What you standing there grinning for, mun? What I keep you for?'

Gwyn tried, unsuccessfully, to click his heels, and made a mock bow. Then he walked round the table and stood in front, of Beth.

'I'm glad, love,' he said. 'He's a good boy.'

'You've always said so.'

'I know so.'

'Get the drink myself, I might as well,' Myra said.

'I'll get it, girl. Keep your tongue in.'

'Should we go in tell Kate?' Myra asked Harold.

Harold nodded.

'Then it can be your beer, boy,' Gwyn said.

'Is she in, Uncle?' Beth asked.

'Aye, upstairs,' Harold said. 'She does this work at home.'

'Can I come with you?'

Harold hesitated.

'I was just thinking I might go down and see Peter. If Beth'll just tell me the way.'

There was a moment's silence, and then the others all spoke at once. Beth went up to Harold and gave him the directions. Gwyn offered to take him down in Mag. Myra said she'd slip round and see Kate. From the tangled conversation, Harold emerged quietly, and said good night and went out to get the bus.

Peter was working at his table by the window, and did not turn as he called 'come in' to the quiet knock. He heard the door open, and looked across. Harold, in a cap and grey raincoat, was standing just inside the door. Peter jumped up.

'I'm not disturbing you, boy, am I?'

'No, of course not.'

'I asked Beth how to find you.'

'Yes, I ought to have let you know.'

Harold walked in a few steps, looking curiously around the room.

'Beth came and told us you were getting married.'

'Yes, I knew she was telling her mother.'

Harold broke in, quickly.

'It's your own affair, boy. We shan't any of us interfere. It's your own lives. You'll have to trust to each other.'

Peter turned back to his desk.

'She had the courage to come and tell us,' Harold said, 'after staying the night with you. And her Mam supported her, which is more than I'd have expected. She came in to me while I was talking to Gwyn and she came straight across to me and put her head on my shoulder. Then she went in to your Mam.'

'Beth isn't frightened of anything,' Peter said. 'Not when she thinks she's done right.'

'And was it right?'

'Yes.'

Harold looked at him carefully, and then went across and sat on the edge of the bed.

'I don't know any more, Peter,' he said, slowly, taking off his glasses. 'Only Myra surprised me.'

'She knows Beth.'

'Beth's a lovely girl. Like Myra herself was.'

'Yes.'

Harold put his glasses down, on the white counterpane. He bent his head forward, closing his eyes and rubbing the vivid red line on his nose.

'You're tired, Dad.'

'Yes, boy, I am.'

'Have you started back yet?'

'No, but next Monday.'

'Beth told me about it, when Gwyn got back.'

'Never mind that now.'

Peter hesitated, and then pulled his chair round so that he sat facing his father. It was very quiet in the room, and suddenly cold. The thin carpet between them was rucked up in the centre, and the grey threads were exposed and broken along the fold. The unshaded bulb accentuated a bareness and shabbiness in the room that Peter hadn't previously noticed. When he had first come in, he had walked straight to the window, and looked at the trees and gardens.

'I've been trying to follow it all, in the papers,' he said. 'Only it was pretty confusing.'

'It's we are confused,' Harold said. 'We get excited by details and miss the pattern. That's the record, this winter.'

'But then, when that's noticed.'

'Noticed?' Harold said, angrily. 'Do you think we're stupid? It's spelled out, in big letters. It's like a bloody rule book, and they're all working to it. It's just chipping away all the time, and with time on their side.'

'And the men won't see it, is that right?'

'See it? They see it all right. But what's the use of seeing it? All they see's where the power is, and they curse and accept it. They have to go where the money comes from, and anything else is just silly bloody talk. There's just a few people, protected, can see it could all be different. But day to day they leave it to us and day to day we get beaten.'

'Not altogether beaten.'

'Nor not altogether alive, either,' Harold said, getting up. 'When you've worked your guts over years for that bit at a time and then a bit again. And the pressures starting fresh every day. We get no help, Peter. That's the plain fact. Talked at, yes, but no help, and it's that that does it. Then we know we're on our own and the heart of it goes, my own heart goes. Everybody wants us for their own private army, but we've had that. We'll stay where we are and look after ourselves.'

Peter shifted in his chair.

'Well, you're right to look after yourselves.'

'Certainly, and we will. It's the way it's set up. Even I know it could be different, but what's the use? We just have to hang on where we are.'

'Uncle Gwyn is getting out.'

'Yes, there's the special cases. Though what's the garage without the works? But yes, the chap you happen to know, the chance through a family. Or your way.'

Peter waited. Harold stood in the centre of the room, looking at him.

'That's what the education is for, isn't it? That's what we watch happening.'

'Always?' Peter asked.

'Well, it's set up for you, isn't it? The teaching, the politics, the management jobs, or then the papers and the television. That's your world, isn't it? So you go.'

'Without any connections?'

'They may be there. I've not noticed them. That's how it is, day to day.'

Peter waited, staring down at the grey threads in the fold of the carpet.

'Yes, Dad, it may be. Or at least, if it's not, I'm in no position to deny it. I've done nothing different.'

'Nor can you afford to,' Harold said, sharply. 'You got to marry, bring up a family, get the job that's going. That's the way it is.'

Peter leaned across to his table. He wanted to say what he intended to do, but he knew, as he looked, that the papers wouldn't help him.

'Something must be possible,' he began.

'Yes,' Harold said. 'Like there was once Christ, and for two thousand years the churches and chapels have lived off him.'

'Plenty of actual workers, and others,' Peter said. 'Over the last hundred and fifty years.'

'Aye, that,' Harold said. 'Keeping our conscience warm on the history, like the chapels. Be brave, be like them, you all fancy a cross. Only not just yet, there's the hymn to sing first. I do believe, I will believe, that Jesus died for me. Only the son of man had to be a son of God after all. That kept it occasional. And praise him, praise him all ye little children. Only who tells his son to behave like that? Anyhow, in the end, there's never the choice. It's down Black Rock after work and a wage.'

'Then,' Peter said.

'Then and now. Getting married and making your home.'

'But still with choices. Still really with choices.'

'No, Peter. There isn't that much choice, when the preaching's stopped. And that's one thing for certain, for us, now. Not the bloody preaching again. Not that from anybody.'

Peter did not answer.

'Still it wasn't all that I came down here for,' Harold said.

Peter waited for him to go on. He was still nervous.

'I've said I'm glad, boy, about you and Beth. It's your own lives, you decide. And Gwyn and Myra are glad. Gwyn has a lot of respect for you.'

'Has he?'

'He's talked to you. He told me. I don't know, I don't ask.'

Peter felt the blood in his face, and got up.

'It hasn't always been easy,' he said, lamely.

'I know. I'm not saying it has. But it's your Mam I'm thinking about.'

'Yes?' Peter said. As he spoke he walked back to the window. He saw his papers spread over the table, and the pen and the half-finished sentence, when the knock at the door had come.

'Whatever there's been,' Harold said, 'it must come right now. When your son gets married, it matters, Peter. You expect him to tell you.'

'I was coming to tell you.'

'And your Mam?'

'When Beth told them,' Peter said, 'you mentioned the others. Does that mean Mam objects?'

'Objects? What's the matter with you?'

'Well tell me just what you're saying.'

'What your Mam and I do, what your Mam and I decide, is our own business, Peter. We've twenty years yet, twenty years on our own, and we make the decisions. You made your own judgement and you left us. All right, you do that, you do what you want. But it's not your business. You're not set in judgement on us, Peter. Not on me. Not on her.'

'I wouldn't claim that. I went for my own reasons. I went because I had to.'

'You made it like a judgement. It's how we see it. You condemned your Mam and you pitied me.'

'No.'

'Don't lie now, Peter. We can't stand lies from our son.'

'Lies from anybody,' Peter said.

Harold looked away, and then sat on the bed. He put his hand over his face. He seemed collapsed into himself, and beyond the effort at concealment. Peter wanted to go over to him, but the barriers were still too strong. To go with pity would only make matters worse. He wanted to go with respect, but though he knew its language he did not know its actions, and he could not yet trust himself.

Harold lifted his head, and looked around the room, avoiding his son's eyes.

'Your Mam has talked to me, Peter, but I don't understand. She says I won't try but I can't and that's the truth. So it's been a long silence, till just these last few days.'

'Yes.'

'It's coming all right, Peter. It'll be all right.'

'Well, I'm glad.'

332

Harold stood up, getting back his strength.

'Only she'd be pleased, now, if you came and talked to her. If you came to your Mam about Beth and getting married.'

'Does she really want that?'

'We've both wanted it. You can't see it our way, but we've brought you this far. That's why I came myself. And that I wanted to see you.'

'I wanted to see you, Dad. I wanted to talk to you. I always have wanted to talk to you.'

'Yes, well there it is,' Harold said, and again sat on the bed. He crossed his ankles, and lifted his feet a little way from the ground. His hands were close together, palm to palm, between his knees and his thighs. His thin shoulders were hunched forward, and his head seemed the only part of himself that he could move, jerkily, against the control of the rest of his body.

'Shall I come with you now, to see Mam?'

'Not now, no. Tomorrow, better.'

He stood up, and looked again round the room.

'I'd better get back now.'

'I'll come down as far as the car.'

'I haven't got the car. I haven't licensed it. I've not had the money.'

He turned to the door. As he went down the stairs, Peter followed him closely. They went out together to the street.

'I've not yet apologized,' Peter said, 'for taking the car.'

Harold didn't answer. He looked up at Peter for a moment, and then took his hand.

'Go on back in, boy. You'll get cold.'

Chapter Eighteen

On the following day, in the late afternoon, Peter went back to Goldsmith Street. But when he got off the bus at the familiar corner, by the furniture store and the record shop and the garage, he didn't go up the usual way. Instead he walked on, along the road through the works: the public road that was part of its system.

From the road the noise of the works was muffled. The air above it was grey, and the cowls of the ventilators were open. Lorries were moving down the wide concrete roads, behind the high wire fence and the numbered gates. The works policemen walked up and down at their posts, keeping moving in the thin, cold easterly wind.

Peter walked slowly down on the opposite side of the road, under the older sheds. In that great complex of buildings, laid out like a model, Harold and Gwyn had been working, day in, day out, since before he was born. It was a strange but now customary settlement: lines drawn on paper, the earth flattened, and then men and machines inside the lines. When the hooters blasted, the roads would be filled with the men turning out and dispersing, with the daylight going, and the sodium lamps glaring red and then orange along the crowded streets.

A car drew in to the pavement, a few yards in front of him. Two men got out and stood talking back to the driver. He heard the sharp Welsh accents even before he distinguished the words, but they were men he had never seen before. The driver leaned across and passed out a bunch of daffodils. The younger man on the pavement, small and dark, about Peter's age, wearing stained overalls, took the daffodils and folded them in his arm, in the same movement bending to touch them with his forehead, feeling their yellow coolness tingling on the skin. The car drove on, and the men crossed the road to the works.

Above the pavement, a high transporter drew up, with a long hiss of air from its brakes. On its angled skeletal frame, six red bodyshells seemed to hang in the air. The transporter turned, to Gafe Seven. The works policeman, an elderly man, moving stiffly, his face reddened with tiny burst veins, stepped out and spoke to the driver, who gave down his papers. There was a brief conversation, and then the transporter pulled away, in a cloud of black oil fumes, and turned in at Gate Nine.

Peter crossed the road, and made his way up the hill. There was a sound of shouting from the school. A class was out in the long yard, doing what used to be drill. The boys and girls, eight or nine years old, were clambering over a complex scaffolding of aluminium tubes to a diving-board from which they leaped to a wide copra mat. A girl in her twenties, in a white blouse and red skirt, stood on the mat to touch their shoulders and balance them as they landed. One boy who stumbled she held by the head, the hands suddenly white on the close black hair. Laughing down at him, she pulled his head close to her thighs, and then let him go to run back. Beyond the yard, the wide glass windows of the main school showed the other children working. Several of them were moving about, carrying books and papers.

He looked at the scaffolding, tracing its structure as if in his hands. The children were climbing over and through it, again and again, and then jumping, lifting their arms, to the mat. He watched, intently, feeling the hold of the fingers on the long bars, and then the pull through the back, and the knees and feet finding a new hold. There was a moment of balance, looking out, and then the launch into air, and the arms lifting, the stumble of feet on the mat and the quick hand on the moving shoulders.

He held the bars in front of him, as the children ran round again. Then he turned, letting go of the bars, and walked on up to Goldsmith Street. The blue and white of the two houses stood sharply out, in the grey air. He ran his hand along the low iron-work, on the wall fronting the street. Then he turned and walked down the gravelled side-passage, to the kitchen door. He walked through the house to the sitting-room at the front, where the door was ajar. He pushed the door open quietly, and looked in.

Kate was sitting in a chair drawn close to the electric fire, with her legs curled up. Her book was lying on the arm of the chair, and she had twisted her head and shoulders to look down at it.

Peter held his breath. He was alarmed that she didn't move as he entered. Then she looked across at him and smiled, and he turned to close the door.

'No, don't close the door, Peter. I'd rather go out.'

'Would you?'

'I'll get my coat. We'll go for a walk, shall we?'

'Yes, if you like.'

She got up, and laid her book on the mantelpiece. She shook back her hair and her whole body seemed to move. It was as if she had more energy than could be used in any particular action. The sudden movement from her stillness in the chair was startling, though he had seen this break so often before.

He stood aside, while she fetched her coat, and then went out ahead of her to the street. She had turned her collar right up, and was walking with her hands deep in her pockets. Yet she walked quickly, and he had to change his pace to keep up with her.

They walked up the hill towards the church and the old school and the fields beyond.

'Do you remember me bringing you this way?' Kate asked. Her head was still bowed, and she was staring at the lines of the paving-stones just ahead of her shoes.

'To school, I mean.'

'Yes, Mam. Yes, of course.'

'I keep going back to that time and thinking about it. I don't suppose you really remember.'

'Some of it, Mam, yes.'

'I knew what I was doing then, Peter. That's the only difference.'

'Yes, with a child it's clearer.'

'You were going to be everything we hadn't a chance for. And even then you did more than I ever expected. I kept raising my expectations, and every time you went past them.'

'Until now.'

'No, Peter. It's still true. I can feel it.'

'But you oughtn't to feel it.'

'Not even that?'

'Not as you do, Mam. Not as being fulfilled in me. You mustn't write off your own life like that. You've done so much.'

'Have I? Nobody else seems to think so.'

'I think so.'

They turned along the path to the fields. Kate pulled her hands from her pockets and began looking around. There were several birds in the bare thorn hedge, and she looked at them with a sudden interest. She didn't even know their names, though she would know the word if someone else said it. They had black and white heads, with olive-green wings running back to brown and grey tail feathers. The breasts were black, and then all the under-

336

parts were a clear, vivid yellow. She stood watching them for some moments, and then reluctantly walked on.

They climbed the stile, and went out across the field path.

'I'm glad about you and Beth.'

'Are you?'

'Yes, glad, Peter. Glad in myself.'

'All right, then.'

'I hope you'll be happy. I think you will. You've had a lot of the difficulties first.'

Peter hesitated.

'They were still wrong, though, Mam. As they actually came.'

'Yes, I expect so. We were all wrong for you.'

'No, not just that. Or we shouldn't have been here at all.'

Kate pushed her hands in her pockets again.

'It may be easier now. At least for you, with good jobs. You'll have just that bit more margin.'

'You gave us that bit more margin.'

'I don't know, Peter. We passed it all on to you, the good and the bad. But I meant, at least, no love on the dole.'

'I know you did.'

Kate turned and looked up at him. He was so much bigger than her own tiny body that she could hardly believe he had once been a movement inside it.

'And when I think of that I can feel warm for a change. Especially because you're being nice to me, Peter.'

'It's not a question of being nice to you.'

'Well, I notice it. And I'm glad and happy. Yet at the same time, when I think about my own life, I'm bitter. It isn't only me. I try to look at the whole of it. I walk down the street and I say all right, so it isn't love on the dole, but what else is it?'

'We don't know, do we?'

'No, but I get bitter and it all starts over. All the edge and the hardness. I want to say, all right, it isn't love on the dole, it's just love on hire purchase. We pay a moderate deposit and then regular weekly instalments. By the time we've finished paying, the thing itself is worn out.'

'Yes,' Peter said. 'That's a quite different voice.'

'I know it is, and I hate it. But at the same time it satisfies me. It's what I'm wanting to say.'

'It's a voice I've heard elsewhere.'

'Yes,' Kate said. 'At least you understand that.'

They walked on in silence for some time, under the high thorn

337

hedge. The bare darkness of the wood was ahead of them, and at the gate leading into it they instinctively stopped.

'You don't mind me talking like this,' Kate said, still turned from him.

'I don't know, Mam.'

'It's just the pressure, all the time, you can't begin to understand. If I can't say what I feel I shall break.'

'The feeling itself may be breaking.'

'Yes,' Kate said, and turned and leaned on the gate. The wind through the wood caught her loose hair, and blew it back from her face. In the stiff white raincoat, her tiny body seemed tense and coiled. 'And now you know why I'm bitter,' she said quickly. 'Why it seemed, in the end, that I still had a right. Harold said I was corrupt and it's true, Peter. They say power corrupts and perhaps it does. What I know, in myself, is a quite different thing. That power corrupts the people it is exercised over.'

'All the people?'

'Yes, Peter, it seems so to me. Mine was just one way and that's why I'm nót apologizing, at least not to them. They've twisted themselves so deep, into an acquiescence they can't now even notice. If I'm picked out as the bad one, it's just as a sacrifice to protect their complacency. I'll agree that I'm wrong when they stop pretending they're right.'

Peter was moving his shoe over a dead stick that had fallen from the tree by the gate. He looked up now, and back across the field, where the wind was moving. He was thinking of Beth, and of the children at the school, but they seemed too far away.

'You're still very young,' Kate said, 'and you've been more or less protected. But I've had so much of it it's not a question of studying or observing. I just know it, now, like I know the air.'

'Know what exactly?' he asked, looking out over the field to the lines of houses, and the works below them, and the city in the distance.

'That we've settled for so little, and called it normal. And then twisted body and soul to avoid seeing more. Seeing what life could really be like.'

'What life is like,' Peter said, watching the smoke rising from the houses and caught by the wind at different heights down the slope. 'Because we've got this wrong, this contrast we make between potential and actual. In the end it breaks us, because it is no way to live. If we keep reducing the present, by some idea of

338

the future, nothing good can happen. We have to take hold where we are, and know good from bad. We've lived in this break too long. All it's taught us is breaking away. But the change will only come when we've learned to confirm.'

Kate swung away, impatiently, driving her hands deep into the stiff pockets.

'Confirm, conform, we've had enough of all that. It's only the break that has ever changed things. And the only people that matter, now, are the misfits like us who still go on kicking. Everybody knows this, even the tame ones. In public, of course, they pretend quite different, they pretend they're all right.'

'No, Mam, really. Nobody pretends it's all right. But the life is still here, that's the point. It isn't some future, it's now: between one life and another.'

Kate smiled, reluctantly.

'I wish you were right, Peter. But you simply don't know how far it's all gone. You're like Robert Lane, seeing the world through his own haze. If you actually tuned in to it, you wouldn't be able to stand it. It isn't only the conditions, that we think we can alter. It's what has been done to the actual people, crushing them down in the shadow, till they're glad to be as they are. And one way or another, they'll break any challenge, because they don't want to change. Any disturbance terrifies them, and their only enemies, the only people they hate, are the few who are trying to change them.'

'You really think that?' Peter said.

'Yes, I've learned it, though I didn't want to. Because who do you think keeps the violence and the ugliness and the triviality going? A few at the top? They don't need to any more. The system runs by itself.'

'Then it can't be changed?'

'Yes, it can, but it will break those who do it. It will break them to pieces, even inside themselves. We used to say, be humane and tolerant, make a better life. But to be humane now we can't be tolerant. We have to break and fight, and go dry and hard in the process. All that's left to us now is this struggle.'

'Yes, I've thought this. But I'm still not certain.'

'You'll need to be, if you mean to do anything. And not just hardness: that can be learned. But being broken, yourself, while you try to change things. Not just broken in their terms, but finally in your own. And you can agree to break yourself for the others to walk over, or you can have some sense and contract out. It's as

339

hard as that, and nothing fine about it, anywhere. You can take your choice between the one tragedy and the other.'

'Even if people make their own changes?' Peter asked, watching her.

'That's the textbook answer. Why don't you go down the streets and see?'

'But it's not changing others,' Peter said angrily. 'What right have we got to do that? That's the world, in fact, that we're trying to change.'

'But why should it happen, Peter? Are we any advertisement for it? The few who try go to pieces quite quickly, one way or another. Not just the strain either, but that the effort is quite different from the life we're making the effort for. Have you ever really thought when we say fighting for peace? It's quite real, that contradiction. The feelings we learn from the fighting disqualify us from the peace, yet there's still no alternative, we still have to fight. I tried for years to suppress this, but it's time for the truth. We'd be the worst people, the worst possible people, in any good society. And we're like this because we've exposed ourselves and we've hardened. We're just disorganized people fighting for a better organized life. Every sneer we get is quite right, for it's the truth about us.'

'Not the whole truth.'

'No, not the whole truth. But it's the part we won't recognize. And while the rest can despise us, they get the complacency to go on as they are. They can be sure they're right while they see, so easily, that we're wrong.'

Peter bent and picked up the stick. Its bark was quite loose, and came away in his fingers. He kept turned from Kate, who was moving away, looking along the hedge. The intensity of her argument seemed quite overwhelming: not because he accepted it, but because its energy, suddenly, seemed to alter the world. He looked away to the distance, beyond the city. The sky was darkening, but there was one pale ribbon of light, at the edge of the hills, the wide new motorway he had driven over, on the way to Trawsfynydd. He thought of Gwyn going there, and of the field behind the garage. He needed, now, to see the shape of another life; even a shape beyond him. For within her intensity a different life moved, in his own body. He would probably fail if he tried to express this, yet the feeling was absolute. He turned and looked for her. She was walking slowly back, with her head down. Her hair had dropped forward, over her cheeks and shoulders. She was walking with slow jerky steps, almost kicking at the ground. As he watched her coming towards him, the perspective altered, suddenly. What she had said was an explanation, a definition of her life. And even while he recognized that it was also an apology, a definition shaped and narrowed to an apology, he hadn't the blood to reject it. He wasn't that separate, and didn't want to be separate.

She stopped in front of him, and looked up to his face. She had thrown back her hair, and now her heavy cheeks, her dark eyes, seemed suddenly naked in front of him. He tried to look away, but he couldn't move.

'I need to tell you about Arthur,' she said.

'No, Mam. It isn't my business. Dad said it wasn't my business.'

'He was just trying to be kind.'

'He was being kind.'

'Yes, every time. He's been kind to me.'

'Well then?'

'It released me, Peter. For the time it released me. From myself. From my world. And I needed release. But now it's sprung back at me. It's hit me in the face. Not just being found out, though that was bad. But finding myself out.'

'This happened to me.'

'There was nothing there. He was so weak he dissolved through my fingers, and I used to cry after him, cry out in the pain. But then I tried again, because there was so much I needed. And I never got it, except from myself. That's been my adventure.'

'Don't call it that.'

'It was that, Peter. Didn't you see while it lasted? That in fact it released me, going out like that on my own.'

'But you just said it was nothing.'

'Yes, because I'm ashamed. And in fact he was nothing. I was merely using him. It's not him to be blamed, but me.'

'To consent to being used is as bad.'

'Well, perhaps. But it's over now. And I still have to live, having disgraced myself and my husband. I've emptied myself, Peter. The formal disgrace I could bear, but not this.'

'You're not the only one.'

'But does that help? It's not the comparisons, it's the feeling inside.'

'You're still living with Dad.'

'Yes, and I mean to. I've got to learn it again, being really married. Being alive together, we've both got to learn it. Only it still comes hard, the learning comes hard. When you feel in yourself, Peter, the days and the nights aren't long enough, the years aren't long enough, for the life you still want. And our bodies too small and too tired. Only don't look in and say it's just choosing. If you respect us at all, you'll see what we've paid and just why we've paid it. Don't rub out the lines and the dirt to make it seem easy. If it's a word, it is easy, but this is year after year, really giving your life.'

'That makes you the good people,' Peter said, slowly.

'Do you think so? Do we look it?'

'You and I may be wrong, Mam. At least we've been wrong. But we're not the whole of it. We live with good people. And Dad, who's really been fighting, he hasn't gone wrong.'

'Don't insult him, Peter.'

'Insult him? That isn't an insult. I've seen what it means to keep going that long.'

'So have I seen it, Peter. I've lived it, with him. If you say it's not twisted and broken him, you've got no idea, no idea of respect.'

'Not broken,' Peter insisted.

'Nor have I broken,' Kate said, clearly. 'I've taken this into myself, as he has, and we've not broken. It's mad to turn round, after all that's happened, and simply assert our dignity. But that's still what we're going to do.'

'Not much dignity left to stand on,' Peter said, smiling.

'I'm not saying we ought to do it, or that we have a right to do it. I'm saying we must do it, Peter. Do you know what I mean?'

They walked across the field, with the wind behind them, in the fading light. At the stile Kate moved quickly in front, and got neatly over, as if on her own. He had to hurry to catch her, as the street-lamps appeared at the end of the path.

'Only one thing, Peter,' she said, without turning. 'Don't push your generation at me. Don't try all these songs about youth. I've had all that, being proud and twenty, condemning the middle-aged for the mess they've made of it, and then getting middle-aged and seeing all the connections. It's a smug little game, and I won't kneel to it. Even when the generations pass and some of the changes happen. All that really matters is to go on seeing it, as you did then. Only now inside, where it hurts. Just seeing what happened, and how it mightn't have happened.'

She turned and smiled at him.

'I still feel like a girl, Peter. I make a girl's judgements. And I

342

contradict myself, but I know what I'm saying. And I can still feel young, even with you beside me.'

'Dont you want me beside you?'

'You're going to Beth. It's all right.'

They reached the street, and crossed to the side of the houses. Kate pushed her hands in her pockets, and hunched forward her shoulders. As the houses closed round her, she seemed to shrink and withdraw.

There was a light in the front room, and Peter could see Beth there. Kate stopped at the entry, and closed the ironwork gate. There was a sombre silence in the street: an effect they had often noticed, before the hooters sounded at the works. As the familiar blasts came, Kate touched Peter's hand, lightly, and then went on down the entry. He kept some distance behind her, following her through the house. Harold was sitting with Beth and Myra, in the warm front room. They got up as the others came in.

Kate stood in the doorway, taking off her white raincoat. As she turned to put it away, Harold moved and took it from her. She smiled, and he hesitated. The others were watching them, involuntarily.

'Thanks, Harold,' Kate said, quietly.

'It's all right, girl.'

'Yes.'

Kate moved and kissed his lips. He did not pull away, as she still half expected, but put his arm round her and held her close for some moments. Then he went to put away the coat and Kate moved on into the room.

'Gwyn won't be long,' Myra said. 'I asked him to bring home some beer.'

Kate went across and stood by the mantelpiece. Peter could see her hair reflected in the curving round mirror.

'There's some wine,' she said. 'I got in for Christmas. Only we were all too busy to drink it. And it's not gone bad, Myra, if that's what you're thinking. It's a French wine, Hermitage, from the Rhone valley. We'll go there, Harold and I, and see where it's grown.'

'Catch you in a hermitage,' Harold said, coming back.

'And you watch,' Kate said, 'my French will be good, I've not kept much else, but I've kept that.'

There was a sharp hoot in the street, and they looked out to see Gwyn turning in next door, drawing Mag up close under the rowan. They saw him get out and step over the low dividing wall, carrying a crate against his hips. Harold went and opened the door, and Gwyn came in and put the crate down.

'We going to drink to these two?' he said to Harold.

'Drink, anyhow,' Harold said. 'They don't go in for ceremony, this lot. Only I had it clear in my mind. Peter getting this other degree, and then him and Beth marrying, and we'd all have dressed up and it'd have been an occasion.'

Gwyn smiled, and looked round at Peter and Beth. He was taller than Harold and in his dark overalls looked much leaner and younger.

'That's half the trouble,' he said, 'working out the occasion. But get someone like me, all they want is the drink.'

He smiled at Peter, as if sharing some secret.

'You haven't told us,' he said, 'what this new work of yours is.'

'It's not an occasion, either.'

'No, but the detail of it,' Gwyn said, tying him down.

Peter knew it was time to speak, to explain his decision. But still he needed their questions.

'Beth said you were settling here.'

"Yes, Dad, I'm trying to settle. There are other places, but for me, inevitably, this is the place to begin. What I shall try to do, here, is a new kind of inquiry, with ourselves involved in it. And for our own understanding, not just for report.'

'A survey, you mean?' Harold said, frowning.

'No, Dad, not a survey. That's just what's been wrong.'

'I've read a bit of it,' Harold said. 'Like we're the new tribe, and they hack through the jungle to find us. Then they measure us up, opinions and attitudes. Or what they call kinship and we call family. I tell you I've seen it, myself, in print. Adult male, semi-skilled, 45, married.'

'They ought to put mated, mun.'

'You can laugh, Gwyn, yes. But I've actually seen it. They come over the hill and survey us: how we vote, what we buy, why we come out on strike, and how fast we can work if there's some-body watching us.'

'You ought to write a report on them, Uncle,' Beth said, moving beside him.

'Don't worry, we have, Beth. It just happens not to get so wide a circulation.'

'Then get Peter to write it,' Gwyn said.

'No,' Harold said, bending again to the fire. 'Because from what I can see he's in the same trade. And it makès no difference, that he happened to be born here. He wants the same, just to measure and see what we're good for.'

'I've not found the words,' Peter said. 'And that's where it starts, where I still have to learn. Only take this report that you say you've made. You haven't, you know. It's never got past the swearing. And while you can only swear, you can only lose. You'll even end up accepting their measurements.'

'Not yet,' Harold said.

'All right, not yet, though you've gone a long way.'

'We're under too much pressure, all of us, here.'

'Yes, I know. But still the pressure is part of us. In myself I've been weak, taking only the pressure of others. But it's all been like that, that's why I can see it. In you and Mam, or down in the works.'

'Not only the works.

'I know. I'm starting from that. This is a single city.'

'Living different lives.'

'But inside the same form.'

Harold glanced across at him, then took off his glasses and rubbed his eyes. Beth stayed close to him, and he felt her closeness and turned towards her.

'Only one thing, Peter,' Gwyn said. 'You'll have to try it, down there in the works. Nobody else can tell you, just watching.'

'I mean to, Uncle. If I can get Dad's permission.'

'After eighteen years,' Harold said. 'Eighteen years' education, and you want to go back where I started.'

'Not where you started. Where we all now are, because you started.'

'No,' Harold said, 'you'll never know that. Because for one thing you can always get out. You'll see it different, whatever you do, because that can't be altered.'

'I don't want to alter it. It took eighteen years.'

'And you're getting married. Beth's entitled to something.'

'I want what Peter is doing,' Beth said, quickly. 'I shall go on working. And Peter will earn what he can.'

'You'd live on your wife's wages?' Harold said, irritated and surprised.

'I shall be working, remember. Working harder, in fact, than I've ever had to.'

'It's not the effort. You talk like a kid. Work is what you get paid for.'

'Yes,' Peter said, 'that's where it all starts. So while I have this margin, I'm bound to use it. And in respect to you, who gave me the margin.'

Harold, numbed, did not answer. Peter saw how the lines on his face had hardened, as always in argument. The head was still, and its strength was held for a moment. The deeply weathered skin ran into the faded coppery hair, so that the whole shape of the head was single and clear.

'In the end it isn't what I'm doing. It's what we're doing,' Peter said clearly.

Kate came back, with the wine and the glasses. Myra was behind her, with cakes on a tray.

'I've heard this before,' Kate said, putting the wine on the table. 'The child among us, taking his notes. Only you're not a child, Peter. We none of us are.'

Peter stared at her, taken aback. There was an edge in her voice that he had not expected, though it was very familiar.

'We'll start from that then,' Beth said, clearly. She moved quickly and stood beside Peter. Kate, bending over the glasses, looked across at her, and then again, smiling, at Peter.

'Only what you'll find, Peter, is that we're not together. Make no mistake about that. You say what you have to, and do what you have to. We'll listen, we'll challenge it, different ways.'

'And the other way round,' Beth said, accepting the challenge.

'All right, Beth,' Kate said, pushing back her hair. She was suddenly alive and certain again, as she had been in the autumn.

'It's come time for it, anyway,' Gwyn said, seriously.

Kate poured the wine, and Gwyn and Myra handed the glasses. There was a moment's silence, when they were all ready to drink.

'Like standing before a journey,' Gwyn said.

'Yes,' Kate said. 'And for you and Myra it is.'

'For us all,' Gwyn said. 'Different ways.'

'To Beth and Peter,' Harold said.

They drank, formally. There was again a silence, in the sudden awareness of ceremony. Then Myra and Kate went across to kiss Beth and then Peter. Gwyn and Harold followed them, shaking hands.

There was a spatter of rain on the window, as the wind blew from the west up the hill. Myra shivered, glancing at the undrawn curtains.

'And now to you,' Peter said, looking quickly around: Gwyn, Myra, Harold, Kate.

He touched glasses with Beth, and they drank quickly and
346

deeply. Hurried by the wind, the rain was beating against the windows, all along the street. Far to the west, the wind was blowing over the mountains, where the thorns had grown to its shape. A grey sail of rain moved down the valley to Trawsfynydd, past the white cottage and the garage and the field with the caravans. On the scarp of Brynllwyd, the wind moved through the dark houses around the deserted ironworks. Down Black Rock, it blew fiercely, and then over the hills into England, the broad green valley and the long switchbacks of the road. In the city the bells were ringing, from the high floodlit towers, where a gust caught the sound of the bells and dispersed it, the chimes fading and rising above the race of traffic and the crowded pavements of the centre. Over the long bridge, the wind cut through the stone balustrade and swept the rain along the gleaming surface of the road, where pools edged with the iridescence of oil were forming to drain to the silent river. Along the road to the works the wind blew past the smaller houses and the lighted shopfronts. In the ordered lines of the works, picked out by the lights, the rain shone on the parked cars and the wind was loud in the high silvered funnels of the ventilators and the squat dark cowls of the older sheds. The wind blew through the diamond-wired fences, round the perimeter of the works, and through the lines of houses running up the hill to the church and the fields to High Wood. From Between Towns Road the whole city could be seen, the lines of light marking the settlement by the river: the cathedral, the colleges, the yards and sheds of the works, the lighted windows of the houses. The wind blew through the city, bringing the spring rain.